The Management System Auditor's Handbook

Also available from ASQ Quality Press:

The Internal Auditing Pocket Guide
J.P. Russell

Quality Audits for Improved Performance, Third Edition
Dennis R. Arter

The Process Auditing Techniques Guide
J.P. Russell

Automotive Internal Auditor Pocket Guide: Process Auditing to ISO/TS 16949:2002
Roderick A. Munro

The Process Approach Audit Checklist for Manufacturing
Karen Welch

How to Audit the Process-Based QMS
Dennis R. Arter, Charles A. Cianfrani, and John E. (Jack) West

TS 16949: Insight from a Third-Party Auditor: With a Process Approach Audit Checklist
Karen Welch

Process Driven Comprehensive Auditing: A New Way to Conduct ISO 9001:2000 Internal Audits
Paul C. Palmes

Internal Quality Auditing
Denis Pronovost

Fundamentals of Quality Auditing
B. Scott Parsowith

ISO Lesson Guide 2000: Pocket Guide to Q9001:2000, Second Edition
Dennis R. Arter and J.P. Russell

To request a complimentary catalog of ASQ Quality Press publications, call 800-248-1946, or visit our Web site at http://qualitypress.asq.org.

The Management System Auditor's Handbook

Joe Kausek

ASQ Quality Press
Milwaukee, Wisconsin

American Society for Quality, Quality Press, Milwaukee 53203
© 2006 by ASQ
All rights reserved. Published 2005
Printed in the United States of America

12 11 10 09 08 07 06 05   5 4 3 2 1

Library of Congress Cataloging-in-Publication Data

Kausek, Joe, 1957–
    The management system auditor's handbook / Joe Kausek.
       p. cm.
    Includes bibliographical references and index.
    ISBN-13: 978-0-87389-670-2 (hard cover : alk. paper)
    ISBN-10: 0-87389-670-X (hard cover : alk. paper)
    1. Management audit. 2. Compliance auditing. I. Title.

    HD58.95.K38 2005
    658.4'013—dc22   2005024894

ISBN-13: 978-0-87389-670-2
ISBN-10: 0-87389-670-X

Publisher: William A. Tony
Acquisitions Editor: Annemieke Hytinen
Project Editor: Paul O'Mara
Production Administrator: Randall Benson

ASQ Mission: The American Society for Quality advances individual, organizational, and community excellence worldwide through learning, quality improvement, and knowledge exchange.

Attention Bookstores, Wholesalers, Schools, and Corporations: ASQ Quality Press books, videotapes, audiotapes, and software are available at quantity discounts with bulk purchases for business, educational, or instructional use. For information, please contact ASQ Quality Press at 800-248-1946, or write to ASQ Quality Press, P.O. Box 3005, Milwaukee, WI 53201-3005.

To place orders or to request a free copy of the ASQ Quality Press Publications Catalog, including ASQ membership information, call 800-248-1946. Visit our Web site at www.asq.org or http://qualitypress.asq.org.

 Printed on acid-free paper

Quality Press
600 N. Plankinton Avenue
Milwaukee, Wisconsin 53203
Call toll free 800-248-1946
Fax 414-272-1734
www.asq.org
http://qualitypress.asq.org
http://standardsgroup.asq.org
E-mail: authors@asq.org

Table of Contents

CD-ROM Contents

The following files are available on the CD-ROM accompanying this book. To access them, you will need word processing software such as Microsoft Word. These files are intended for the reader's personal use only. They should not be reproduced for any other use without the prior written permission of the publisher. All such requests should be directed to ASQ Quality Press at 800-248-1946 or qpress@asq.org.

Audit Checklists

14001 and 18001 Checklists

File names:
Combined EHS Management System Audit Checklist.doc
EMS Management System Audit Checklist.doc
OH&S Management System Audit Checklist.doc

ISO 9001 Checklists

File names:
9001 Audit Checklist—Quality Planning and Design.doc
9001 Audit Checklist—Management Responsibility.doc
9001 Audit Checklist—Monitoring Measurement and Improv.doc
9001 Audit Checklist—Production Support.doc
9001 Audit Checklist—Resource and Support Activities.doc
9001 Planning Checklist—Production Process.doc
QMS Audit Checklist 1—Area Manager-Owner Interview.doc
QMS Audit Checklist 2—Basic Production Process.doc
QMS Audit Checklist 3—Basic Preservation Process.doc

TS 16949 Checklists

File names:
16949 Audit Checklist—Audit and Corrective Action.doc
16949 Audit Checklist—Quality Planning and Design.doc

16949 Audit Checklist—Analysis and Improvement.doc
16949 Audit Checklist—Management Responsibility.doc
16949 Audit Checklist—Resource and Support Processes.doc

Best Practices Checklist
File name:
Best Practices Checklist.doc

Forms and Surveys

File names:
Audit Findings Form.doc
Audit Nonconformance Report.doc
Audit One Liner Form.doc
Audit Program Survey.doc
Audit Report Form.doc
Survey for Determining Relative Process Importance.doc

List of Acronyms Used

A2LA	American Association for Laboratory Accreditation
APQP	advanced product quality planning
ASL	approved supplier list
ASTM	American Society for Testing and Materials
BOM	bill of materials
BPI	business process improvement
BSI	British Standards Institute
CAR	corrective action request
CFR	Code of Federal Regulations
DFA	design for assembly
DFE	design for the environment
DFMEA	design failure mode and effects analysis
DFM	design for manufacturability
DVP	design verification plan
EH&S	environmental health and safety
EMS	environmental management system
EPA	Environmental Protection Agency
FDA	Food and Drug Administration
FIFO	first in–first out
FMEA	failure mode and effects analysis
GR&R	gage repeatability and reproducibility
HAZOP	hazard and operability study
IT	information technology
JHA	job hazard analysis

MBNQA	Malcolm Baldrige National Quality Award
MRP	materials requirements planning
MSA	measurement systems analysis
MSDS	Material Safety Data Sheets
MWO	maintenance work order
NC	nonconformance
NIST	National Institute of Standards and Technology
NNPP	Naval Nuclear Propulsion Program
NVLAP	National Voluntary Laboratory Accreditation Program
OEM	original equipment manufacturer
OFI	opportunity for improvement
OHSAS	occupational health and safety assessment series
OJT	on-the-job training
OSHA	Occupational Safety and Health Administration
PFMEA	process failure mode and effects analysis
PPAP	production part approval process
PPE	personal protective equipment
PRR	product rejection report
QMS	quality management system
QPR	quality problem report
QSP	quality system procedure
QSI	quality system instruction
SIP	state implementation plan
SIPOC	supplier–inputs–process–outputs–customer
SPC	statistical process control
VOC	voice of the customer
VPP	voluntary protection program

Preface

As a management system auditor for the last 20 years I have been both encouraged and frustrated by the changes in management system auditing that have taken place over the last decade. Auditing practices have evolved toward more value-added functions. Companies are streamlining their management programs, with a focus on efficiency and the elimination of waste. At the same time, more attention is now being placed, and rightly so, on the effectiveness of auditing systems, both in terms of final products and services and in the operation of internal processes. Importance is now being placed not just on what we do, but how well we do it. Together, these changes have provided an opportunity for auditors to take a larger role improving the quality and productivity of their organization's operations.

While the management systems standards and practices have rapidly evolved, the competency and capabilities of auditors have failed to keep up. Auditing continues to be seen as a collateral duty performed by part-time and often ill-prepared auditors. Auditors still tend to identify administrative deficiencies over more important weaknesses in system support or effectiveness, and management teams still grumble about audit results.

This handbook attempts to address these shortcomings by providing a detailed and structured examination of the audit process. It seeks to address the whys of auditing as well as the whats and the how-tos. Extensive focus is provided on auditing for effectiveness, in addition to conformance. In addition, this book shows how you can use your audit program to drive continual improvement and alignment throughout the organization through the identification of best practices and waste. Unlike other audit books on the market, this handbook seeks to give the auditor sufficient understanding of the intent of auditing and of techniques for auditing to allow the development of an audit program that is uniquely fitted to the auditor's industry, processes, and company culture.

The handbook is meant for both new and experienced auditors. New auditors will benefit most from chapters 1 through 6, while experienced auditors will find chapters 5 through 14 most useful. The section on senior management's responsibilities in Chapter 4 and auditing for strategic performance in Chapter 14 should be required reading for every executive and middle manager in the company. Audit program managers will find chapters 4, 5, 7, and 11 particularly useful. And while many of the fundamental concepts of auditing apply to any management system audit, separate chapters have been devoted to the unique aspects of quality, environmental, and health and safety management system audits. These can be found in chapters 8, 9, and 10. Finally, a chapter has been provided on how to integrate these into one combined audit, making the audit both more effective and more efficient.

Included on the accompanying CD are electronic checklists that can be used to plan and guide the auditor in the evaluation of both the conformance and effectiveness of the management system to the corresponding standard's requirements. In addition to the questions that an auditor might ask, many of these checklists contain pop-up notes that provide the auditor with tips on how to verify the auditee's response. When combined with knowledge of the process or area being audited, they provide a powerful tool for ensuring the consistency and effectiveness of internal audits.

Acknowledgments

Certainly, writing a book that attempts to capture a lifetime of learning and experience does not come about without the assistance and support of others. Most importantly, I would like to thank those who had the patience and persistence to show me the right way to audit, starting with Cynthia Clark, Steve Eslinger, Gerry Starnes, John Button, Ron Argenta, Ray Wiesniewski, and Dave Curtis, all members of the Naval Nuclear Propulsion Program. Appreciation is also extended to all of the other dedicated men and women in the U.S. Navy Submarine Program, who taught me that excellence is the standard, not the exception. Special thanks goes to George Smith, my mentor, still the best auditor I've ever known.

Thanks also go to my friends and colleagues at Eastern Michigan University's Center for Quality and QualSat, who took a retired naval officer and gave him a chance to practice his skills in the automotive industry. Thank you Barbara Hopkins, Walter Dimantova, John Lindland, and Mark Lindsay. Thanks also to all of those companies and individuals who allowed me into their organizations and graciously provided the feedback that allowed me to improve my techniques and tools.

Thanks also to George Raub, Anton Camarota, Ronald Berglund, Jonathan Kovach, and the many others who took the time to review the manuscript and provide comments. Your insights were invaluable and led to many additions and improvements. Thanks also to Paul O'Mara and all my friends at ASQ Quality Press who had the patience and talent to coordinate this project.

Finally, thanks to my wife and family, without whose support and understanding this book could never have been written.

Part I

Management Systems and the Audit Program

P art I examines the structure and intent of the most common management systems in use. The section starts in Chapter 1 with a look at what any management system should do and then briefly reviews the structure of ISO 9001:2000,[1] ISO/TS 16949:2002,[2] ISO 14001,[3] and OHSAS 18001.[4] Of particular note is the section that discusses management system evolution from conformance through effectiveness and toward improvement.

Chapter 2 builds on Chapter 1 by examining what a management system audit should do. It defines and expands on the types of findings documented during the audit and when they should be expected. This chapter also presents the concept of audit program evolution, theorizing that the audit program should evolve to meet the changing needs of the management system. It also discusses important organizational benefits that should flow out of the audit program and provides a survey that managers and audit professionals can use to determine to what extent they are realizing these benefits. Both chapters 1 and 2 focus on the commonalities between quality, environmental, and health and safety management systems, and strategies and techniques for evaluating them.

The different types of audits and the skills required to perform them are addressed in Chapter 3. This chapter also explains the concepts behind *process-based* audits and why auditors should be performing them. It finishes with a short discussion on regulatory compliance reviews, which are not management system audits per se, but may be integrated at least partially into the management system audit program.

Chapter 4 completes this section by examining the components of any audit program. It starts by discussing the roles and responsibilities of auditors, lead auditors, clients, and auditees. A very thorough analysis of the pros and cons of using part-time auditors versus full-time auditors follows. An extremely important section is devoted to the role senior management fills in the support of the audit program. Auditor selection, training, and qualification are discussed next, followed by examples of audit forms and aids that may be used to support the audit program. The chapter and section concludes with a detailed review of the strategy and mechanics that go into the development of an audit schedule.

Part I should be required reading for all managers and executives within the organization, with special emphasis on management's role in support of the audit program in Chapter 4. Audit program managers will find chapters 2 and 4 particularly useful, although all sections should at least be quickly skimmed. Management system auditors will be most interested in chapters 1 through 3.

1

What a Management System Should Do

This chapter examines the structure of a typical management system, along with the intent, or purpose, of its major elements. The term *management system*, herein refers to quality, environmental, and health and safety management systems, not financial management, information management, or personnel management systems. Although each of these other management systems do indeed have structural elements similar to the ones we will examine, they are not the focus of this handbook.

In general, any management system is composed of three primary components:

- The *primary, or core, processes* that focus on the primary outputs of the system and the processes that produce them. In the quality management system this is the product realization process, while in the environmental management system it is the identification and control of significant environmental aspects.

- The *key supporting processes* that provide direct inputs into the core elements or measure the results of the outputs. These would include the processes used to ensure competency and awareness, an adequate infrastructure, and internal communications. It would also include the process, product, and customer satisfaction monitoring process.

- The *management system supporting elements,* such as document control, record control, and internal auditing.

For a management system to be effective, all of these components must be aligned and performing as they are intended. While most of the attention is given to the primary processes, failure to adequately monitor or control any of the supporting processes will impact the quality of the primary outputs.

THE PURPOSE OF ANY MANAGEMENT SYSTEM

The primary purpose of any management system is to implement the chosen strategy of an organization by focusing resources on areas critical for organizational success. For a quality management system this means providing high-quality products and services that meet or exceed customer requirements and expectations. For an environmental management system this means reducing or eliminating the negative environmental impacts of its products, services, and activities and/or increasing their positive impacts. For a health and safety management system it means providing a safe and healthy workplace for the organization's employees and surrounding community.

To meet this purpose, all management systems establish requirements and guidelines that, when followed, should provide reasonable assurance that the outputs from the system will be as expected (that is, high-quality products or services, minimal negative environmental impact, or a healthy and safe workplace). The purpose of the management system standards and specifications is to provide these general requirements. Note that the ISO 9001, ISO 14001, and OHSAS 18001 standards are nonprescriptive; that is, they detail what should be done, not necessarily how to do it. Organizations then develop and implement internal systems, processes, and procedures that provide more detail on how these general requirements are met within their unique operating environment.

Much of an internal auditor's focus will be on verifying that these internally defined policies, procedures, and practices are actually in place and are being used throughout the organization. This is the *conformance verification* aspect of the internal audit. The assumption is that if we follow the procedures and practices specified, we should produce the desired result.

Note that the *assumption* is that if we conform with the management system requirements, we will produce high-quality outputs. This is just an assumption. Because of the complexity of most modern management systems, and because it is possible that we may not have correctly designed the controls and methods used to realize the output, it is important that the auditor also examine the actual outputs of the processes being reviewed to confirm that the desired outputs are, in fact, being achieved. This is the *effectiveness confirmation* aspect of the internal audit.

Although the primary purpose of any management system is to ensure the quality of its outputs, it is also important that the activities that are used to accomplish this purpose be efficient and provide maximum value. In today's ultracompetitive business environment, organizations do not have the time, money, or other resources to support inefficient or non-value-added activities. This means that the internal processes that make up the management system components must be in alignment and must fully support the other processes that they input into. The general trend in management system standards is to reinforce this need to align processes into integrated systems of processes, all focused on providing the highest quality outputs from the system.

This is an important concept for internal auditors. In essence, the movement is away from the "silo approach" to management to an integrated systems approach. In the silo approach, individual departments seek to optimize their outputs, often at the expense of the organization (and customer) as a whole. As an example, the primary output of the marketing department is to bring in orders. A marketing department that narrowly focuses on bringing in orders will sometimes seek to optimize that objective by bringing in orders that the company really can't do. Or, it may spend less time interacting with the customer to determine exactly what the customer needs or expects, since that time could be better spent tracking down new prospective customers ("Besides, that's engineering's job, anyway."). In essence, the marketing department throws the order over the departmental wall to engineering who has to figure out how to design a product that will meet the customer's often ill-defined needs.

The engineering department, whose primary job is to design a product that will meet the customer's requirements, will do its best but in light of the absence of information about the customer's application environment will probably overdesign the product, which will lead to manufacturing problems later. In reality, the engineering department should go back to the customer to get more information, but "that's marketing's job" and detracts from time spent optimizing the overall goal of product design and development. Instead, assumptions are made of the customer's expectations based on past experience and the design is finalized. The engineering department has done its job and throws the design over the departmental wall to the production department, whose function it is to manufacture the product. Rarely does the engineering department involve production during the design of product, since it's not their job to worry about manufacturing. Of course, without good communication between departments during product design the likelihood is that the product will be difficult to produce or very costly to manufacture. This is shown graphically in Figure 1.1.

Even though each department optimizes its own departmental processes toward its primary goal (bringing in orders, developing new products, and so on), this silo approach can have disastrous effects on the business as a whole and on its ability to meet the customer's expectations. In fact, the customer is forgotten once the order is received, until it comes time to deliver the product. The new quality management standards, in particular, have been revised to reinforce the need to integrate and align internal processes like sales, engineering, and production into horizontal processes focused on

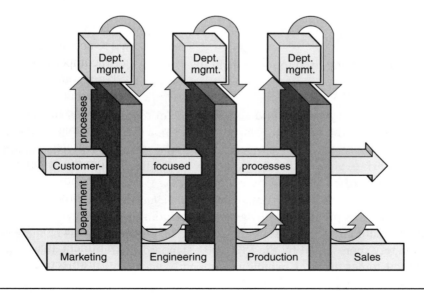

Figure 1.1   The silo approach to management.

the customer and not individual department functions. Customers do not care about these vertical processes that exist within an organization; they care only about the horizontal, or cross-departmental processes that focus on meeting their needs. Another primary purpose of any management system then is to align and integrate separate activities and functions into an interdependent system of processes that focus on the primary outputs of the organization and its customers.

What does this mean to the internal auditor? In addition to verifying conformance to and the overall effectiveness of the management system, internal auditors should also evaluate the extent to which the internal processes are aligned and supportive of each other. This means that the auditor will also examine the inputs into the process being evaluated to see if they are adequate and sufficient, along with the outputs from the process to see if they are supporting the downstream processes that they feed.

Value Streams and Customer-Oriented Processes

A *value stream* is a set of interrelated activities that provide value to your customers. From the customer's viewpoint, value-adding activities are described as things that the customer would be willing to pay for, were they to be itemized on the price list for the product. Value streams may reach down to your suppliers and up to intermediate customers between you and the end user. There are three primary value streams of importance to your customers. These three value streams are (1) concept to launch, (2) raw material to finished product, and (3) order to cash.

The *concept to launch* value stream represents the traditional design and development process that has been included in ISO 9001 and most other quality standards for years. The concept to launch value stream includes some important activities not always included in the formal quality management system. Some of these additional activities include:

- New idea generation

- Upstream marketing used to understand the voice of the customer

- Pricing and target costing

The *raw material to finished product* value stream represents the standard manufacturing process, or in the case of a company that primarily offers services, the service delivery process. These activities are well represented by the processes included in clause 7.4 (Purchasing) and 7.5 (Product and Service Realization) of the ISO 9001:2000 quality system standard.

Finally, the *order to cash* value stream represents everything from getting the order from the customer, the processing of the order, including production scheduling and delivery, to invoicing and receipt of payment from the customer. Most of these activities are adequately represented by the ISO 9001 standard, with the possible exception of processing customer invoices, which until recently was generally seen as extending beyond the scope of the traditional quality management system.

Each of these value streams and the processes that make them up represent customer-oriented processes in that they focus specifically on adding value to the customer. In addition, together these activities start with the customer and end with the customer, and in so doing reflect the customer-focused process represented by the horizontal arrow extending through Figure 1.1. The important point here is that by focusing our energies on those activities that add value to the customer, we will be able to better satisfy our customers, expand our markets, generate more sales, and grow the business. Any action or item that does not add value to the customer or is not necessary to support the processes that do is waste.

This handbook will emphasize the evaluation of these value streams. Evaluating related customer-oriented processes together greatly increases both the efficiency and effectiveness of the management system audit. Such an audit can be challenging, but ample discussion is provided to allow the auditor to successfully plan and conduct the evaluation.

Muda or Waste

Once we understand and accept the importance of customer-oriented processes, we can start to appreciate the concept of *muda*, or waste. Waste is considered to be anything that adds cost without adding value. Examples of waste in the workplace include:

- Excessive inventories

- Rework and repair

- Excessive travel between workstations

- Interim storage of materials and parts

- Time spent waiting for parts and materials

- Unnecessary equipment downtime

- Unnecessary equipment

- Unnecessary reviews and approvals

- Waiting in line for the copy machine

- Wide distribution of a report that only a few need

Many other examples could be given, and undoubtedly you have a few of your own. The identification of waste represents an opportunity for improvement and, as such, is within the charter of the internal auditor, especially as the company moves from the conformance phase into the effectiveness phase of maturity.

A final purpose of any management system is to provide a mechanism for continual improvement. Considering the pace of change and the intensity of competition today, the organization that is not improving is constantly losing ground. Improvements may focus on many areas such as quality, efficiency, or value, but the constant is that change for the better is mandatory in today's marketplace. A management system must establish the mechanisms and culture of improvement to be successful. Internal auditors can support this purpose by reviewing these mechanisms and by identifying opportunities for improvement within the organization. They can also drive improvements by identifying best practices that should be shared throughout the organization.

To summarize, the purpose of any management system should be to provide the following:

- High-quality outputs that address customer needs

  - For a quality management system (QMS), high-quality products and services that meet or exceed customer requirements and expectations

  - For an environmental management system (EMS), products, services, and activities that have minimal adverse impact or that produce positive impacts on the environment

  - For an occupational health and safety system (OH&S), a healthy and safe environment for employees and the surrounding community

- Efficient operations along the entire value stream, with minimal waste

- Aligned operations, optimized for the organization as a whole and focused on customer satisfaction

- Mechanisms for continual improvement of the organization's products, processes, and practices

EXPECTED BENEFITS

Another way to look at the purpose of a management system is to examine the benefits that it should provide. Possible generic benefits include:

- Higher-quality outputs

- More consistent operations

- Higher customer satisfaction (customers being consumers, the environment, employees)

- More efficient operations

- Higher profitability

The extent to which these benefits are achieved is dependent on how mature the organization's management systems are, which is reflected by how well they are accomplishing the functions or purposes just described.

Unfortunately, many companies fail to achieve all of the expected benefits after implementing an ISO 9001, ISO 14001, and/or OHSAS 18001 management system. As a management system trainer, I have conducted hundreds of seminars on these management systems, and I always ask for a show of hands of those participants who believe that they have indeed realized all of the five basic benefits just highlighted. I've never had more than a few hands go up. Often I have none. I then go on to explain how they must evolve their management system toward the benefits that they seek.

MANAGEMENT SYSTEM EVOLUTION

Management systems, like other systems, must evolve. Initially when an organization puts in a management system, the focus is on implementation and conformance with the new procedures and practices. Corrective action is taken when nonconformances are found. The focus is on getting a basic system in place. I call this the *compliance phase*.

The benefits realized at this initial level of maturity are dependent on how well the informal practices that existed prior to implementation of the management system worked and how consistently they were followed. If a company had reasonably good quality practices in the past, then just "saying what we do" in the form of procedures is unlikely to significantly improve the quality of the outputs unless they were not consistently followed. These companies comprise a large share of the organizations that complain that they have not benefited from implementation of ISO 9001, ISO 14001, and/or OHSAS 18001. Organizations with good preexisting practices must rapidly move to the next level of maturity to benefit from their management system.

On the other hand, organizations without good preexisting systems or practices should realize significant improvements in quality, consistency, and customer satisfaction in the compliance phase. It should be noted that improvements in efficiency and effectiveness may be minimal in this phase, since it's possible to consistently do things in an inefficient and nonproductive manner. The goal should be to move rapidly through the compliance phase toward the effectiveness phase. Unfortunately many companies never leave this phase, and after realizing initial benefits, complain that the management system no longer adds value. This phase is characterized by internal audits with numerous conformance deficiencies. For EMS and OH&S systems, this phase normally focuses on compliance with regulatory requirements.

As the management system matures, and conformance becomes less of an issue, more attention is focused on results. This is the *effectiveness phase*. In this phase both process owners and internal auditors focus more attention on the results being produced by the system and by the internal processes that make up the system. In any large system with multiple interdependent processes, it is inherent that some processes will not be producing the results that they should. The key to improving the overall primary outputs from the system is to improve the results of each of the interdependent processes that feed into the system. In this phase the management team and process owners will develop more robust systems of metrics to measure how well these internal processes are performing. Areas where results are not being obtained will be targeted for improvement. Internal auditors will spend more time looking at process effectiveness and less at conformance. Auditors will be able to focus their attention on processes where the metrics say a performance issue exists. In these processes, auditors will then identify nonconformance to existing practices, which could be a cause of poor performance, and at process design and improvement. Internal audits will uncover more findings relating to effectiveness and opportunities for improvement. Nonconformances will be primarily associated with processes that are not performing adequately. Organizations in this phase will see improvements in their effectiveness, productivity, and bottom-line profitability.

The final level of maturity is the *continual improvement phase.* In this phase there is a complete system of metrics on all important processes and the processes have been optimized to produce results. Although effectiveness and conformance will continue to be monitored, more attention will be placed on efficiency and deriving additional value out of existing processes. This is the level at which innovation, creativity, and the implementation of best practices become widespread throughout the organization. In addition to auditing for effectiveness and conformance where results are not being achieved, auditors will look to measures of efficiency associated with waste, time, and value and will note opportunities for improvement when weaknesses are identified. Auditors may also more aggressively seek out best practices that should be communicated throughout the organization. At this phase all of the primary benefits will be realized, with significant improvements in profitability. This evolutionary model of quality management system (QMS) development is illustrated in Figure 1.2.

The bottom line is that the management system is what you make it. If you are not realizing the expected benefits from your management system, ask yourself what level of maturity you are currently at and then take the steps needed to proceed to the next level. ISO 9001, ISO 14001, and OHSAS are nonprescriptive minimal standards. They do not tell you exactly what to do, nor do they tell you how to do it. They are minimal in that they provide the minimum requirements for quality, environmental, or health and safety management; it is up to you to go beyond the minimum in areas of importance to your company and your customers. Internal auditors can identify weaknesses in these

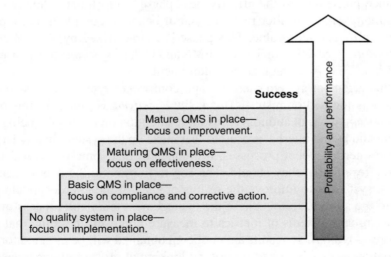

Figure 1.2 Quality management system evolution.

systems, both in terms of conformance and effectiveness, and opportunities for improvement. As such, internal auditors can be a driving force for change and performance improvement in areas of real importance to the organization.

Now we will examine the basic framework of several of the more common management system models. An understanding of these concepts will be used during audit planning and audit execution and will define the flow of an efficient and effective audit. Note that auditors must be knowledgeable of the standards to which they are auditing, including their detailed requirements. This discussion is not meant to replace such standard-specific knowledge or training. Rather, it is to ensure that the auditor can see the big picture needed to plan and conduct the audit.

ISO 9001:2000 BASICS

The ISO 9001:2000 quality system standard defines a management system model for developing, implementing, and improving the effectiveness of an organization's quality management system focused on meeting customer requirements. Although ISO 9001 is defined as a quality management system model, it has truly evolved into a business management system model through its inclusion of all internal processes that impact on the organization's ability to satisfy its customers.

The discussion that follows applies equally to industry-specific variations of ISO 9001:2000, including AS9100:2004[5] (aerospace industry), ISO 13485:2003[6] (medical device industry), and TL 9000[7] (telecommunications industry). Each of these industry variations has their own focus and supplemental requirements, but all have the same basic requirements regarding management system audits. This handbook will expand on one of the industry variations, ISO/TS 16949:2002 (automotive industry), as a means of demonstrating how the auditor should evaluate the industry-specific requirements of the management system. Important considerations for some of the other industry-specific standards will be highlighted as appropriate points in the chapters that follow.

The Process Approach

The ISO 9001 model promotes the adoption of the process approach when developing, maintaining, and improving internal activities and services. A *process* can be defined as any activity that transforms inputs into outputs. As an example, consider the process of developing a conceptual design for a new product. The process model might look like Figure 1.3.

The older versions of the standard, and many other current quality models, focus almost exclusively on the transformation step of the process. That is, they provide the requirements that must be met and the controls to be used during the transformation, with only minimal consideration of the inputs and only generic requirements for the outputs. Companies implemented the earlier models by developing procedures that laid out the steps needed to properly conduct the activity, in this example, conceptual design. This transformation-focused model was reinforced in earlier standards by the

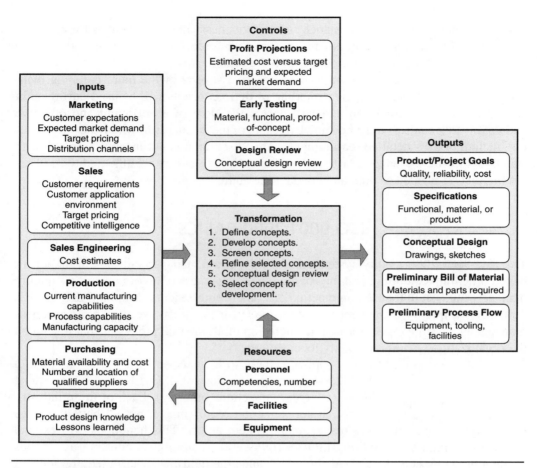

Figure 1.3   Simplified example of a typical process.

grouping of requirements into elements, with each major element focused on a major transformation activity (for example, contract review, design control, product identification, and so on).

Unfortunately, experience has taught us that the old adage, "garbage in–garbage out" is still as true today as it was yesterday. Even if we do everything exactly right during the transformation step, the outputs will still be bad if the inputs were bad. For example, if the sales and marketing departments do a poor job of defining customer expectations and requirements, then the product will not satisfy customers no matter how well it was designed. Likewise, if the cost estimates produced by sales engineering are inaccurate, we may end up with a well-designed product that can't sell because it must be priced too high to cover costs and thus fail to meet customer expectations regarding price. The process approach embedded in the ISO 9001:2000 models emphasizes the understanding and control of the critical inputs and resources into a process as much as it does on controlling the transformation process.

On the other side of the example, the new ISO model emphasizes understanding how the outputs of the process support other processes needed to satisfy the customer. Indeed, these outputs become inputs into these downstream processes and, as such, also need to be monitored and controlled as inputs. To truly embrace the process concept, the supplier of these outputs (in this case, the product development team) would go to these internal customers and determine what they need in terms of the quality, information, timeliness, accuracy, format, and other attributes of these deliverables in order to fully meet their needs. This would continue until all of the organization's important processes were aligned to meet both its external and internal customers' needs and expectations. In effect, what is created are systems of processes all oriented and operating together toward the achievement of system goals, most typically to satisfy the customer.

The Five Processes of ISO 9001:2000

The revised ISO 9001 standard has accomplished this shift to the process approach by regrouping the requirements contained in the previous version's 20 activity-focused elements into five major interdependent processes as follows:

Clause 7.0 Product realization. Clause 7.0 now contains all requirements that directly relate to producing products and services, from understanding customer needs and requirements to delivery and any post-delivery servicing. This clause represents the major horizontal process illustrated in Figure 1.1 and is the primary focus of the management system. In the big-picture view of the management system, this clause represents an integrated transformation activity, with the qualifier that it also includes the primary customer inputs and expected outputs from each process activity.

Clause 6.0 Resources. Clause 6.0 contains requirements related to the control of critical inputs into the product realization and key support processes. These resources may be in the form of competent operators, infrastructure, or the work environment. In the big picture, this clause represents some of the critical inputs and resources needed to support the transformation process.

Clause 8.0 Measurement, analysis and improvement. Clause 8.0 monitors the outputs of the management system and its processes and products. It is focused on ensuring that the outputs from each step are producing the expected results, in terms important to both the external customer (that is, meeting defined requirements and overall satisfaction) and internal customer (process effectiveness).

Clause 5.0 Management responsibility. This clause can be considered as a necessary input for the overall management system and its related processes. It reflects the importance of management's involvement and support in the operation of internal processes and in providing vision and direction for the organization.

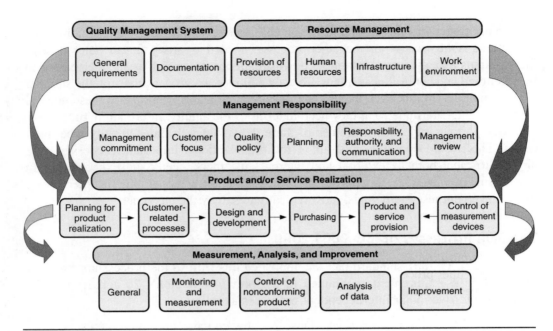

Figure 1.4   General structure of ISO 9001:2000.

Clause 4.0 Quality management system. Clause 4.0 defines two important processes needed to support the quality management system, document and record control, and lays out the general framework for developing and implementing a QMS that complies with the ISO 9001 standard. The structure of the QMS is shown in Figure 1.4 and consists of the five main processes just described, each of which contains more detailed requirements related to that process. Note that clauses 4.0, 5.0, and 6.0 provide inputs, resources, and support for product or service realization, while clause 8.0 monitors the output of these activities.

ISO 9001:2000 Development, Implementation, and Improvement

The requirements outlined in clause 4.1 provide the framework for the development and implementation of an ISO 9001–compliant quality management system. This clause also provides an overall summary of what a process-based management system should do. The standard requires that the organization:

- *Identify the processes needed for the quality management system and their application throughout the organization.* Note that the processes that should be controlled are no longer limited to those defined by the 20 elements of the old standard. Processes such as information management, customer relationship management, and customer invoicing are now candidates for inclusion since they directly impact the ability of the organization to satisfy its customers. This is why we say that ISO 9001 is now a business management system versus a quality management system.

- *Determine the sequence and interaction of these processes.* Understand how the organization's processes interact and support each other, linking the outputs from one process to the inputs to another. Define the system of processes important to meeting customer requirements.

- *Determine criteria and methods needed to ensure that both the operation and control of these processes are effective.* Identify the actions needed to properly perform these activities, including standards and criteria needed to ensure their performance.

- *Ensure the availability of resources and information necessary to support the operation and monitoring of these processes.* Provide adequate resources for proper process operation and establish a system of metrics to measure process performance.

- *Monitor, measure, and analyze these processes.* Perform the monitoring and measurement just identified, and analyze the results to determine process performance.

- *Implement actions necessary to achieve planned results and continual improvement of these processes.* Take action to correct and/or improve the process if it is not performing as expected.

The rest of the standard expands on these core requirements, but the heart of the model is the repetitive application of these actions to each of your processes that impact on your ability to satisfy your customers. Auditors evaluating an ISO 9001:2000 quality management system must be able to evaluate processes, including the adequacy of their inputs, resources, controls, and outputs. This has important implications for how the audit is planned and conducted, and will be examined in detail in later chapters.

ISO/TS 16949:2002 BASICS

The ISO/TS 16949:2000 specification is an industry-specific version of ISO 9001:2000. All of the previous discussion relating to ISO 9001 also applies to ISO/TS 16949. In addition, the ISO/TS 16949 specification adds supplemental requirements unique to the automotive industry. The most important of these relate to what are referred to as the automotive core tools, which include:

- *Advanced product quality planning (APQP).*[8] This methodology provides common guidelines for a structured approach for defining and establishing the steps needed to ensure a quality product and robust production processes.

It provides a framework to pull together the other requirements and tools presented in ISO/TS 16949 and associated reference manuals.

- *Production part approval process (PPAP).*[9] This methodology defines generic requirements for production part approval. It is used to determine if all customer engineering design record and specification requirements are properly understood and that the process has the potential to produce product consistently meeting these requirements during an actual production run at the quoted production rate.

- *Failure mode and effects analysis (FMEA).*[10] This provides general guidelines for preparing a failure mode and effects analysis of products and processes, including the application of techniques used to conduct the analysis. It provides guidance on how to use the FMEA to improve current and future product and process designs.

- *Measurement systems analysis (MSA).*[11] This methodology provides an introduction to measurement system analysis, along with guidance on how to conduct measurement system studies to ensure the quality of data used for product and process evaluation.

- *Statistical process control (SPC).*[12] This methodology provides an introduction to statistical process control and presents general guidelines for the selection and application of statistical techniques to monitor, analyze, and improve production and supporting processes.

Evaluating an ISO/TS 16949 QMS requires that the auditor understand the requirements of these and the other additional automotive-specific requirements, and how they fit within the overall structure of the quality management system. Strategies, techniques, and tips for evaluating the automotive core tools will be provided in Chapter 12.

ISO 14001:2004 BASICS

The ISO 14001 environmental management system standard is a model of environmental stewardship that combines regulatory compliance with sustainable development initiatives. The standard was developed to help address the rash of environmental issues that generated global concerns in the 1980s such as greenhouse gas emissions (global warming), ozone depletion in the upper atmosphere, the loss of biodiversity, deforestation, and depletion of the earth's natural resources. The standard embraces the concept of sustainable development, which is development that meets the needs of the present without compromising the ability of future generations to meet their own needs. To achieve this, the standard requires that an organization commit to environmental performance that goes beyond compliance, or beyond the minimum required to satisfy regulatory and legal requirements.

The ISO 14001 standard is developed around Deming's famous plan–do–check–act (PDCA) model of improvement. Its planning elements consist of the development of an environmental policy that must include the organization's commitment to the environment. Of note, a commitment to comply with regulatory and legal requirements is mandatory, as are commitments to continual improvement and the prevention of pollution. As part of planning its environmental management system (EMS), the organization must also identify those products, services, and activities that could have an impact on the environment. These are called environmental aspects. The organization then evaluates these aspects to determine those that could or do impact the environment in a significant way. It then identifies controls and methods to minimize those impacts that could harm the environment or to expand on those that benefit it. This typically includes substitution of environmentally friendly materials for hazardous materials, resource conservation, reuse, recycling, and process modifications. Planned improvements, in the form of environmental objectives and targets, must also be established along with plans on how to achieve them.

The *doing* component is titled Implementation and Operation, and in this phase the organization implements the controls and methods identified in the planning phase. In addition, the standard requires that operators be trained in the performance of environmental duties and be made aware of their impact on the environment, that roles and responsibilities be defined and communicated, that documents used to support the EMS be controlled, and that emergency plans be developed, maintained, and tested.

The checking and corrective action elements represent the *check* component of the PDCA cycle. Here the organization monitors how well its environmental controls are working, along with the performance of its management system. Records of actions and performance must be maintained and controlled. Compliance to regulatory and legal environmental requirements must also be reviewed. If deficiencies or nonconformances are noted, then corrective action is initiated to restore the performance of the system.

The *act* component of the PDCA cycle is represented by the management review requirements, which mandate senior-level review of the overall performance of the EMS and its related components. The output of this review should lead to actions and decisions to correct or improve performance.

It has been shown that a mature ISO 14001 EMS leads not only to improved environmental performance, but also to improved profitability. Significant cost reductions in the handling and disposal of hazardous materials and solvents, in energy costs, and increased revenues from recycling and the sale of byproducts are all commonly cited by companies that have learned that it pays to go beyond compliance.

The ISO 14001:2004 EMS model is shown in Figure 1.5. The standard was recently revised. The major changes were the combining of the requirements for objectives, targets, and management programs in clauses 4.3.3 and 4.3.4 and the separation of the requirements for environmental performance monitoring in clause 4.5.1 into two separate clauses—4.5.1, Monitoring and measurement, and 4.5.2, Evaluation of compliance. The core requirements and intent of the standard have essentially remained intact.

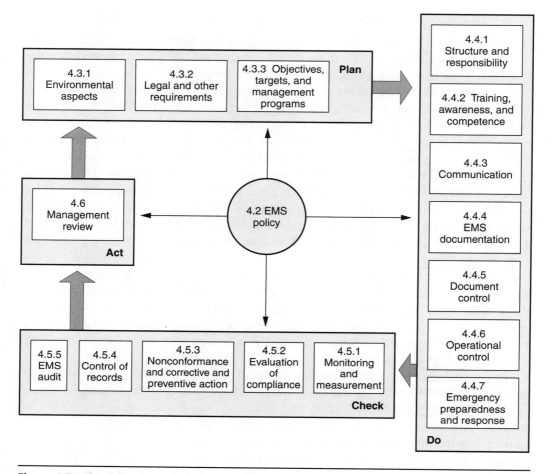

Figure 1.5   The ISO 14001:2004 EMS model.

OHSAS 18001 BASICS

The Occupational Health and Safety Assessment Series (OHSAS) 18001:1999 specification was developed by the British Standards Institute (BSI) as a model to assist an organization in the identification, evaluation, control, and minimization of occupational health and safety (OH&S) risks in the workplace. The model provided in OHSAS 18001 mirrors the model of ISO 14001:1996. Indeed, many of the requirements of the specification are almost verbatim the requirements for the environmental management system. This allows an organization that has already implemented an ISO 14001 EMS to more easily expand its current management system to include health and safety risks to its employees.

A review of the structure of OHSAS 18001 shows that it follows the same PDCA model of the ISO 14001 model. The major elements of the specification are illustrated in Figure 1.6.

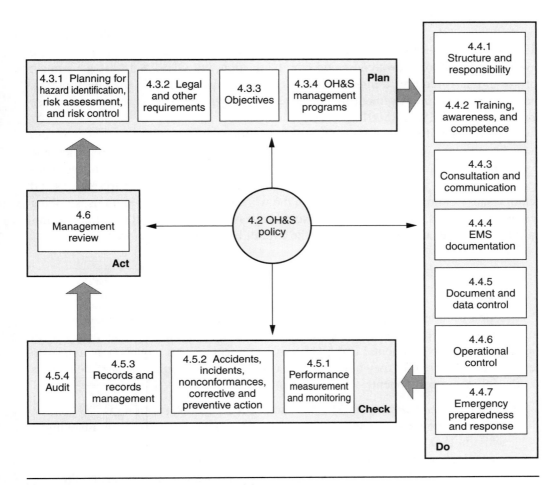

Figure 1.6   The OHSAS 18001:1999 model.

The primary differences between ISO 14001 and OHSAS 18001 lie in the planning activities. To develop and implement an EMS, an organization identifies the environmental aspects associated with its products, services, and activities and then determines those that could significantly impact the environment, in line with its environmental policy commitments. This is normally done during the performance of an initial environmental review. In 18001, the organization identifies the hazards associated with its workplace and workplace activities and then determines the risks that these hazards represent. This is accomplished through the systematic application of job hazard analysis (JHA) methodology. Once these hazards and their associated risks are identified, the organization then implements appropriate controls to minimize the risks associated with these activities. It should be noted that whereas an initial environmental review for an EMS may be completed in a matter of weeks or even days, a full JHA of all of an organization's hazards may take from several months to a year or more. Indeed, the JHA process is a continual process owing to the constantly changing nature of workplace activities and processes.

Another subtle, but important, difference between the EMS and the OH&S management systems relates to the level of employee involvement. Both systems require a high level of organizational awareness and communication, but OHSAS 18001 goes much further in that it requires a higher level of employee involvement in the development, maintenance, and improvement of the management system. This is termed *employee consultation* in OHSAS 18001.

The overall performance of the OH&S management system can be judged by reduction of workplace injuries, accidents, and near-misses. In progressive companies, the overall health of the workforce may also be used to gage the performance of the management system as judged by measures such as number of absences due to sickness and health issues not normally associated with the workplace. Nutrition programs, smoking cessation programs, and company-sponsored fitness programs are all examples of initiatives companies may use to improve the overall health of its workforce.

SUMMARY

This section introduced the internal auditor to the management systems that they may be asked to evaluate. Although the differences between the quality management system models and the environmental and OH&S management system models may appear to be pronounced, in reality they have much in common. In particular, each of the models has the following components:

- *A planning component.* In ISO 9001 and ISO/TS 16949, planning is represented by management system planning and product realization planning; while in ISO 14001 and OHSAS 18001, planning is represented by the identification of significant environmental aspects or hazards and risks associated with the organization's products, services, and activities, and the identification of appropriate methods to control them. Note that all of the standards require the establishment of an organizational policy that declares the company's commitments for quality, environmental performance, and/or health and safety performance.

- *An operational component.* In ISO 9001 and ISO/TS 16949 this is represented by the management system, resources, and product realization processes. In ISO 14001 and OHSAS 18001, requirements focused on operation and maintenance of the system are specified in the implementation and operation clauses.

- *A monitoring and corrective action component.* In ISO 9001 and ISO/TS 16949 these activities are defined in the monitoring and measurement, internal audit, control of nonconforming product, analysis of data, and corrective action processes. In ISO 14001 and OHSAS these activities are defined in checking and corrective action elements.

- *An improvement process.* In all of the standards, improvement is embedded in similar requirements for preventive action, for the setting of improvement objectives, and in the conduct of management reviews. In the ISO 9001 and ISO/TS 16949 model, additional requirements are added to address process improvement as needed based on the results of process performance monitoring.

These primary components, or processes, are important in that they provide insight into strategies useful for planning and conducting internal audits, either of individual systems or of an integrated quality, environmental, and OH&S system. These strategies will be more fully developed in Chapter 5 and Chapters 8 through 11.

2

What a Management System Audit Should Do

This chapter builds on Chapter 1 by examining what a management system audit should accomplish. As with the management system, a company's audit program also goes through a maturing evolution. Auditors normally learn first how to verify conformance. Once that skill set is mastered, the auditor reaches out to identify opportunities for improvement. Unfortunately, this is the limit of most auditors' skill sets. To be truly effective, the auditor must extend to auditing for effectiveness. At this point management support becomes truly critical. If the auditor can master these essential skills, and if the management team supports the audit program, then the auditor can further extend his or her focus to auditing for best practices. This evolution is diagrammed in Figure 2.1.

Note that this evolution mirrors the management system evolution discussed in Chapter 1. In a newly implemented management program the focus of auditors should be on conformance. As the management program progresses to the effectiveness phase, auditors should spend more time looking for opportunities for improvement and auditing

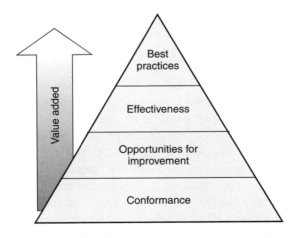

Figure 2.1 Audit evolution.

for effectiveness. Finally, as the management program moves into the continual improvement phase, auditors should lend support by seeking out best practices.

This also implies that there should be an auditor training program that provides for a progression in the mastery of these skills. New auditors would be overwhelmed if they were expected to be able to demonstrate all of these skills during their first few audits. Initial training should equip auditors to audit for conformance and obvious opportunities for improvement. Subsequent training for experienced auditors should focus on auditing for effectiveness and best practices. Auditor training will be discussed more fully in Chapter 4.

To state in simple terms, the objectives of any management system audit are fourfold:

- Identify any weaknesses that exist in the management system.

- Identify opportunities for improvement.

- Identify best practices that should be communicated throughout the organization.

- Determine how effectively the management systems support the strategy of the organization.

The extent to which these objectives can be met will depend on the maturity of the management system itself, the skill and training of the internal auditors, and the level of support provided by the management team for the realization of these objectives. At the end of this chapter you will find a survey that can help pinpoint how well your audit program is performing relative to these objectives and to what extent it is realizing the additional benefits described in the last section of this chapter. We will now look at the methods auditors use to accomplish these objectives, in terms of the types of findings normally generated.

VERIFYING CONFORMANCE

A fundamental purpose of any audit is to verify that the organization is conforming to the relevant standard and to its own internal policies and procedures. A management system cannot produce results if it is not followed. Although there are some practitioners who feel that conformance verification is a thing of the past, auditing for conformance has always been, and always will be, the foundation of any management system audit. Noncompliance is a weakness that will lead to inferior performance of the management system and such instances must be identified during the audit.

Conformance means that the organization is adhering to the requirements set forth in its internal procedures, policies, and guidelines and to external requirements set forth by the standard, customers, and/or adopted industry practices. Basically, it verifies that we are "doing what we say we do." Auditing for conformance is typically the easiest skill to learn since the auditor has a clear requirement that must be met. The auditor can compare the actual practice to the specified requirement and determine if the auditee is complying. Although conformance verification is the easiest skill for a new auditor to master, it is by no means always easy to do. As organizations move away from text-based procedures toward flowcharts and visual controls, the level of detail regarding the requirements that must be met evaporates. Compounding this is the fact that many of the management standards no longer require a written procedure for many of the processes. Auditors generate *nonconformance findings* (NCs) to document areas where deviations from the requirements are noted. Techniques and tips for conformance verification will be examined in chapters 4 and 5 and reinforced through all subsequent chapters in this handbook.

Auditors must be careful in how they view their role in accomplishing this purpose. Some auditors use an optimistic interpretation of this objective. It normally goes like this: "I'm not here to look for what you're doing wrong—I'm here to verify what you're doing right!" Unfortunately, this interpretation is misleading at best. I've heard it used by overzealous registrar auditors looking to put the auditee at ease or assuming that such an approach will result in continued business with the client. Usually when I hear it I recommend to my client that he or she request another auditor or possibly even look for a different registrar.

Except for those occasions where the auditor finds a best practice, which will be discussed in Chapter 13, no action is likely to result from focusing on what is being done right. In addition, complacency may set in or it may become harder to sustain a mind-set of continual improvement. While an auditor needs to give credit where exceptional practices are noted, an effective audit does not *focus* on verifying what's right with the system. Value is added when the auditor identifies weaknesses and opportunities for improvement.

IDENTIFYING OPPORTUNITIES FOR IMPROVEMENT

Opportunities for improvement (OFIs) are any areas where improvements in a process, typically associated with results, are obviously possible. Typical examples may include:

- An auditor notes high levels of scrap or rework in a production process.

- An auditor evaluating an enrollment process notes that student information is redundantly entered into an electronic database and a paper-based system because of concerns with the reliability of the electronic database.

- An auditor notes significant drafts or a high level of heat loss in an area during an EMS audit.

- An OH&S auditor notes through interviews that the instructions for conducting job hazard analysis are unclear, leading to some confusion among those performing the JHAs as to how they should evaluate risks.

In each of these cases, the auditor cannot generate a nonconformance because there is no definitive requirement relating to the observed practice and/or results. In the first situation, the auditor finds that the scrap and rework are being properly controlled, but notes that there are no criteria or objective established for the level of scrap or rework that can be tolerated without action. Still, in the auditor's judgment, the levels of scrap and rework are unusually high, thus the auditor generates an OFI. In the second example, the auditor notes that there is no requirement to insulate all areas of the facility, but he or she understands that energy conservation is an important aspect that directly affects environmental performance and thus notes the energy loss as an OFI. In the last example, the auditor finds that the evaluators are following the stated requirements for performing the JHA, but because of a lack of detail and/or clarity, confusion exists, which causes some inconsistency among the evaluators.

An opportunity for improvement does not require action on the part of the auditee, since there are not any defined requirements that must be met. Auditors often issue an OFI when they do not feel comfortable with what they find, but cannot find a requirement directly related to it. Auditors also often use the OFI to voice their opinions about how an operation should be conducted. This is not really in line with the purpose of the OFI and should be avoided in most cases. The widespread use of OFIs to offer opinions on methods or on how process owners should manage their processes can lead to disenchantment with the audit program over time. A better way to approach the issue of methodology is to use the audit program to develop a database of related best practices that could then be made available to process owners as a standard part of any audit of a targeted area, perhaps as a standard component of the audit report.

Because there is no clear requirement related to the practice being observed, the auditor must use judgment and perspective when generating OFIs. This is why the generation of opportunities for improvement is more difficult than conformance verification. It takes experience and some level of familiarity with a process to generate meaningful OFIs. Auditor training should provide clear guidelines for generating opportunities for improvement and meaningful examples. It should be noted that in some third-party registration schemes, such as ISO/TS 16949, the generation of OFIs by third-party auditors is no longer allowed.

In certain cases, what appears to be an opportunity for improvement may actually be better documented as a nonconformance. In particular, when an examination of results shows that a specified objective has not been achieved or that a long-term adverse trend is developing (such as a high scrap rate) and no action is being taken to achieve the objective or reverse the trend, then an NC would be appropriate. In these cases, the auditor is really auditing for effectiveness, the topic of the next section.

VERIFYING EFFECTIVENESS

As noted in Chapter 1, conformance with system policies and procedures does not guarantee performance of a management system. Ideally, when an organization initially develops its systems and procedures it would standardize on the most effective, efficient methods for performing the activity. This is not always the case. It is possible that the organization specified incorrect or inefficient methods for accomplishing its tasks. Therefore, it is important that the management system auditor also evaluate the effectiveness, or results, of the processes being audited.

Verifying effectiveness is one of the most important objectives of any management system audit, especially for those organizations progressing into the effectiveness phase of their management system evolution. This objective goes beyond basic correction of identified weaknesses and evidence of some improvement and focuses on the primary purpose of the process and the extent to which the process is accomplishing that purpose. In today's lean organization, all tasks must add value—they must provide results. While management may see broad, overall metrics relating to strategic objectives, auditors are in a unique position to identify waste and inefficiencies at the process or subprocess level. Furthermore, when auditors identify areas where expected results are not being achieved, they must then be able to thoroughly investigate those areas to help identify the reasons why. In most organizations these reasons will be associated with poorly designed and poorly validated processes, poor-quality inputs from or alignment with other processes, or nonconformance to established policies and procedures.

In some instances this is not difficult to do, such as when the organization has in place a well-defined system of process metrics that accurately reflect why the process exists. Auditors evaluating TL 9000 quality management systems, in particular, will have a robust system of process metrics in place that can be used to assess effectiveness, thanks to the standard's rigorous requirements for metrics and monitoring. In this case the auditor can evaluate trends or performance to goals to determine if the process is performing adequately. In other instances, however, such metrics will not exist, or the metrics will be at too high a level to directly correlate to the actions represented by the process being evaluated. In these situations, auditors must be able to identify and state the primary purpose of the process in terms that everyone, especially the process owner, can agree with. Then the auditor must be able to develop a strategy for collecting relevant and sufficient audit evidence to establish whether the process is accomplishing its primary purpose. How to do this, and how to present the findings relating to process effectiveness requires a new way of thinking on the part of the auditor and will be discussed in later chapters on planning, conducting, and documenting the audit.

Long term, the goal is to establish a mind-set where the auditor is always looking for evidence that actions are effective, not just on an overall process basis but also for each activity within the process. In effect, the auditor also performs an informal value analysis of the process, looking for opportunities to improve the effectiveness and efficiency of the process by identifying instances where the resources and inputs are not providing the expected outputs or results. Once this is achieved, attitudes relating to the value of the audit itself will start to change. Of course, this is a lot easier to say than to actually do, and requires strong management commitment and support. Chapter 4 will discuss more thoroughly what management must bring to the table in order to realize these benefits.

IDENTIFYING BEST PRACTICES

This is a valid objective of an audit, but one that requires significant perspective and objectivity. Experienced internal auditors, in particular, are in a very favorable position to identify best practices during audits so that they can be communicated and implemented throughout other portions of the organization, as appropriate. This is difficult for new auditors, who typically lack the baseline for comparison needed to identify best practices. Properly designed, the internal audit program can serve as an element of an internal benchmarking program in addition to its many other benefits.

As noted in Chapter 1, organizations moving into the improvement phase of their management system evolution will need to be more aggressive in identifying best practices than those at lower levels of maturity. Indeed, without a common and robust system of metrics it may not even be possible to establish the baseline of comparison needed to identify best practices. I recommend that specialized training be provided to experienced auditors who will be seeking out best practices during their internal audits, focused on concepts of internal benchmarking, performance measurement and comparison, and training in the documentation, communication, and dissemination of best practices. The structure for such a training program will be explored in Chapter 4.

It should be noted here that the identification of best practices described here and in Chapter 13 goes well beyond the practice of commenting on areas of strength as is common during any audit, including external audits. Citing an area of strength is appropriate when the auditor finds performance to be significantly better than average and well beyond the minimum required to comply with the standard or the organization's basic requirements. The systematic identification of best practices, however, looks beyond the performance numbers and seeks to identify the enablers of performance so that others within the organization can judge whether the practice should be adopted by another team, department, or business unit. This type of deeper dive is primarily within the realm of internal auditors. External auditors should typically refrain from such research as it may violate confidentiality of the client and it may detract from the primary purpose of the external audit.

OTHER POSSIBLE BENEFITS

Auditing for effectiveness, for opportunities for improvement, and for best practices in addition to auditing for conformance will result in processes that are more efficient and productive, which will result in higher profitability and more satisfied customers. A robust internal audit program should also provide a number of additional benefits to the organization. Audit program managers and senior management should use these as benchmarks of the health of their audit program. Take the survey at the end of this chapter to see how your audit program measures up.

Benefit: Provide Training and Awareness

Training is not a primary objective of the audit. It is true, however, that audits typically do have a training benefit. Establishing training as one of the primary objectives of the audit risks compromising the other goals of the audit. Auditors may spend more time coaching an auditee about a process than looking for the weaknesses and opportunities for improvement.

As an alternative, it is important to recognize that the audit does provide training opportunities through the questions that are asked and the methods used to evaluate the process. As auditors focus more on evaluating the effectiveness of activities, auditees should be oriented to the importance of looking at process performance and how to gage it. This indirect training provides significant value and does not compromise the primary objectives of the audit.

Benefit: Promote Teamwork, a Spirit of Cooperation, and Respect

Auditing by its very nature is an interpersonal process. The way that the audit is planned and conducted can either support the concept that all are on the same team, or it can reinforce the image of auditors as the police. Respect means recognizing and acknowledging the value of the auditee's knowledge, expertise, and opinions in relation to the process being reviewed, and treating the auditee as an equal member of the audit team. Specific practices that promote this benefit are:

- Process owners/managers are requested to participate in determining the audit scope (areas to be reviewed) prior to the audit.

- Process owners/managers are asked to identify their primary challenges or concerns relating to the process being evaluated during the initial interview. Any areas so offered are then given special attention by the audit team.

- Auditees are informed that they are part of the audit team during introductions prior to starting an interview.

- Auditees are asked if they have any suggestions or opinions about the process or procedures being reviewed.

- Auditors use the words *we* and *our* instead of *you* and *yours* wherever possible during interviews.

- Auditees are asked if there are any areas that the audit team overlooked.

- Auditees are informed of any findings prior to terminating the interview.

Benefit: Promote a Spirit of Continual Improvement and a Focus on Performance

An effective audit program will support the development of a culture of performance excellence through continual improvement. Significant findings should be celebrated, not debated, as they represent opportunities to improve the performance of the process and the organization. Employees will not be fearful of the audit, but will cooperate and assist in the identification of weaknesses and process improvements. Audit findings must focus on effectiveness and performance in addition to conformance for this benefit to be realized. Specific practices that promote this benefit and/or measures that reflect how well it is being realized include:

- Audit findings frequently (well over 30 percent) focus on performance/ effectiveness issues and not just compliance or conformance.

- Process owners/managers are usually willing to volunteer information on process weaknesses and problems with the audit team.

- Process operators are usually willing to volunteer information on process weaknesses and problems with the audit team.

- Process owners/managers are generally willing to accept findings relating to performance when accompanied by objective evidence indicating the need for improvement.

- Process owners/managers are generally willing to accept findings relating to known, chronic, but previously undocumented, weaknesses when found by the audit team.

- Employees at all levels are free of fear of the audit process. When weaknesses are found, management focuses on fixing the system, not punishing the individual.

Benefit: New Skills Add Significant Value to the Organization

Auditing can be tough work. Why would anyone volunteer to be an auditor? To be truthful, many auditors are not volunteers. In organizations where management sees little value in the audit process and where time and cooperation are in short supply, auditors may need to be appointed. This is almost always a reliable indication of a dysfunctional audit process. In a properly administered audit program, many individuals want to be auditors, in part because of the valuable skills they gain, and in part because of the value that they add to the organization. Personal benefits include:

- Auditors gain a better understanding of how processes other than their own operate. This helps them manage their own interdependent process better and helps their career growth and development.

- Auditors learn how to evaluate and manage a process or system of interrelated processes. The importance of the inputs, controls, and metrics that support the actual transformation activities becomes more apparent as the auditor conducts process-based audits and sees the impact these can have on process performance. Process-based auditing exposes the auditor to systems thinking, a key skill set of the modern employee or manager.

- Auditors learn how to analyze information to make judgments relating to process performance. This skill should then carry over into their monitoring of their own processes.

- Auditors learn important interpersonal communication skills. Being able to commence and maintain a dialogue, to listen effectively, and to enlist the support of an occasional reluctant auditee are important skills that an auditor can apply in everyday situations. In addition, conflict management techniques learned during auditor training, even though not much used during internal audits, can be important assets in other team settings.

- Auditors learn the importance of writing clearly and of supporting their conclusions with facts. Auditors need this skill to communicate audit findings to the auditee. This skill can be applied to routine business and technical writing.

Benefit: Reinforce the Systems Approach to Management

The systems approach to management can significantly improve organizational effectiveness and efficiency, not to mention customer satisfaction. Process-based audits can be used to support the systems approach to management. Keep in mind that there are different levels of process-based audits. For example, a process-based audit can be performed on a subprocess, such as data entry, or it can examine a more complete value stream, such as order processing from receipt of customer order to scheduling of production and shipping of the final product. The first audit scope doesn't do much to support the systems approach to management, while the latter audit will touch on many of the interdependent processes needed to make the whole system work.

Internal management system audits should include as much of the value stream as possible since most problems occur at the interfaces and handoffs between subprocesses and inputs within a value stream. Most organizations have three primary value streams that directly impact the customer. These are the:

- New product/service concept to launch (design and development)

- Raw material/inputs to finished product or service delivery (product/service realization)

- Order to cash (administrative order processing)

Note that there may be more than one value stream in each of these categories because of differences in product or service characteristics or customer expectations. The chapter on audit planning will go into more detail on determining the proper audit scope.

Specific practices that promote this benefit are:

- The organization has identified its primary value streams, generically and/or by specific customer or product segments.

- Inputs, outputs, and interrelationships between processes within the value streams have been identified and mapped.

- The audit schedule reflects at least one audit annually of each type of primary value stream.

- Auditors are provided sufficient time to understand, plan, and conduct audits of an entire value stream.

Benefit: Support Value Stream Management and the Conversion to Lean Operations

The previous benefit touched on value streams. The knowledge obtained from auditing can be further put to use in helping to manage the value stream. Value stream management is lean management, and the audit skills relating to process analysis and mapping can be very beneficial in value stream mapping and improvement. Specific practices that promote this benefit are:

- The pool of auditors reflects all components of our primary value streams.

- Auditors are provided training in value stream mapping and are often used to support process teams during value stream analysis.

- Audit checklists contain elements for evaluating the use of lean operations, including areas such as 5S, total productive maintenance, and waste reduction.

Benefit: Support the Organization's Strategy and Deployment of Strategic Initiatives

As noted by Kaplan and Norton in their popular book, *The Balanced Scorecard,*[1] most organizations fail to achieve their strategic objectives not because of poor strategies, but because of poor execution. Auditors can provide early indicators of organizational weaknesses in the deployment of the strategy, if this is made a part of the audit objectives. Equally important, auditors can uncover the reasons why performance is lacking during their in-depth evaluation of a poorly performing process. Senior executives should recognize this strategic benefit and align their audit programs and focus with the strategic direction of the organization. Chapter 14 will discuss auditing for strategic impact in more detail.

AUDIT PROGRAM SURVEY

This survey is based on the benefits and practices discussed in this chapter. Audit program managers should candidly complete this survey to gauge the maturity of their internal audit program and to identify areas where it can be improved. Portions of the survey should be completed by process owners/managers, some may be completed by the company's internal auditors. Consider any items where respondents answer *no* to be potential candidates for improvement in your audit program. The survey has been included on the CD accompanying this handbook to allow you to excerpt specific sections for different groups of respondents.

Use this survey to evaluate the level of maturity of your audit program and the extent to which it is realizing all of its potential benefits. You can also use it to gauge how well your management team supports and believes in the audit program. The survey should be completed by the audit program manager. Other auditors may be questioned, to the extent needed.

1.0			**Survey topic:** *To what extent are auditees made to feel that they are respected and part of the audit team?*
	Yes	**No**	**Specific question/practice**
1.a			Process owners/managers are requested to participate in determining the audit scope (areas to be reviewed) prior to the audit.
1.b			Process owners/managers are asked to identify their primary challenges or concerns relating to the process being evaluated during the initial interview. Any areas so offered are then given special attention by the audit team.
1.c			Auditees are informed that they are part of the audit team during introductions prior to starting an interview.
1.d			Auditees are asked if they have any suggestions or opinions about the process or procedures being reviewed.
1.e			Auditors use the words *we* and *our* instead of *you* and *yours* wherever possible during interviews.
1.f			Auditees are asked if there are any areas that the audit team overlooked.
1.g			Auditees are informed of any findings prior to terminating the interview.
2.0			**Survey topic:** *To what extent is the audit process seen as value-added by management?*
	Yes	**No**	**Specific question/benchmarks**
2.a			Process owners/managers willingly provide auditors to the audit program.
2.b			Process owners/managers allow auditors under their control sufficient time to plan and conduct assigned audits.
2.c			Process owners/managers make themselves and their people available during the audit.
2.d			Process owners/managers will, on occasion, request that an audit be conducted on their areas/processes independent of or in addition to those already assigned on the audit schedule.
2.e			Process owners/managers are generally supportive and appreciative of the audit findings, and react appropriately and in a timely manner.
3.0			**Survey topic:** *To what extent does the audit program promote a spirit of continual improvement and a focus on performance?*
	Yes	**No**	**Specific question/practice**
3.a			Audit findings frequently (over 30 percent) focus on performance/effectiveness issues, not just compliance or conformance.
3.b			Process owners/managers are usually willing to volunteer information on process weaknesses and problems with the audit team.
3.c			Auditees are usually willing to volunteer information on process weaknesses and problems with the audit team.
3.d			Process owners/managers are generally willing to accept findings relating to performance when accompanied by objective evidence indicating the need for improvement.
3.e			Process owners/managers are generally willing to accept findings relating to known, but previously undocumented and hidden, weaknesses when found by the audit team.

Continued

	Yes	No	Specific question/practice
3.f			Employees at all levels are free of fear of the audit process. When weaknesses are found, management focuses on fixing the system, not punishing the individual.
4.0			**Survey topic:** *To what extent are audit skills seen as desirable beyond the audit process itself?*
	Yes	No	Specific question/benchmarks
4.a			More employees volunteer to be auditors than there are auditor slots to fill.
4.b			Managers often volunteer to be auditors.
4.c			Audit skill attainment is reflected in the organization's performance and recognition system.
4.d			At least 25 percent of the organization's supervisors and midlevel managers have at some point in their career functioned as internal auditors.
4.e			Managerial and leadership training courses as a minimum provide an overview of the process approach to management and how to evaluate process performance.
5.0			**Survey topic:** *To what extent do our internal audits focus on systems of related processes, as opposed to stand-alone activities?*
	Yes	No	Specific question/benchmarks
5.a			The organization has identified its primary value streams, generically and/or by specific customer or product segments.
5.b			Inputs, outputs, and interrelationships between processes within the value streams have been identified and mapped.
5.c			The audit schedule reflects at least one audit annually of each type of primary value stream.
5.d			Auditors are provided sufficient time to understand, plan, and conduct audits of an entire value stream.
6.0			**Survey topic:** *To what extent does our internal audit program support our lean initiatives and value stream management?*
	Yes	No	Specific question/benchmarks
6.a			The pool of auditors reflects all components of our primary value streams.
6.b			Auditors are provided training in value stream mapping and are often used to support process teams during value stream analysis.
6.c			Audit checklists contain elements for evaluating the use of lean operations, including areas such as 5S, total productive maintenance, and waste reduction.
7.0			**Survey topic:** *To what extent does our internal audit program support the execution of the organization's strategic plan?*
	Yes	No	Specific questions/benchmarks
7.a			The organization has developed a balanced scorecard and has mapped the scorecard indicators to the internal business processes that support them.

Continued

Continued

	Yes	No	Specific question/practice
7.b			Internal auditors are aware of the organization's scorecard, strategy maps, and strategic goals.
7.c			Internal auditors routinely examine the alignment between internal business processes and their related metrics and the organization's strategic goals and indicators as represented by the scorecard.
7.d			Internal auditors routinely examine the performance of key internal business processes toward achievement of the organization's strategic goals.

Use the results to plan improvements to your audit program. If you answered *yes* to 30 or more of the questions, then congratulations! You have a robust audit program that is adding significant value to the organization. Focus on improving the remaining areas where your answer was *no*.

If you answered *yes* to between 10 and 30, then consider your audit program to be at a moderate level of maturity. Work with management and your audit team to improve the effectiveness of the program by focusing on key topics where you scored the lowest. Don't be disheartened; most audit programs fall into this range. With some effort you can rapidly make yours one of the best.

If you answered *yes* to fewer than 10 of these questions, consider major modifications to your program. Work with management to build support for the audit program by focusing on the potential benefits of the program. You may need to retrain your auditors. The remainder of this book will help you develop your training program.

SUMMARY

In this chapter we have described the primary objectives of any audit program and laid out a sampling of the benefits that a robust, healthy internal audit program can and should provide. The primary objectives of any audit program are to:

- Verify conformance to the standard.

- Identify opportunities for improvement.

- Verify the effectiveness of the management system and its related processes.

- Identify and help disseminate best practices.

We can simplify these primary objectives with the following overall objective: *The purpose of any internal management system audit is to identify the systemic weaknesses, opportunities for improvement, and best practices within the management system.*

We then examined several additional benefits an organization may expect to receive from conducting internal audits, along with some of the specific practices that support realization of these benefits. More specifically:

- The audit program should promote teamwork and a spirit of cooperation and respect within the organization.

- Internal audits should promote a spirit of continual improvement and a focus on performance.

- Auditors learn new skills that add significant value to the organization beyond the audit process.

- Internal audits can be used to reinforce the systems approach to management.

- Internal audits can be used to support value stream management and the conversion to lean operations.

- Internal audits can be used to verify the alignment of internal business processes with the organization's business strategy and progress toward the achievement of strategic goals.

- Internal audits can be used to verify the alignment of internal business processes with the organization's business strategy.

The extent to which your organization realizes these benefits is dictated by the time and effort management invests in training its auditors and then supporting them with time, moral support, and acknowledgement of their efforts. The remainder of this handbook provides you with specific techniques and methods, but you have to supply the vision and commitment!

3

Types of Audits

T his chapter describes the primary types of audits and how they differ. This handbook contains information that can used for all types of audits and should equip the auditor to perform any of these audits except for the third-party audit and compliance reviews, where additional training and/or experience is required.

The generic classification of audits are as first-party, second-party, and third-party audits. Each of the remaining audit types can be placed within one of these three categories. A visual description of the three main types of audits is shown in Figure 3.1.

FIRST-PARTY AUDITS

First-party audits are audits performed by the organization on itself, hence the name. The more common name for these audits is internal audits. In an internal audit the organization commissions the audit and uses its own auditors, or subcontracted auditors, to

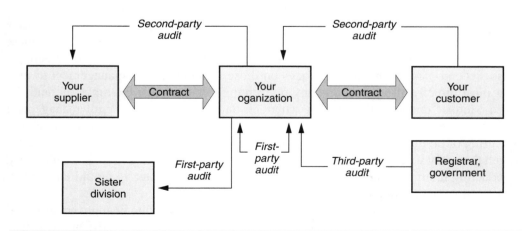

Figure 3.1 The three general audit types.

evaluate the management system or related processes. Each of the management system standards requires that the organization perform internal audits to verify conformance and effectiveness of the management system. Note that an audit of a sister division or plant is also a first-party audit since the auditee is still a member of the same parent organization.

The first-party audit should be the most thorough and effective of the audit types, owing to the existing familiarity of the processes to be evaluated by the auditors, the increased frequency of audits, and because internal auditors should have more time to plan and conduct the audit. One of the goals of the internal audit is to identify any systemic weaknesses before the outside auditor does. Unfortunately, this is not always the case. Many companies fail to adequately train their auditors or give them sufficient time to plan and conduct the audits. As a result, these companies tend to rely on outside auditors to identify weaknesses and use internal audits merely to fulfill the standard's requirements to conduct internal audits.

First-party audits may consist of management system audits, process audits, compliance reviews, or layered audits, as needed. The essential concept is that the first-party audit is commissioned and performed by the organization itself.

SECOND-PARTY AUDITS

Second-party audits are audits of an organization by its customers, or an audit by a company of its suppliers. Many companies refer to second-party audits as customer audits and supplier audits. Second-party audits are therefore audits of an organization by an outside entity, typically a customer. The distinguishing characteristic of a second-party audit is the existence or potential for an ongoing contractual relationship between the two organizations. Since there is an existing or potential contract, there is dependence between the two organizations and the potential for bias to affect the audit. Although, in theory, bias should not be allowed to affect the results, this potential is the main characteristic that distinguishes a second-party audit from a third-party audit.

Second-party audits of a management system differ in practice from first-party audits in two primary ways. First, customer and supplier audits tend to be a little more formal than internal audits, especially in regard to the opening and closing meetings. Also, second-party audits tend to focus on those elements of the management system that most directly affect the company performing the audit. For example, an audit by Ford Motor Company of one of its suppliers may evaluate the overall management system, but the processes picked for evaluation would be those involved in the manufacturing of product for Ford. These processes would typically be evaluated to a greater depth than they would be if audited by a third-party auditor, or registrar. Scheduling and conducting internal value-stream audits, as discussed in Chapter 1, should ensure that an organization is ready to support customer audits.

The concepts, practices, and methods discussed in this handbook apply equally well to first-party or second-party audits, with the exception of the identification of best practices discussed in Chapter 13. As noted in Chapter 2, best practices identification and communication will normally be a function of internal auditors.

THIRD-PARTY AUDITS

Third-party audits are audits performed by an outside organization that is independent of the audited organization. This independence is assumed to free the auditor from any outside pressure to come to a predetermined conclusion and is thus seen as the most reliable type of evaluation by other external companies, including customers. Examples of third-party audits include audits performed by quality, environmental, or OH&S registrars; by government agencies such as the Environmental Protection Agency or OSHA; and by large national accreditation bodies such as the American Association for Laboratory Accreditation (A2LA). Because these audits are used by many organizations as a basis for using a company's products or services, these audits tend to be very structured, formal, and standardized. Special training and experience are required to become a third-party auditor. Although many of the techniques and strategies found in this handbook would be useful to third-party auditors, it is not the intent of this handbook to equip you to perform third-party audits.

A question I routinely get when training auditors is how a registrar conducting a certification audit can be considered to be independent when the organization is maintaining a contract with the registrar and pays for the auditing services. The answer is that the auditor who performs the evaluation is not being paid by the audited company and should have no vested interest in the results. In addition, various oversight boards maintain a close watch on the registrars, which is a control feature not found in routine second-party audits. Even so, reports of bias by registrars, typically toward leniency in the reporting of management system deficiencies have been received and will probably continue, although to a far lesser extent than in the past.

Interestingly, this improvement in the objective reporting of results is being driven not so much by the oversight boards, but by the audited companies themselves. In the early days of ISO 9001, QS-9000, and ISO 14001, companies put intense pressure on outside auditors not to report major deficiencies, primarily because of the fear and uncertainty they had with the management system itself, the certification process, and customer reactions to deficiencies. Registrar auditors reacted by giving the company the benefit of the doubt, sometimes going too far by overlooking deficiencies, reporting solid nonconformances as opportunities for improvement, or major nonconformities as minor nonconformities. The results were registration and surveillance audits that resulted in few identified weaknesses. More recently, however, companies have started to question the value that they receive from such shallow audits, especially in light of the costs they pay for these services. More and more organizations are now demanding that their registrars identify weaknesses so that improvements can be made. This, along with a more active evaluation on the part of some of the oversight boards, has now resulted in a steep improvement in the thoroughness and quality of third-party assessments.

From an organization's viewpoint, however, it should not matter how thorough the third-party auditor is. The organization should be capable of finding all systematic weaknesses through its internal audit process well before they are found by an outside organization. Indeed, one of the ways to measure how effective an internal audit program is performing is to compare what your internal audits found against what outside auditors found. If outside auditors find systematic weaknesses in the management system in areas where the internal auditors did not, then this is a strong indication that the internal audit program is not effective. Note the use of the word *systematic* in the previous sentence. Internal auditors should never be expected to find all of the isolated deficiencies that exist in any management system since auditing is a sampling process, but they should be expected to be able to identify systematic deficiencies since these should show up in any reasonable sampling of items.

When viewed from this perspective, the real value that the third-party audit provides is to drive or force action when action is lacking. All too often, internal audit findings are given very little attention, resulting in repeat findings and outstanding, overdue corrective action. Third-party auditors always review the results of the organization's internal audits and corrective actions. A failure to respond to the findings of internal audits will result in a nonconformance from the registrar. Nonconformances resulting from a third-party audit tend to receive quite a bit of attention, thus the registrar can be viewed as a driver for action when action is lacking.

MANAGEMENT SYSTEM AUDITS

A management system audit is any audit, whether first-, second-, or third-party, that evaluates the management system or a portion thereof. This is the type of internal audit required by ISO 9001, ISO/TS 16949, ISO 14001, and OHSAS 18001. Management system audits may be conducted by examining specific portions of the management system or by examining systems of interrelated processes such as a value stream. Management system audits focus primarily on the inputs, controls, and transformation activities that make up the management system, which differentiates them from product audits (that is, inspection and test) and compliance reviews (detailed examination of compliance to regulatory and legal requirements).

Since the introduction of ISO 9001:2000, the trend has been to conduct management system audits by using a process-based audit methodology. This audit methodology is discussed next.

PROCESS AUDITS

In Chapter 1 we examined the concept of process-based management. Here we expand on that discussion and introduce the concept of process-based auditing.

Prior to the introduction of ISO 9001:2000, most internal audits were based on the specific elements of the standard. *Element-based audits* normally focused on auditing one or maybe two of the 20 elements of the ISO 9001:1994 or QS-9000 quality management system standard, or one of the 17 subclauses of the ISO 14001 environmental management system standard. More problematic, however, is how these audits were normally conducted. The process was typically:

1. Pick one of the 20 elements of the standard according to a predefined schedule.

2. Gather all the procedures, policies, and instructions relating to the process.

3. Review these procedures, and build a checklist to verify the *shalls,* or things we say we do.

4. Conduct the audit, verifying during the audit that we are doing those things that we say we do, or, in other words, we are following our procedures.

In essence, we were following the well-known and often cited ISO philosophy illustrated in Figure 3.2.

What was wrong with this? First, performing audits to a predefined schedule did little to address the current needs of the organization. Even though the 1994 version of the ISO 9001 standards clearly stated that audits should be scheduled "according to the status and importance of the activity" it was rare to find any audits performed other than those on the annual schedule.

In many cases this was due to a shortfall of meaningful metrics to tell the audit manager where and when audits should be conducted. The new emphasis on process metrics embodied in clauses 4.1 and 8.2.3 of the revised ISO 9001 standard should help alleviate this limitation. In addition, auditing individual elements did little to really evaluate process problems, which could potentially involve any of a number of the 20 elements. The typical reaction—do what was necessary to comply with the requirement to conduct internal audits—normally was met by auditing each element at least once a year.

Second, auditing one or two elements during an audit did not provide for a full verification of the interfaces between processes. Any process expert will tell you that most problems happen at the handoffs between processes or at the interface with key inputs. Auditing a single process or instruction did little to identify these common problems.

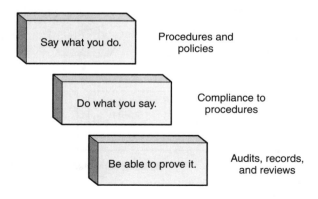

Figure 3.2   The old ISO philosophy.

Likewise, the "shotgun" approach to auditing, or pulling random samples from many different processes (as was typically done during audits of document control and training), was usually ineffective in finding anything but minor administrative errors. Take an audit of inspection and testing, element 4.10 of the 1994 standard, as represented in Figure 3.3. The auditor would normally focus on the following steps, as called out in the inspection instruction and represented by the darker shaded portions of the graphic:

- Sample selection (if other than 100 percent inspection)

- Inspection per the inspection instruction

- Inspection device calibration

The other supporting processes (represented by the lighter shaded boxes in Figure 3.3) would only be spot-checked, if at all. For instance, the auditor would probably verify that the measurement device in use was calibrated, but typically would not check the measurement systems analysis results that would provide information on whether the results obtained from the inspection could be relied on. Similarly, the auditor would verify that the verifications called out in the inspection instructions were conducted, but might not verify that these inspections matched those required by the control plan, or that they were being performed with the correct measurement device, or at the required frequency and sample size. Compliance to the inspection instruction will not ensure that the product

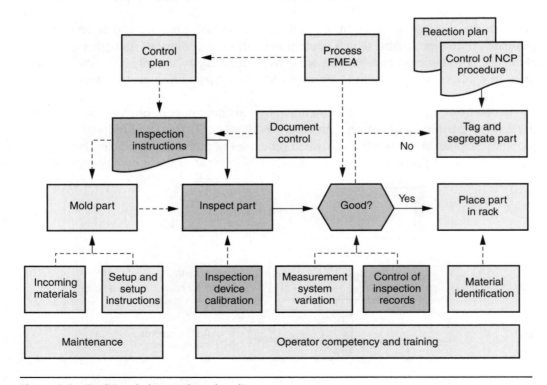

Figure 3.3   Traditional element-based audit.

meets requirements, if the instruction itself is incorrect or obsolete or if the measurement results are suspect.

Similarly, the auditor probably would not ask the operator what he or she would do if the product was found to be nonconforming. Failure to properly handle nonconforming product could result in its release to the customer even if it is caught during inspection. Additionally, failure to follow the reaction plan, or the absence of such a plan, could result in the ongoing production of a large amount of defective product that, even if caught, drives up costs due to scrap or rework.

How would the auditor know that such a deeper dive into the process was necessary? An auditor could gain this insight by looking at indicators of process effectiveness, preferably as part of the planning for the audit. For example, if warranty reports and product returns indicated a large number of inspection escapes (that is, items that should have been caught by the inspection but slipped through) then the auditor should anticipate weaknesses in this process and should be prepared to more thoroughly evaluate it. Which brings us to the last weakness of the traditional audit process—auditors have not been very diligent at verifying the effectiveness of the processes they are assigned to audit.

What is needed is an audit process that evaluates all components of the process such as shown in Figure 3.4. This greatly increases the chances of finding the real weaknesses and opportunities for improvement.

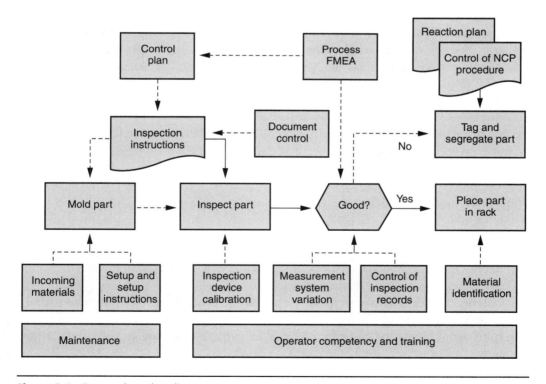

Figure 3.4 Process-based audit.

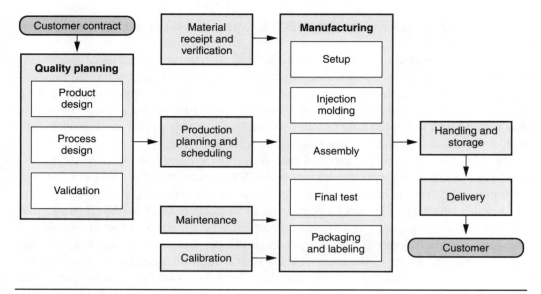

Figure 3.5   Example process audit scope.

Keep in mind, however, that this is a relatively simple example. The greatest benefit comes from looking at overall value streams made up of many processes. An example of such an audit is outlined in Figure 3.5.

In addition to excessively narrowing the scope of the audit, auditing by element also typically focused on the transformation process. Auditors typically verified that we were doing what we said we did, and what we said we do was outlined in the steps of the procedure or instruction. These steps focused on the physical transformation of inputs into outputs. They did not specifically define the inputs or the standards or criteria for those inputs, nor did they adequately define the resources or controls (beyond inspection and testing) needed to ensure the quality of output. Often the procedure or instruction did not even specify the quality or essential characteristics of the outputs. As previously noted, the old saying "garbage in, garbage out" certainly applies to manufacturing and business processes. And during conformance-focused, element-based audits, process inputs were rarely considered. As an example, consider the order entry process illustrated in Figure 3.6.

Many auditors simply were not trained to look at inputs, resources, controls, and outputs. They would verify that the order was entered into the computer per the instruction, but not question how the customer inputs were communicated or collected, or that the various process controls worked effectively.

Assume that the customers typically order from a catalog or Web site where product features and applications are described. If the Web site or catalog is not correct because it is not being updated when there are changes, then there is a strong possibility that the customer will not receive what is expected.

The procedure may only require that the order entry clerk ask the customer for a part number, without verifying the catalog the customer is ordering from. As a result, the auditor only ensures that the field for part number is filled in. In this instance, failure to verify the adequacy of a critical resource (the Web site or catalog) would result in the auditor missing an opportunity to identify a weakness that results in customers getting products other than what they expect.

A knowledgeable auditor could also ask to see the data relating to the percent orders correct to determine how well the process is functioning, which then can be used to determine how deeply the auditor needs to delve into this activity. In effect, the new ISO philosophy needs to be as shown in Figure 3.7. Note the addition of the emphasis on results.

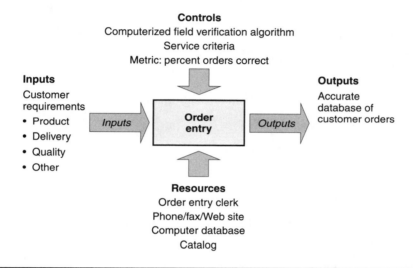

Figure 3.6   Order entry example.

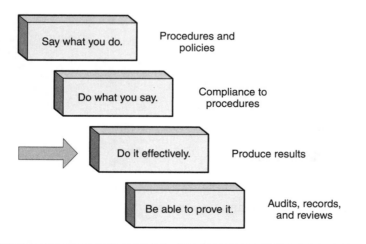

Figure 3.7   The new ISO philosophy.

COMPLIANCE REVIEWS

Both ISO 14001 and OHSAS 18001 require that the organization verify its compliance with regulatory and legal requirements. These are detailed reviews that typically require more specialized knowledge than that possessed of management system internal auditors. Environmental and health and safety regulations are complex, and typically require an in-depth understanding of the regulations and how they apply to the evaluator's organization. A partial listing of some of the federal environmental regulations that may apply include:

- Resource Conservation and Recovery Act

- Clean Water Act

- National Permit Discharge Elimination System

- Clean Air Act

- Superfund Amendments and Reauthorization Act

- Toxic Substances Control Act

- National Environmental Policy Act

- Pollution Prevention Act

- Safe Drinking Water Act

- Comprehensive Environmental Response, Compensation, and Liability Act

- Emergency Planning and Community Right-to-Know

A partial listing of some of the Occupational Safety and Health Act (OSHA) provisions that may apply include:

- Chemical storage

- Compressed gases

- Confined spaces

- Cranes

- Electrical hazards

- Electromagnetic radiation

- Emergency action plan

- Emergency response program

- Ergonomics

- Fire prevention

- Flammable and combustible liquids

- Hazard communication program

- Hearing conservation program

- Heat stress

- Ionizing radiation

- Laboratory chemicals

- Local exhaust ventilation

- Lockout/tagout

- Manual lifting

- Personal protective equipment

- Portable power tools and equipment

- Powered industrial trucks

- Powered machinery and machine guarding

- Process safety management

- Respiratory protection program

- Scaffolds

- Stairways and ladders

- Toxic substance exposure monitoring

- Walking surfaces, wall openings, and other passageways

- Welding, cutting, and brazing

In addition, many states have been granted the authority to implement these federal requirements in the form of state implementation programs (SIPs). The state programs must be at least as restrictive as the federal programs, but may include additional requirements. One can easily see the difficulty of expecting internal management system auditors to also evaluate regulatory compliance. Most organizations use environmental, health, and safety professionals to perform these compliance reviews. Of course, if some of these individuals are also trained as internal management system auditors, then they can perform both management system audits and compliance reviews.

Having said that, internal auditors are expected to verify that these reviews have been conducted and should conduct spot checks of regulatory compliance during their management system audits. Checklists of common environmental and health and safety regulatory requirements can be used by auditors during internal audits to spot-check regulatory compliance.

PRODUCT AUDITS

Product audits verify conformance of products to specified requirements. They are common in all industries and are reflected in the product verification requirements of the standards. Verification of product conformance is not normally within the scope of the management system audit. For example, the Food and Drug Administration (FDA) states in its *Guide to Inspections of Quality Systems*[1] that, "Quality audits should consist of a formal, planned check of all elements in the quality system. They are *not* product audits." Having said that, the management system auditor must ensure that product audits (product verifications) are being conducted as required by the customer, regulatory requirements, and/or internal requirements. To do this the auditor may need to watch product verifications being performed and must be familiar with the basic requirements for such verifications as called out in inspection plans, control plans, and other requirements documentation.

In addition, the FDA has indicated that full quality system audits of products may be required for complex products. Selecting a complex product as the object for the audit and then systematically following it through the requirements, design, development, and production processes as described later in this handbook will provide for a full audit of all quality management system processes that could impact the acceptability of the product.

While conducting audits of supplier quality management systems within the Naval Nuclear Propulsion Program, we commonly required the supplier to conduct overinspections of product during the evaluation. The purpose of these overinspections was to ensure that the product audits were being conducted according to all inspection requirements and to verify that consistent results could be obtained. The auditor has a responsibility for ensuring that product verification is being properly carried out. If overinspection of product is necessary to do so, then the auditor should consider factoring that into the audit plan.

SUMMARY

This chapter reviewed the general audit types and went into some detail on process-based audits. The remaining sections of this handbook provide techniques, strategies, and methods that can be used to perform each of these audits, although the focus is on first-party (internal) and second-party (supplier) audits using a process approach.

4

Audit Program Structure and Organization

This chapter examines roles and responsibilities unique to the internal audit program and provides suggestions relating to audit program training, structure, and organization. Of particular note is the section on management's responsibilities relating to the audit program. This section should be reviewed by every manager in the company, since their support, or lack thereof, is the single largest contributor to the success or failure of the audit program.

ROLES AND RESPONSIBILITIES

Before we look at audit program structure we will review some of the roles and responsibilities of those involved in the audit program. Many of these responsibilities are taken from the ISO 19011 standard, which provides guidance on audit program organization, management, and execution. Audit program managers should consider documenting significant roles and responsibilities in job descriptions, the organization's audit procedures, or in the organization's policy manual(s). More importantly, they should be communicated and discussed with auditors and potential auditors as part of the organization's auditor training. Most of these will be clarified and expanded on in subsequent chapters of this handbook.

The Auditor

The following roles and responsibilities apply to management system auditors:

- Follow the directions of and support the lead auditor.

- Plan for the assigned areas. Planning includes reviewing the processes to be evaluated, including related procedures, instructions, key inputs, and metrics.

- Carry out all assigned tasks objectively, effectively, and efficiently within the scope of the audit.

- Collect and analyze relevant and sufficient audit evidence to determine audit findings and to reach audit conclusions regarding the quality management system. This will be discussed in more detail in Chapter 6.

- Prepare working documents and document audit findings. This also will be discussed in more detail in Chapter 6.

- Safeguard documents related to the audit and return such documents when the audit is completed, as needed. Documents, records, and lists must be returned to the auditee prior to the completion of the audit.

- Assist in the development of the audit report, as required.

The Lead Auditor

Every audit has a lead auditor or team leader. If the team size is one, then it is particularly easy to identify who the lead auditor is. The lead auditor has the following roles and responsibilities in addition to the auditor responsibilities.

- Ensure the efficient and effective conduct and completion of the audit. The lead auditor is responsible for the overall success of the audit, from planning through reporting.

- Obtain relevant background information. The lead auditor should collect relevant information about how well the process is working to help focus the audit. This may include information contained in corrective action reports, previous audit reports, and reviews of process performance over time.

- Assist in the selection of the audit team. Although team selection is normally the responsibility of the audit program manager, the lead auditor should have a say in the selection, since not everybody plays well together and it is the lead auditor's responsibility to ensure that the audit team is cohesive and professional.

- Prepare and communicate the audit plan. Audit plans will be discussed in more detail in Chapter 5, but, in essence, the audit plan shows the processes or topics to be evaluated, who will be interviewed by which auditor, and provides estimated times for each interview. It establishes the structure for the audit.

- Recognize when audit objectives become unattainable and report the reasons to the audit program manager and the auditee. For example, when an auditee is not available for the audit but that particular interview is essential to the objective of the audit. Another example might be when a primary purpose of the audit is to evaluate a specific activity and that activity cannot be conducted. This normally happens as a result of bad audit planning.

- Direct the activities of the audit team.

- Serve as central spokesperson for the audit team. The lead auditor runs the opening and closing meeting and takes on any difficult issues that arise during the audit.

- Resolve any problems that arise during the audit.

- Notify the auditee of any critical audit findings. Auditors do not wait until the closing meeting to notify management of critical audit findings. Deficiencies that are affecting current product, safety violations, and noncompliances that could result in significant environmental degradation and possible EPA violations should be reported immediately.

- Issue the draft/final audit report. This will be discussed in chapters 6 and 7.

- Make recommendations for improvements to the QMS. Normally the lead auditor will decide which OFIs go into the audit report.

Technical Experts

The ANSI/ISO/ASQ QE19011S-2004 guidance standard[1] defines a technical expert as a "person who provides specific knowledge or expertise to the audit team." Such expertise may be needed during evaluations of highly technical areas such as software development, materials testing, and regulatory compliance reviews. An audit team will not normally need a technical expert if it has access to the requirements that the process or activity must meet and can understand the basic intent of the requirements. If the auditor or audit team cannot understand the basic requirements or cannot assess the relative importance of the requirements so as to be able to plan an effective audit, then a technical expert may be necessary.

Note that the 19011 document stresses that technical experts do not act as auditors in the audit team. They are present to provide consultation and explanation to the auditors. They are not trained auditors and do not conduct interviews. Ideally, their participation would be limited to the audit planning phase, but they may be needed during the conduct of the audit. In such cases they must be carefully briefed on their role and limitations. They should operate under the direct control of an audit team member.

The Audit Program Manager

The audit program manager is the individual who manages the audit program. In most organizations this is the management representative or quality, environmental, or OH&S manager. Primary responsibilities of the audit program manager include:

- Identify the need for an audit. Typically this is done through the issuance of the audit schedule, although the audit program manager may identify the need to perform an unplanned audit as a result of poor process performance.

- Establish the scope of the audit. Which processes will be audited, which areas, and what key inputs need to be examined will normally be determined by the audit program manager.

- Make the initial contact and obtain the auditee's cooperation. Although the audit schedule is published well in advance of any audit and should be available to all process owners and managers, the audit program manager should also follow up with the process owner a week or two in advance to remind them of the upcoming audit and to ask them to notify personnel that an audit will be conducted.

- Establish the audit team. The audit program manager should also verify audit team makeup with the lead auditor, especially for large audits where three or more auditors are assigned.

- Approve the audit plan, when part of the organization's policy. As noted, the audit plan provides a structure for the audit. The audit program manager may review the audit plan prior to the audit to ensure that the structure is appropriate for the audit objectives and to provide an opportunity to provide consultation on the audit flow. I recommend this review for new auditors.

- Issue the final audit report to the appropriate distribution. This is really up to the organization. I personally favor audit program manager preparation of the final audit report, although many organizations assign this task to the lead auditor. For a large audit, such as an evaluation of the entire management system or of a primary value stream, I recommend the final audit report be prepared by the audit program manager.

The Auditee

The auditee also has certain responsibilities during the audit. Sometimes it might be necessary to remind them of these:

- Inform personnel within the audited organization/unit about the audit and its objectives, as needed. It really helps if people within the area to be audited are aware of and expecting the auditors before they show up for interviews.

- Provide facilities as needed by the audit team. Facilities include procedures, instructions, and access to processes and areas. For off-site audits, logistical consideration such as a room to work and lunch arrangements are also necessary.

- Appoint guides, as needed, to the audit team. This is not normally required for an internal audit, but possibly needed for off-site audits and always for second-party audits.

- Cooperate with the audit team and provide access to facilities, personnel, information, and records as requested by the auditors. This is the one that may need subtle reinforcement during the audit.

FULL-TIME VERSUS PART-TIME AUDITORS

One of the most important decisions that an organization will make involves the use of full-time, dedicated auditors or part-time auditors. There are advantages and disadvantages of each. First we will examine the most common practice of using part-time auditors.

Part-Time Auditors

In an audit program where auditing is a collateral duty, auditors are normally selected from many different functions and levels of the organization. Auditors are typically provided training in the standard that they will be auditing to along with internal auditor training. They are then placed on the audit schedule as needed during the year. The number of part-time auditors needed to support the audit schedule is often quoted to be between five percent to 10 percent of the organization. Thus an organization with 600 employees would train between 30 and 60 internal auditors. I personally recommend the lower number, since this will give each auditor more opportunity to perform audits. An auditor who only performs one or two audits a year will never develop the competency and proficiency needed to be truly effective.

Using a larger number of part-time auditors provides the organization with a sizable pool of auditors that in turn provides for multiple perspectives since the audit program manager can assign a different auditor to subsequent audits of the same area. It also exposes a larger number of personnel to the audit process and the skills needed to be a successful auditor. As noted in Chapter 2, this can provide far-ranging benefits to the organization outside of the audit itself. Another frequently quoted advantage of using part-time auditors is that it saves money, since auditors are taken from existing resources. This advantage, however, is arguable and will be examined in our discussion of the use of full-time auditors.

Disadvantages with reliance on part-time auditors include time, proficiency, and personality. Part-time auditors are not normally assigned to the audit program and must rely on their direct supervisors and managers to give them the time needed to properly plan and execute the audit. Since their absence from their primary duties is a strain on their departments, they rarely are given the time needed to plan and conduct an effective audit. This is especially true in companies that have rightsized. Few departments have personnel to spare. Although the auditor is released to perform the audit, he or she is not provided time to plan. They are expected to use prepared checklists that include standard questions to find common deficiencies. The auditor in essence picks up the checklist from the audit program manager and starts auditing. This results in shallow audits that rarely identify the deep-seated weaknesses that plague many organizations. Although the comprehensive checklists provided on the CD included with this handbook may help this situation somewhat, it is not a solution to the problem of inadequate preparation.

This disadvantage is compounded by the fact that part-time auditors rarely develop the competencies and proficiency needed to accomplish all of the objectives of an effective audit. Part-time auditors rarely perform more than two or three audits per year, and turnover among auditors can be high. While a professional auditor may be able to skimp a little on planning owing to extensive experience, part-time auditors cannot.

A final disadvantage to the use of part-time auditors is that some people just by nature are better auditors than others. These auditors possess traits such as open-mindedness, curiosity, persistence, and superior communication skills. While most anybody can become an auditor, these individuals become superstar auditors. In any large pool of auditors, the audit program manager will have some individuals who have these traits and some who don't. The worst situation is when a sizable number of auditors in the part-time pool don't want to be auditors. These individuals rarely perform well in this role.

Full-Time Auditors

In a program that uses full-time auditors, the audit program manager is assigned a small pool of permanent auditors whose sole responsibility is to support the internal audit program. These auditors plan and conduct the audits and follow up on auditee corrective action. In an organization of 600 employees the audit group might have three to six full-time auditors in addition to the audit program manager. The advantages are many. Because of the smaller number of auditors involved it is easier to schedule and provide more thorough training to the auditors. Since their primary purpose is to plan and execute audits, the relevancy of the training is higher, which leads to better learning.

Probably most important, since their full-time role is auditing, they tend to develop a much higher level of consistency and proficiency than do part-time auditors. They develop and refine their own personal strategies to identify weaknesses, which allows for more efficient and effective audit planning. They can carve out more time to plan audits, if needed, since they report directly to the audit program manager. This is especially important if the organization conducts value-stream audits since these tend to be more complex and wide-ranging (and also more effective). They can optimize their audit strategies through practice, since instead of performing only two or three audits a year, they will be conducting dozens. They also become more comfortable with auditing and, as a result, are better prepared, both intellectually and emotionally, to track down difficult-to-find or sensitive issues that may be affecting the organization. In addition, full-time auditors are by definition independent of those having direct responsibility for the areas being audited since they report directly to the audit program manager.

Since there is a far smaller number of auditors in the audit pool in a program that uses full-time auditors, it is also possible to be more selective. Auditors can be screened so that only those who possess the desired characteristics of open-mindedness, curiosity, persistence, and superior communication skills are selected. This can have a huge impact on the quality of the audit program. And finally, because of the ability to conduct advanced training with this dedicated group, it may be feasible to use them to conduct some of the compliance reviews discussed in Chapter 3 that are typically outside of the capability of part-time auditors.

The main disadvantage to the use of full-time auditors is perceived to be cost. Instead of using existing resources, the organization must allocate dedicated personnel to the audit group. This may require the hiring of a few additional personnel to serve as auditors or to replace those chosen from existing departments. I believe this perception is dead wrong. Full-time auditors can plan and conduct audits more efficiently than part-time auditors, and can relieve the burden on other departments of having to supply part-time auditors to the audit process. More importantly, the many potential benefits of auditing discussed in Chapter 2 are much more likely to be realized in an organization that develops a cadre of full-time, competent, and professional auditors. These benefits should dwarf the direct costs of any audit program in the long run.

There are some real disadvantages in the use of full-time auditors, however. First, some of the cultural benefits of auditing cited in Chapter 2, such as wide exposure to the audit process skill sets of process mapping, analysis, and performance monitoring and the exposure that auditors get to other department processes would be lost. Second, the assumption is that those selected to be full-time auditors would be those best suited to be auditors, having the right blend of personal dynamics, desire, and the behavior traits previously cited. If, instead, the wrong personnel are selected to become dedicated auditors, the effects on the audit program could be devastating, far more so than if a larger pool of part-time auditors is used.

Considering the pros and cons of each structure, what then is the best solution? My recommendation is to match the audit program to the management system maturity and evolve it as the management system evolves. For a discussion on management system maturity, refer to Chapter 1. For organizations that are in the compliance phase of system maturity, use a larger pool of part-time auditors. Auditing for conformance is the easiest skill for an auditor to learn and is within the capability of most auditors, even considering the limitations of training and proficiency noted in previous paragraphs. During this phase the audit program manager should carefully note which auditors seem to have an inclination and desire to be an auditor. The audit program manager should identify the natural auditors or those that have the desired blend of characteristics to allow them to become superstars.

As the management system matures into the effectiveness and then the improvement phases, shift over to a program that uses a smaller cadre of full-time auditors. Those selected will be those that demonstrated the desire and characteristics to be truly effective auditors in the previous phase. They can be given additional training in how to audit for effectiveness and how to identify best practices. Since they are conducting many more audits, their proficiency will dramatically improve, as will their exposure to potential best practices throughout the organization.

To preserve the cultural benefits of auditing, do not completely disband the part-time auditors, but instead pare them down. Instead of having a pool of five full-time auditors *or* 30 part-time auditors, consider a blended solution that consists of a dedicated audit group of three full-time auditors and 10 to 15 part-time auditors. Focused process audits and layered audits could be assigned to both part-time and full-time auditors, larger value stream audits could be assigned to a team of one full-time auditor (the team leader) and one part-time auditor. Compliance reviews could be assigned to outside professionals or to the full-time auditors once an acceptable knowledge of regulatory requirements is obtained. In each case, the full-time auditor would bear the overall responsibility of planning for the audit, which will correct the major deficiency in most audits of failure to adequately prepare.

Using this kind of a team approach, full-time auditors paired with part-time auditors, will result in more effective and efficient audits while preserving the benefits cited in Chapter 2. Part-time auditors will benefit through exposure to the now professional full-time auditors and will be able to pick up the more advanced auditing techniques more quickly. Department managers will be required to provide auditors less frequently, since the number of part-time auditors required to perform an audit is fewer.

As a final consideration, consider rotating your auditors (full- or part-time) every three or four years. Full-time auditors can develop proficiency much more rapidly than part-time auditors, so it is possible to rotate these auditors more frequently than part-time auditors with less impact on audit program effectiveness.

At General Electric, the accumulation of Six Sigma skills was considered a prerequisite for anyone wishing to move up in the organization. This institutionalizing of the culture of Six Sigma is a major reason why GE had such success with the program, while others who have tried it have not. The skills learned as an auditor are just as valuable and are even more practical than the skills learned through the Six Sigma process. Imagine an organization where every manager and executive had the skills to comprehensively evaluate the processes they were responsible for in terms of conformance, effectiveness, and efficiency and understood the need to align their operations with those of the rest of the company. Consider using auditor assignments as another means of preparing the future leaders of the organization.

THE ROLE OF SENIOR MANAGEMENT

Any discussion of audit program roles and responsibilities would be incomplete without a section detailing the role that senior management plays in the success or failure of the audit program. These responsibilities go far beyond providing resources in the form of personnel, time, and money to providing and reinforcing a culture that allows the audit program to drive improvement throughout the organization. Some of management's most important responsibilities will be discussed in the sections that follow.

Providing Resources

The most fundamental of management's responsibilities is the provision of resources in the form of personnel, time, and training for the audit program. Personnel resources include the assignment of adequate numbers of auditors. If part-time auditors are used, then management must be willing to release a relatively large number of auditors to attend the training required to become an auditor and to continue to release them to conduct the audits. If full-time auditors are used, then management must willing to hire or release personnel to fill this role.

Perhaps even more important, management must be willing to provide the time for auditors to plan and conduct the audits. This is especially important in situations where part-time auditors are used. A general rule is that it takes up to twice as much time to properly plan an audit as it does to conduct one. Therefore, if an auditor is assigned to an audit that will take four hours to perform, management must be willing to release the auditor for up to a day and a half. The use of well-designed checklists can help to shorten the planning time somewhat, but they cannot replace all planning. One of the reasons why I generally favor the use of full-time auditors is because of the difficulties that part-time auditors have in getting the time allocated to plan their audits.

Money is also required to support the training that auditors need in order to develop the competencies needed to become effective auditors. Training is discussed in the next section of this chapter, but suffice it to say, you get what you pay for. Training expenditures are normally higher when part-time auditors are used because of the larger number of auditors that must be trained and the disruption that such training creates in the auditor's normal departments.

Direction and Vision

Another responsibility of senior management is to provide vision and direction to the management system and to the audit program. Senior management must be involved in the shaping and operation of the management program and must ensure that it quickly moves through the compliance phase into the effectiveness and improvement phases. Senior management must demand accountability for performance from process owners and its internal auditors. Establishing a culture of performance and accountability will go a long way toward ensuring that all managers and supervisors take the audit program seriously.

One of the most important actions that management can take to speed the transition from conformance toward effectiveness is to implement a robust system of metrics that monitors the performance of all of its important processes. Criteria and related metrics should be developed at the individual process level to be used by supervisors and mid-level managers on an ongoing basis to measure how well their processes are performing. System metrics should be implemented at the senior management level to monitor overall system performance in areas important to the customer and to execution of the organization's strategic plan. Some of these measures should be standardized across business units to allow benchmarking and the identification of best practices. In addition to improving accountability, such a system of metrics allows auditors to focus their audits on areas of nonperformance and to evaluate process effectiveness.

I strongly recommend that business leaders develop balanced scorecards to execute their strategy. The scorecard metrics should then be mapped to the internal processes that drive performance toward achievement of the strategic goals represented by the scorecard. Once these critical processes are identified, process criteria and metrics should be developed to align with the scorecard metrics and to allow day-to-day monitoring and evaluation of process performance during internal audits. When aligned like this, the quality, environmental, and/or OH&S system and the internal audit program become vital tools in achieving the organization's strategic goals. This in turn provides improved acceptance of the audit program and more motivated auditors.

One of the greatest weaknesses in today's quality, environmental, and OH&S management systems is a lack of involvement in the development and approval of system metrics by senior management. Most organizations just continue to use existing measures of performance, or management delegates the development of new metrics to the process owners, who often select measures that are easiest to obtain. This can lead to a lack of alignment between what senior management and what process owners think is important. Realize that auditors do not cite a process as ineffective based on their opinion. They are trained to base their conclusions on facts, which, in the case of ineffectiveness, is a failure to achieve planned results with no action being taken to correct or improve the situation. An NC due to ineffectiveness will most often be generated when the auditor notes that a process or system metric is far beneath its goal or, when there is no formal target established, has a long and sustained trend going in the wrong direction. The auditor then looks at the actions being taken to address the situation. If no actions are being taken, then the auditor can generate an NC citing sections 4.1 or 8.2.3 of the ISO 9001 or ISO/TS 16949 standards, which require that action be taken to achieve planned results.

When such a weakness is reported to the auditee, it is not uncommon for the auditee manager to respond that it really isn't a problem worth worrying about. Even if the auditee manager accepts the issue as important, senior management may state that the issue can be lived with, it isn't a big enough concern to provide the auditee manager with the resources needed to correct it. Both of these reactions indicate that little thought was given to the metrics used to measure process and/or system performance. If you find yourself reacting in this way to auditor findings related to effectiveness, then evaluate your system of metrics used to measure process performance. You do not need to establish hundreds of metrics to satisfy the requirements of the various management system standards, but those that you do establish need to be important enough to mobilize action if they indicate that the system is not performing as expected. It is for this reason that I strongly endorse the development and deployment of balanced scorecards down to the process level. These scorecards become the alignment tool between what senior management believes is important (achieving strategic objectives) and what process owners measure and control to.

Self-Accountability

The most important role of managers at all levels, however, is the role of self-accountability. When auditors shift their focus from auditing for conformance toward auditing for effectiveness, more of the audit findings will relate to areas where processes are not achieving expected results. Many of these areas will already be known to process owners. Reasons for nonperformance may include insufficient resources, other priorities, or a lack of time to correct the problem. Process owners may already feel frustration at the current level of performance and may react with anger or resentment when the lack of performance is noted during an internal audit. Even so, these areas must be addressed if the organization is to move forward. Documentation of the weakness in an audit report provides additional visibility and possibly additional resources to address the problem area. Let me provide an example.

As a part of internal auditor training at one automotive manufacturer, a series of floor-level audits was conducted. One of the requirements in ISO/TS 16949:2000 clause 5.5.3 is to communicate performance information to the workforce. In this organization a primary method of communicating this information was through the use of zone controls boards in each manufacturing area. Each board had important information about quality performance, environmental performance, safety performance, and throughput relative to that area. In the past, auditors had focused on conformance, which, in this case, meant verifying that the required information was reflected on the board and that it was current. Since a large part of the seminar involved training internal auditors to look for effectiveness, we also asked each of the audit teams to survey a number of personnel in each area to see if the boards were effective at communicating the required information. We asked them to focus on two key areas: What are the major quality issues? And what are the major safety concerns in the operator's area? This information was prominently indicated on each board, and we felt that is was important that operators and supervisors be aware of both of these issues.

In each case the team reported that the communication boards were compliant to requirements in that they had the required information posted and they were up to date. More interesting, however, is that only three of the 33 personnel interviewed could state what the major quality and safety concerns were in the area in which they worked. Although compliant, the boards were not effective in communicating performance information to the workforce. It was further noted that significant effort was expended in maintaining these boards. Considering the lack of effectiveness of these boards, this effort was essentially non-value-added. Value-wise, it would have made more sense to shift the resources used to maintain the boards toward an activity that provided some value than to waste it on an activity that provided little. Since this was the organization's primary method of meeting the ISO/TS 16949 requirement to communicate information on process performance, this was not an option, so the organization lived with this waste. Unfortunately, instances of such waste abound in all organizations.

What is more revealing, however, was the plant manager's reaction when the finding was presented. Although the finding itself was not challenged, since the evidence was factual and overwhelming, the decision by the auditors to note the weakness was severely questioned. "What do you expect me to do about it?" he demanded. "I can't make them read it!" Such reactions, if allowed, will quickly result in auditors refocusing on conformance. Managers must be willing to accept the findings of the auditors when backed up by objective evidence, no matter how painful. To do otherwise virtually guarantees an ineffective audit program.

An interesting note in this example is that in the past the communication boards were maintained by the area operators themselves. There was ownership of the boards and the information they contained. In an effort to standardize the boards, control was taken away from the process operators, against their wishes, and was given to a special team of analysts. Although it is not the responsibility of the auditor to determine the cause of the weakness nor to recommend how to fix it, I think that this revelation does bring to mind several solutions that could actually result in the boards being read. The general rule for action in all cases, however, is this: add value, fix it to add value, or stop doing it. Organizations simply cannot afford to waste effort on non-value-added activities anymore.

Problem Resolution

The final management responsibility to address is support for problem resolution or, as normally stated, corrective action. The best audit in the world provides no value if action is not taken to address the weaknesses found. Management, both auditee and senior management, needs to ensure that timely and comprehensive action is taken to identify the cause(s) of the nonconformity and to eliminate it. Failure to correct audit nonconformities has several negative consequences:

- First and foremost, the problem will continue to exist and will continue to affect the performance of the management system.

- Auditors find it extremely discouraging to discover the same deficiencies audit after audit, or to find that weaknesses noted in the previous audit are still outstanding. Professional, well-trained auditors are motivated by their desire to drive improvement. If they are repeatedly frustrated by a lack of action on what they find, they may stop trying.

- Failure to require timely corrective action weakens the culture of accountability needed to create a high-performing management system.

- Management needs to realize that failure to take corrective actions on a previous nonconformity will lead to another nonconformity during the next audit. In the case of registrar nonconformities, this often leads to a major NC, which in some cases can trigger the decertification process. It should also be understood that auditors are trained to follow up on previous audit results, so the chances of the auditor not noting the lack of action are slim.

When it comes to action, managers will struggle most with nonconformances related to effectiveness. I find it amusing that in the past, managers often complained because audits tended to identify mostly administrative deficiencies like document control errors, missing sign-offs, and the like. Audits, they said, were more nuisance than value-adding. Now that auditors are focused more on effectiveness, they are identifying clear performance issues in their audit reports, and managers are now complaining that these weaknesses are too intractable and hard to correct. I imagine that there are quite a few managers out there who long for the good old days when findings were mainly a nuisance, but easily correctable. Yet, to drive improvement, issues of effectiveness must be addressed.

Most issues with effectiveness are caused by either a lack of resources or a lack of alignment between processes. The alignment issues are normally easier to correct than are the resource issues, which in today's lean environment are always in short supply. Internal auditors may document a number of areas where processes are not providing planned results. Not all of these may be correctable right away because of resource limitations. The manager needs to develop a system for documenting and tracking these deficiencies, and for assigning action plans to address them, in a prioritized fashion. As long as reasonable progress is being made to address the issues, then the next audit team should find the corrective action acceptable. It must be emphasized that reasonable actions and progress must be evident for the auditor to accept it. Taking no action on a list of three process nonconformities because the highest priority item requires a new hire, which will not occur for at least six months, is unacceptable. Other options in the interim might be to reallocate existing resources, identifying and targeting non-value-added activities for elimination to free up resources, or task redesign. There is so much waste in most processes that additional resources can almost always be found through waste reduction activities.

The second additional consideration for managers relating to problem resolution is how managers react to reported weaknesses. Management must not punish those responsible for the situation, but should instead provide the resources needed to correct the situation. Accountability to correct the problem, not personal blame, is the goal. Punishment goes beyond termination and includes more subtle forms such as strongly assigning blame, significantly reducing performance evaluations, working through the weekend when the problem doesn't warrant it, and so on. If fear of retribution is allowed to infuse itself into the audit program, then auditees will attempt to cover up problems and generally will not support the internal auditors' attempts to find the weaknesses. This will greatly lower the effectiveness of the audit program.

The only exception to this is when the same finding is noted on multiple audits. While managers should not punish individuals for mistakes, they do have a right to expect them to learn from their errors. In the rare case where individuals refuse to learn, then the manager has a right and responsibility to take the issue on in order to preserve the concept of accountability. In these cases some form of punishment may be appropriate. What about instances where workers haven't made a mistake, they knowingly broke the rules? Before managers dole out punishment, they should evaluate the rewards system to see if it is unwittingly reinforcing such problem behaviors.

AUDITOR TRAINING AND QUALIFICATION

Developing an effective audit program begins with the proper selection and training of internal auditors. In this section we will examine selection criteria for internal auditors and the components of an auditor training program.

Auditor Selection

Selecting auditors with the right blend of experience, knowledge, and interpersonal skills is the first step to building a successful audit program. Some people just aren't cut out to be auditors, others are naturals. The audit program manager should always strive to select auditors who have the desire, willingness, and skills to be good auditors.

An important and often overlooked attribute of potential auditors is desire. It amazes me how many times people are assigned as auditors when they don't want to be. During my auditor training seminars I often ask for a show of hands of those who volunteered to be auditors. It's not uncommon for fewer than 50 percent to raise their hands. While unwilling employees can do a credible job auditing, they rarely turn into superstars. I'll never forget one seminar when I asked the students to state their first impression when someone said the word *audit* or *auditor.* One gentleman slowly stood up, and replied, "My first impression is now I'm never be able to look at myself in the mirror again. I hate audits and I hate auditors!" Needless to say, despite our best attempts to change this attitude, chances are that this individual will probably not become a superstar auditor.

You need to examine the health of your audit program if you find it difficult to enlist auditor volunteers. The survey presented in Chapter 2 provides a means to identify structural problems that may be creating reluctance toward becoming an internal auditor.

Even though they may be willing, some employees do not have the interpersonal skills needed to become good auditors. Some of the characteristics of an ideal auditor are listed and can be used to screen auditor candidates. Auditors should be:

- *Open-minded.* Auditors must be willing to accept methods and practices they disagree with if they are compliant to the standard and internal policies and procedures, and are producing acceptable results. Individuals who always see their way as the right way tend to offer too many opinions and do not make good auditors.

- *Perceptive.* Auditors will find themselves evaluating areas they have never worked in. They must be able to see and understand events and objects around them and relate them to the process under evaluation.

- *Possess perspective.* This is a critical trait, especially when the focus shifts away from compliance toward effectiveness and improvement. Auditors must be able to see the big picture and focus on activities and requirements that are truly important. They should not go looking for minor administrative errors that can damage the credibility of the audit program.

- *Tenacious.* Auditors must have the will to dig deeply into problem areas, some of which may be sensitive to the auditee. The primary purpose of any audit is to find the weaknesses. Auditors must be willing to pursue the audit threads until they find them.

- *Diplomatic, ethical, and professional.* Although auditors must be tenacious, they must be also be diplomatic and professional when they hunt for the weaknesses. They must not allow themselves to be biased in any way.

- *Effective communicators.* Communication involves more than simply expressing oneself well. It also involves active listening, being able to read an auditee's nonverbal communications, and to hear the emotional side of the message. Up to 90 percent of a good auditor's time is spent listening.

- *Analytical and factual.* Audit findings must be based on facts, not opinions. Auditors must be able to uncover the facts and put them together to support their conclusions.

- *Flexible and adaptable.* Very few audits flow exactly as planned. Auditors should be able to make adjustments during the audit to account for changes to the schedule, interviewees, or objective evidence presented, without becoming rattled.

- *Calm under pressure.* Most people relate pressure during an audit to the auditee. Auditors will also experience pressure. Pressure may be due to time constraints or attempts by the auditee to intimidate the auditor. Auditors must be able to maintain their focus and professionalism in the face of audit pressures.

- *Curious.* This intangible is one of the characteristics of natural auditors. The best auditors just want to understand how things work. They tend to be tenacious in uncovering weaknesses because by nature they dig deeply into how things work. When combined with perspective, this trait makes for a powerful auditor.

It is rare to find all of these traits in a single individual. Note that some of these skills can be learned. The challenge to the audit program manager is the selection of those individuals who posses the greatest number of these traits to be auditors. This chapter previously discussed evolving your audit program from the use of a large number of part-time auditors toward a smaller number of full-time auditors, possibly supplemented by part-timers. If this strategy is adopted, then the audit program manager has ample opportunity to observe a large number of auditors, which should help identify those who posses these traits. Even if the organization sticks with part-time auditors, the audit program manager should observe the auditors in action and coach those lacking these skills or release them from their audit responsibilities.

Auditor Training

All personnel must be competent to perform their assigned tasks. Auditors are no exception. Unless a candidate already has an extensive background in auditing, training will be required. Auditor training should consist of the following components:

• *Training in the standards or specifications that the auditor will be auditing to.* This is a prerequisite for any auditor. You cannot audit to what you do not understand. I strongly recommend at least two-day training sessions for each standard that applies. For auditors that will be auditing to both ISO 9001 and ISO 14001, this would entail four days of training. Ideally the training would be focused on both the requirements and key audit points and strategies. The common practice of sending auditors to a two- or four-hour orientation session on the standards does not properly equip candidates to be auditors.

• *General training.* Auditors need to receive basic auditor training, preferably in the process approach to auditing. This training should include information on how to properly plan an audit, conduct the audit, and report the audit. Planning should include process analysis and/or mapping, the development of audit checklists, and how to develop an effective audit strategy. Sections dealing with audit execution should include how to run an opening and closing meeting, how to conduct interviews, communication skills, the use of the checklists during the audit, how to obtain and evaluate objective evidence, and how to audit for effectiveness. Training on audit reporting should include how to write up audit findings and how to complete the audit report. Training should also include opportunities for the auditees to practice these skills, either through an actual audit or through the use of role-playing or simulations. I recommend three days for this training, although it may be possible to conduct it in two days in some situations.

• *Specialized training, as required.* This training may include training in the automotive core tools (APQP, PPAP, MSA, FMEA, SPC) for quality system auditors, training in pollution prevention and/or environmental regulations that apply to the organization, or training in OSHA regulations and job hazard analysis for OH&S management system auditors. The nature and depth of this training depends on customer requirements and what roles you want the auditors to fill within the audit program. For example, Ford and General Motors require that quality auditors be trained in the automotive core tools. Use of EMS or OH&S auditors for regulatory compliance reviews will require some training on the regulatory requirements. Auditors who will be supporting the identification and communication of best practices should be trained in benchmarking fundamentals. Audit program managers can consider this to be advanced training and not required for all auditors.

This handbook includes sufficient information to develop an auditor training program, except for training in the standards and/or specifications and regulatory requirements. Note that some customers have specific requirements relating to the qualifications of personnel who provide the training. I recommend that unless the organization has experienced trainers with an audit background, outsourcing of auditor training be used. Table 4.1 shows some of the topics that might be included in an auditor training program.

Table 4.1 Auditor training topics.

Training	Length	Audience
Standards Training	2 days	All auditors
Basic Auditor Training	3 days	All auditors

Basic Auditor Training Topics	Day
Introduction—Management System Overview • Management system structure • Management system purpose • The process and systems approach to management • Management system documentation	**Day 1**

Introduction—Management System Audits
• The purpose of the management system audit
• Audit types
• Types of findings
  – Major and minor nonconformances
  – Opportunities for improvement
  – Best practices
• Audit roles
• Auditing using the process approach
• The audit process
	Day 1

Audit Planning • Why planning is important • Determining audit purpose and scope • Audit team makeup • Identifying, collecting, and reviewing audit criteria • Developing an audit strategy • Focusing the audit—reviewing performance metrics • Review of organizational audit forms • Developing audit checklists • Developing an audit plan • Communicating the audit plan • Workshop—planning the audit (real or simulated audit)	**Day 1**

Audit Execution
• The opening meeting
• Interview basics
  – Establishing a rapport
  – Active listening
  – Providing feedback
  – Questioning strategies
• Verifying conformance
• Verifying effectiveness
• Identifying opportunities for improvement
• Handling difficult interviews
• Managing audit conflict
• Documenting findings
• The closing meeting
• Working documents
• Recommendations for action
	Day 2

• Workshop—conducting the audit (real or simulated audit)—2 to 3 hours
• Review of organizational audit reporting forms
• Workshop—documenting audit findings
• Workshop—presenting the audit findings
Postaudit Activities
• The audit report
• Verification of audit corrective action
  – Immediate and containment action
  – Short-term action
  – Long-term action
  – Remedial action
• Audit files and closeout
	Day 3

Continued

Continued

Training	Length	Audience
Advanced Auditor Training (Quality Management System Auditors)	2 to 4 days	Full-time and experienced part-time auditors

Advanced Auditor Training Topics	Day
Auditing for Effectiveness • When metrics and criteria or objectives are available • When metrics are available without objectives or criteria • When metrics are not available	**Day 1**
Auditing for Strategic Alignment and Performance • Review of organizational strategic goals • Mapping of strategic goals to processes and activities	**Day 1**
Evaluating Process Efficiency • Waste and non-value-added activities • Efficiency performance indicators • Identifying waste during internal audits	**Day 1**
Identifying Best Practices • Internal benchmarking concepts • Identifying superior process performance • Identifying enablers of performance • Documenting and reporting best practices	**Day 2**

Auditing Value Streams
• Identification of the organization's major value streams
• Selection of the value stream
• Special considerations when planning the value stream audit
  – Identifying areas of focus
  – Developing the audit strategy
	Day 2

Conducting Combined Audits (assumes auditors have appropriate standards training) • Common elements of ISO 9001:2000, ISO 14001, and/or OHSAS 18001 • Strategies for performing combined audits • Planning the combined audit • Performing the combined audit • Documenting and reporting the combined audit	**Day 3**
Other Topics (as desired) • Evaluating lean operations • Evaluating Six Sigma programs	**Day 3**
Auditing for Strategic Alignment (reference Chapter 14) • The organization's vision, mission, and values • The organization's strategy • The balanced scorecard or other dashboard of strategic indicators used by the organization to measure strategic performance, and how these support the chosen strategy • The strategic plan and initiatives needed to execute the chosen strategy • The organization's strategy maps, or linkages to the specific processes and activities that support the strategy • Key process metrics that were derived to deploy the strategy to these processes	**Day 4**

Table 4.2 lists the training that should be provided to quality management system auditors in the automotive industry. It is required for suppliers to Ford Motor Company and General Motors Corporation. Basic auditor training and some audit experience are prerequisites. The table is an outline of the course for automotive auditors in how to evaluate the automotive core tools.

Table 4.2 Automotive auditor advanced training topics.

Training	Length	Audience
Advanced Automotive Auditor Training (Automotive Quality Management System Auditors)	3 days	Full-time and experienced part-time auditors

Advanced Automotive Auditor Training Topics	Day
Overview of the Advanced Product Quality Planning Process • Advanced product quality planning (APQP) overview • The APQP audit	**Day 1**
Phase 1 Plan and Define • Evaluating planning inputs and outputs • Customer-specific requirements	**Day 1**
Phase 2 Product Design and Development • Evaluating the product design and development process • Design failure mode and effects analysis (DFMEA) • Evaluating the DFMEA • Workshop—evaluating current DFMEAs	**Day 1**
Phase 3 Process Design and Development • Evaluating the process design and development process • Process failure mode and effects analysis (PFMEA) • Workshop—developing a PFMEA • Evaluating the PFMEA • Workshop—evaluating current PFMEAs	**Day 2**
Phase 4 Product and Process Validation • Evaluating the product and process validation process • The production trial run • Statistical process control (SPC)—process capability • Measurement systems analysis • Workshop—conducting an attribute gage study • Workshop—conducting a variables gage study • Workshop—evaluating current gage studies • The production part approval process (PPAP) • Workshop—evaluating current PPAP packages	**Day 2**
Phase 5 Feedback, Assessment, and Corrective Action • Evaluating feedback, assessment, and corrective action • Statistical process control • Workshop—Evaluating control charts	**Day 3**

AUDIT FORMS AND REPORTS

There is no required format for audit reports and forms. Audit program managers are free to use whatever layout and system of supporting forms they choose. Several commonly used forms follow, starting with those used to plan the audit and ending with those used to report the results.

Audit Planning Forms

Audit planning forms most commonly used include auditor planning aids and audit plans. The audit schedule, which is a unique type of planning document, will be discussed separately.

Planning aids are forms that assist the auditor in focusing the audit. They may have an area where the auditor or audit program manager can list the processes or areas to be evaluated along with relevant documentation in the form of procedures, instructions, and guidelines that define these activities and are therefore subject to audit verification. They would also typically include a series of checkboxes or bullets relating to additional information that the auditor should consider to help focus in on the areas where the auditor needs to dig deeper. These items include previous audit reports, corrective actions, customer complaints, recent accidents or near-misses, and environmental incidents and other problem indicators. The aid might also provide an area where the audit program manager can indicate previous audit findings that need to be verified during this audit. Finally, they may also include an area where the auditor can list items that he or she will need to reference or be aware of during the audit. Examples include a list of significant environmental aspects or job hazards that affect the process or area under review and their related controls, any formally defined objectives or target that directly relate to the process (and that process owners should be aware of), and relevant process performance information.

Planning aids, although rarely incorporated into most audit programs, can be a valuable tool toward improving the thoroughness and consistency of internal audits. I favor embedding them into auditor checklists, which helps to ensure they are used by the internal auditors. An example from one of the checklists contained on the CD is shown in Figure 4.1.

An *audit plan* is a commonly used document that identifies the areas to be reviewed, who is to be interviewed, and the approximate times for each interview. Anyone who has participated in a certification audit to ISO 9001, ISO/TS 16949, ISO 14001, OHSAS 18001, or any of their numerous variations is undoubtedly familiar with audit plans. Audit plans serve several functions during an audit:

- First, the audit plan serves to structure the audit by identifying the areas to be evaluated, the sequence of evaluation of these areas, and the approximate time that will be spent in each area.

- The audit plan can be used to clearly define responsibilities among an audit team by associating each audit area to an auditor who will lead the questions in that area.

- The audit plan communicates to those who will be interviewed when they will need to be available. This allows them to plan the rest of their day and helps ensure the availability of these key individuals.

- The audit plan is also normally used to indicate audit events such as when and where the opening and closing meetings will be held and when the auditors will break for lunch.

The audit plan, if used, should be developed and communicated to the auditee management at least a week prior to the start of the audit. This allows the auditee an opportunity to prepare for the audit and to line up key interviews. If personnel are not

Compliance Category: General Requirements	
Standard Requirements	**Reviewer Checks**
Article I. Planning the Process Audit	
Rough Process Flowchart (Show/list key inputs and primary outputs)	Determine the processes/activities to be included in the scope of the audit. The scope may be provided as part of an audit schedule or plan, or it may need to be developed by the management rep. List the process(es) below. Processes Document No.

	Gather information relating to the processes to be examined. The following sources of information should be considered.
	❑ **Previous audit results of process**
	❑ **Current process metrics**
	  Metric Value and/or trend
	
	❑ **Any open or recent corrective actions, complaints**
	  (refer to next page)
	❑ **Control plans/inspection plans**
	❑ **Process flowchart(s)/layouts**
	❑ **Operator instructions (listed above)**
	❑ **Quality objectives and targets**
	
	Objectives and/or targets to review:
	1.
	
	2.
	
	Previous audit findings to verify:

Figure 4.1   Example of a planning aid embedded in a QMS audit checklist.

available or the sequence needs to be readjusted to account for interviewee availability, then this information can be provided to the lead auditor prior to the start of the audit. An audit plan such as that described here is not required by any of the standards and specifications that require internal audits. It is really only needed for large audits when multiple interviews of specific personnel are needed or when many different areas will be visited. The lead auditor and audit program manager must decide when an audit plan is needed. An example of an audit plan is provided in Figure 4.2.

Audit No. 9-05 Date: Sept. 6–7, 2005 Audit Scope: Product realization from order entry to shipment Audit Criteria: ISO/TS 16949:2002 and local procedures		Auditor(s): Frank Lewis
Time	**Topic, Area, or Process**	**Interviewee**
Day 1 **8:00–8:30**	**Opening meeting**	
8:30–9:20	**Order generation** Quotation to order entry	John Mach, account manager
9:30–12:00	**Advanced product quality planning** Product design and development	Susan Resnick, lead product engineer
12:00–1:00	**Lunch**	
1:00–2:20	**Advanced product quality planning** Process design and development	Tim Brewsky, lead process engineer
2:20–3:20	**Advanced product quality planning** Production part approval	Tien Lei, quality assurance
3:30–4:00	**Production planning and scheduling**	Tom Gransky, production control
4:30	**Daily debriefing**	
Day 2 **8:00–8:20**	**Production management**	Vicky Summers, first shift production supervisor
8:30–12:00	**Production**	Various
12:00–1:00	**Lunch**	
1:00–2:20	**Production**	Various
2:30–3:15	**Packaging, storage, and shipping**	Allen Copeland, shipping and receiving
3:15–4:00	**Auditor preparation**	
4:00	**Closing meeting**	
Process owners are requested to inform their employees about the audit and to make arrangements to minimize any disruptions during the interviews. Thank you for your support.		

Figure 4.2   Example audit plan.

Audit Forms

Many different types of forms have been developed to assist auditors during the execution of the audit. The most common of these, the audit checklist, will be discussed in Chapter 5. In this section we will discuss the audit finding forms, interview lists, and agendas for the opening and closing meetings. We will also present a specialized form that I found very useful when conducting large audits using a team of auditors, the one-liner form.

Opening meeting agendas are not normally used during internal audits, although they may be useful during full management system evaluations of a sister division or of a supplier. The opening meeting agenda serves as a checklist for the lead auditor to guide him or her through the opening meeting and the items that should be discussed. Some of the topics that might show up on the agenda include the following:

- Introductions (if needed), including guides

- Purpose and scope of the audit

- The way the audit will be conducted

- Areas to be examined, including:

  - Back shift operations

  - Unique activities to be observed

  - Satellite locations to be visited

- Any safety considerations

- Logistics (lunch, conference room, documentation, phone, and so on)

- What will happen to findings

- Time of daily debriefings (if longer audit)

- Time of the closing meeting

- Brief review of the audit plan, including any necessary changes

Instead of bullets, the agenda may use checkboxes, allowing the lead auditor to check off each item as it is discussed. An agenda is particularly useful to new lead auditors, especially when assigned to do an audit outside of their own organization. It provides an air of professionalism to the audit that puts the lead auditor firmly in control of the meeting.

Closing meeting agendas are similar to the agenda for the opening meeting and serve the same purpose. Again, they are not normally used for internal audits unless the audit was broad in scope and reached across several departmental boundaries. Since it would not be convenient to provide an individualized wrap-up with each process owner or department head, a formal closing meeting may be called for, in which case an agenda should be used. Typical items listed on the closing meeting agenda include:

- Thank you for the support shown by the auditee during the audit

- Purpose of meeting

- Statement as to the confidentiality of the audit results (especially important if this is a supplier audit)

- Disclaimer that the audit was only a sampling, weaknesses may still exist

- Brief description of the terms NC, OFI, and BP

- Overall conclusion, if conclusions are part of the lead auditor responsibilities

- Presentation of best practices noted

- Presentation of nonconformances noted

- Presentation of opportunities for improvement noted

- Nonconformance follow-up and response timing

- Request for questions

The agenda helps structure the closing meeting and, more importantly, firmly establishes the lead auditor as being in control of the meeting. For this reason, I always recommend the use of an agenda when a formal closing meeting is held. Details on opening and closing meetings will be presented in Chapter 6.

Interview lists are simply lists of the names of personnel interviewed during the audit. They are sometimes used by registrar auditors when they need to have a record of who was interviewed. They are less commonly used during internal audits. I do not recommend the use of interview lists during internal audits since they can make the auditee feel uncomfortable. I recommend jotting the person's name on the audit checklist when there is a need to note their name for some valid reason. An example of a valid reason might be to verify that employees have received training on the processes they were observed operating by examining training records maintained in human resources.

Nonconformance reports, or audit finding forms as they are sometimes called, come in many shapes and sizes. The following information should be considered mandatory no matter the format used:

- Date, auditor name, and audit number

- Description of the nonconformity

- Reference to the requirement that is being violated

- Background information needed to understand the finding

    - Form or report numbers or other specific identifier

    - Number of deficiencies and the size of the sample

    - Location or area where identified, as appropriate

    - Any other pertinent information that the auditor feels would be useful to the auditee

The exact format of the form is not as important as the information in it. The auditor must remember that the form should be designed with the auditee in mind, as the auditee has to understand and act on the finding. An example of a typical nonconformance report is shown in Figure 4.3. A discussion on how to write up audit findings is included in Chapter 7.

Since this nonconformance report also functions to document corrective action, the following sections have been added:

- Auditee manager assigned responsibility for action

- Root cause(s)

- Actions planned to eliminate the cause(s)

- Estimated completion date of long-term action

- Actual date long-term action was completed and signature of auditee manager

- Verification methods, date, and signature of audit program manager

Finding No. 02-17	Audit Finding Form
Date: Nov. 19, 2005 **Auditor:** R. Tubbs	☑ Nonconformity ☐ Opportunity for improvement ☐ Best practice

Finding: Management reviews do not consider all of the relevant inputs required by ISO/TS 16949:2002, section 5.6.1.

Description: ISO/TS 16949:2002, section 5.6.1, requires that management reviews consider customer feedback and process performance during the management review. One management review has been held since the QMS was upgraded to the new requirements. No evidence could be provided that these essential inputs were considered during the management review, and these items do not appear on the current agenda form.

Auditor	Cognizant Manager

Requirement Violated: ISO/TS 16949:2002, section 5.6.1

Root Cause:

Management Action to Be Taken:

Estimated Completion Date of Action: _____

Date Action Completed: _____   **Action Taken By:** _____
                                                      Cognizant Manager
Verification of Action:

Auditor/Verifier	Management Representative

Figure 4.3   Audit nonconformance report.

An interesting variation on the nonconformance report that I noted in use at one client was the inclusion of cost information along the bottom of the form. The audit program manager would estimate the cost of the nonconformance, including both direct and hidden costs, on the report. This information had a powerful impact in getting management's attention and the resources needed to take the action to eliminate the root cause.

One-liner forms are useful tools to help manage a large audit that extends over several days or involves three or more auditors. We found them to be very useful when leading large audit teams of six to 10 people on multiday audits of supplier facilities. It is common in these situations to find similar or related deficiencies in different areas or by different auditors. Imagine an audit where over 50 findings are noted by the audit team. Grouping of these audit findings is needed to focus the response and to avoid overwhelming the auditee. The one-liner form assists this grouping.

At the beginning of the audit, each auditor is provided with a stack of blank one-liner forms. During the audit, auditors document findings on the one-liner forms, one finding per form. During team meetings the lead auditor collects and sequentially numbers the one-liners. The team then reviews the findings by reading the one-liners together, during which time they agree on the nature of the finding while the lead auditor groups related findings together. As an example, one-liners 2, 6, and 9 might all deal with improper product identification. The lead auditor would give all three of these one-liners to one auditor and assign him or her to write up the nonconformance citing all three as examples. I strongly recommend the use of the one-liner for large audits. An example is provided in Figure 4.4.

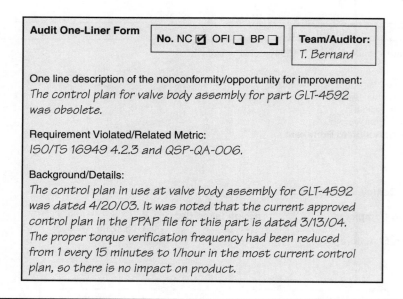

Figure 4.4 Audit one-liner form.

Audit Report

The final form to discuss is the audit report. Audit report formats vary from simply stapling a cover sheet on the nonconformance reports to multipage documents that detail the findings, statistics, instructions, and a host of background information. For internal audits, most organizations favor the former. One example of an audit cover sheet is shown in Figure 4.5. This sheet would be attached to the nonconformance reports that detail the auditor findings. Opportunities for improvement and best practices would be summarized on a separate sheet at the end of the report.

Audit Report Form
February 8, 2005
Date of Audit: February 4, 2005   **Audit No.** 3-05
Audit Team: Thompson (Lead), Cranick

Purpose: To evaluate the effectiveness and implementation of the processes used to evaluate, select, control, and develop suppliers and subcontractors.

Scope: This audit examined all aspects of supplier selection, monitoring, control, and development, including the training and control of on-site contractors.

Audit Criteria: ISO/TS 16949:2002, ISO 14001, and QSP-PUR-01

Key Personnel Contacted:
    Tom Browers, manager, purchasing
    Kim Delanney, buyer
    Ralph Beres, buyer
    George Smith, manager, QA
    Bill Martin, manager, OH&S

Summary: The audit found several significant weaknesses in the processes used to select, monitor, and control suppliers and contractors. Most significantly, the audit found that the documented process used to evaluate potential suppliers is not being followed consistently and that routine monitoring as required by the procedure is not being performed. In addition, it was found that follow-up actions are not being pursued after the issuance of corrective action to the supplier as required by the procedure. It was noted that this deficiency has potential to impact the quality of product provided to our customers.
It was noted that delivery performance of critical suppliers has been steadily deteriorating over the past six months and is well short of the goal of 95% on-time delivery, and that no action has been initiated to investigate or reverse this trend.

Other deficiencies are noted in the audit finding forms attached to this report. Corrective action requests (CARs) Q01-12 through Q01-17 were issued to address these findings.

Response: An initial response indicating the immediate corrective action taken, and an estimated completion date for long-term action, is requested by February 18, 2005.

_____   _____
    Audit Team Leader   Audit Program Manager
1

Figure 4.5 Audit report cover sheet.

Several features of this report are worth mentioning. First, an audit summary statement is not required, and when used, would typically be completed by the audit program manager. The audit team would simply report out on the audit findings during the closing meeting and provide copies of the nonconformance reports to the auditee. The final report, including the cover sheet and summary, would be prepared and issued by the audit program manager within a few days of the completion of the audit. The purpose of the summary section is to provide an overall summary of the results of the audit to senior management. It basically tells them whether they should spend the time to review the report in detail. Executives are busy people, and the summary statement gives them a short and clear indication whether the report warrants their time. Second, the summary statement provides the audit program manager, who is normally the most experienced auditor in the organization, a chance to put the audit in perspective. Summary statements are especially useful for supplier (second-party) audits, where they can be used to get supplier senior management attention. A more common form of summary is to simply list the number of nonconformances, opportunities for improvement, and best practices found during the audit.

The list of personnel contacted can be used if documentation of who was interviewed is desired. Normally this section would only list key salaried personnel contacted during the interview and it should not associate individuals with any specific audit findings. The audit number would be a sequential number used to identify the audit, in this case the third audit of 2005.

Since opportunities for improvement and best practices do not require a response and are therefore not documented on nonconformance reports, some other means of documenting them must be used. A common addition to the audit report is shown in Figure 4.6. The form can be used to document all findings noted during the audit. The

No.	Organization's Procedure No.	Audit Finding	Actions Taken/Observed	Std. Para.	Type
01					
02					
03					
04					

Figure 4.6 Audit findings form.

auditor then cuts and pastes the NCs to the nonconformance reports at the end of the audit. This form is also commonly used to debrief the auditee during multiday audits, as will be discussed in Chapter 6.

Copies of these forms, along with other formats, are provided on the CD included with this handbook. The important thing to keep in mind is that whatever format is used, it must satisfy the needs of the auditee and executive management as well as the audit program manager.

THE AUDIT SCHEDULE

An audit schedule does more than simply identify the dates when quality, OH&S, and/or EMS audits will be conducted. An audit schedule also reflects the audit program manager's strategy for performing management system audits. Indeed, the development of the annual audit schedule is in reality a strategic action.

In the old days of ISO 9001:1987 and ISO 9001:1994, many audit program managers simply assigned an audit to each element of the standard and then apportioned them somewhat equally across each month of the year. Audit schedules were easy to develop since all you had to do was take last year's audit schedule and slap this year's date on it. These audits did not reflect the status or importance of the management system components and rarely found any significant weaknesses.

The ISO 9001:2000 revision started a trend toward process-based management and the systems approach. As noted in Chapter 1, organizations are now managing value streams and systems of interdependent processes as opposed to separate activities or elements. As management methods have changed, so should our methods for planning and conducting audits. Our audit schedule should reflect these changes.

The audit schedule is important because it sets the overall scope of the audits. By scope, we mean what processes and/or areas will be included in each audit. In the old method of scheduling audits, the audit scope was simply one of the elements of the standard. Fortunately, we now recognize that natural processes don't work that way. They don't end at contract review, rather they flow into design and development and quality planning. They don't necessarily flow in series either, but rather mesh with other interdependent processes operating in parallel, series, spiral, and many other geometric patterns. Understanding these flows and interdependencies is the challenge of systems management. It is also the challenge of audit program management. Audits should mirror these natural process flows to the extent practicable since this leads to more efficient and effective audits.

The most effective audits are those that test the linkages and handoffs between related processes. Combining multiple interdependent processes in the audit scope allows the auditor the opportunity to test these linkages. The most effective quality systems audits are typically those that evaluate an entire value chain, from receipt of order to delivery, for a specific product. For an EMS, an audit that starts with the identification of controls for significant environmental aspects and then tracks the deployment of these controls throughout the organization, the monitoring of the effectiveness of these controls, and their improvement, is more effective than are separate audits of their identification, implementation, monitoring, and improvement.

The challenge with optimizing the scope is time. To audit an entire value stream might take an auditor two or even three days. Add on an additional one or two days worth of planning time and you can quickly see the magnitude of this problem, which is especially acute when the organization uses part-time auditors. To address these challenges, audit program managers often lessen the scope by splitting these larger audits into a smaller number of focused audits. Audit program managers must be careful in this balancing of needs versus resources, since splitting the audit into ever smaller chunks impacts on the ability to test the linkages and alignment between interdependent processes, which is where experience has shown most systemic weaknesses exist.

Another important consideration relating to audit scope is audit efficiency. When the audit scope involves multiple interdependent processes, the auditor normally starts at the front of the process and works forward, or at the back of the process and works toward the start. As the auditor works through the process he or she learns more about the system at each workstation or process visited. In other words, there is a building of knowledge about the system and its related processes as the audit progresses. The auditor can bring this increased knowledge to bear during subsequent interviews, allowing for a far more penetrating audit. Because this knowledge is used as it is learned, the audit is also more efficient. The auditor doesn't have to continually relearn the system, as would be the case if the audit was broken up into a series of smaller scope audits. Overall planning and audit time is therefore much less than if the same processes were evaluated using multiple audits. The bottom line is that an audit of an entire system or value stream is both more effective and more efficient than a series of smaller scope audits covering the same processes.

It must be acknowledged, however, that auditing an entire value stream may overwhelm part-time auditors unless they have extensive audit experience or are paired with someone who has. One of the reasons why I favor at least a small cadre of full-time auditors is because they can typically accept the challenge of a larger-scope audit more readily than can part-time auditors.

The challenge for the audit program manager, therefore, is to develop an audit schedule that optimizes the effectiveness and efficiency of the audits performed while accounting for the availability and competency of the internal auditors. There are two additional considerations to throw into this pot, however, status and importance. Each of the management system standards in some fashion require audit schedules to reflect the status and importance of the activities to be audited.

First we will discuss importance. Not all processes are created equal. The bottom line is that some processes are just more important toward meeting customer requirements than are others. Some are more important to being able to achieve strategic objectives. These key processes should be evaluated more frequently than other processes that only indirectly have an impact on customers or competitive strategy. All QMS, EMS, and/or OH&S processes need to be evaluated at some frequency, but I expect to see the key processes evaluated more often than these others. Identifying those processes that are most important to your customers is one of the first steps toward creating an ISO 9001:2000 or ISO/TS 16949 QMS. A similar approach can be used for environmental management systems by replacing *customer* with *environment.* Which processes could have the greatest impact on the environment if not done correctly? For an OH&S system, use *employees* in place of *customers.* Which activities or jobs present the greatest risks to employees if not properly controlled? Strategically important processes can be identified through the development and deployment of a balanced scorecard.

Status represents the current condition or performance of the processes. Status is normally reflected by performance metrics and problem reports. When a system's performance has deteriorated significantly, or when the scrap rate goes way up or the throughput way down, it's time to conduct an audit, even though it may not be scheduled for another six months. ISO/TS 16949, in particular, requires additional auditing when problems occur in a process.

Status also includes planned changes in system configuration. For instance, if you recently completed installation of a new electronic document and record control system to replace the old hard-copy systems, it might be wise to perform an audit of these systems now, rather than wait nine months and find out there are some bugs to work out, which means a lot of documents and records to regurgitate.

Let's use an example to walk through the creation of an audit schedule that embraces the process and systems approach to management. Assume the general structure of your management system is as shown in Figure 4.7.

This organization has implemented an integrated quality, environmental, and safety and health management system. One of the nice things about this diagram is that many of the related activities have been grouped together. We can also see the processes that most impact our customers. These are shown by the heavy flow lines that start with the customer in the upper left-hand corner and end with the customer in the lower right-hand corner. Also shown are the environmental and OH&S planning and compliance activities. The rest of the EH&S activities have been integrated into the original quality management system processes.

Now we will list some of the major processes that need to find their way onto our audit schedule, starting with those needed for product realization (that is, customer focused processes). We will also note some of the subprocesses that could be included in the audit scope.

Business Development Process

Business development is the front end of the product realization system of processes and comprises much more than simple contract review and order entry. Any or all of the activities in the following list could fall within the scope of business development.

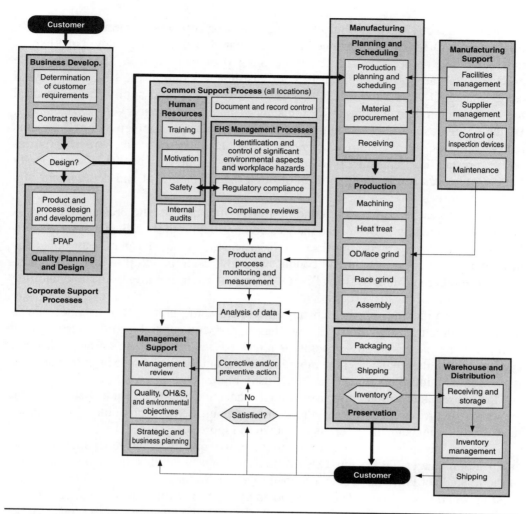

Figure 4.7   Example company structure.

Sales and marketing professionals would undoubtedly add several more. Just for the fun of it, checkboxes have been added where you can check off those that you feel would directly impact on your ability to satisfy your customers (customer column) along with those you feel would directly impact on your ability to achieve your strategic objectives (strategic column). Clean copies of each of these lists are provided on the CD. Ask your quality, engineering, and production managers to complete the customer columns individually, and members of your executive team to fill out the strategic columns. General agreement among the staff would indicate that your organization has done a good job of identifying and communicating its important customer and strategically important processes. Significant disagreement indicates it hasn't. Once agreed upon, you can use the results to help shape your audit program.

Process	*Customer*	*Strategic*
• Market segmentation	❏	❏
• Market research	❏	❏
• Product pricing	❏	❏
• Advertising and promotions	❏	❏
• Market demand forecasting	❏	❏
• Sales	❏	❏
• Proposal generation	❏	❏
• Cost estimation	❏	❏
• Customer relationship management	❏	❏
• Web-based sales and marketing	❏	❏
• Contracting (including requirements determination)	❏	❏
• Contract maintenance	❏	❏
• Order entry	❏	❏

From an audit planning perspective, I would probably group these processes into two main groups of related activities as follows:

- *Market development process.* This includes market segmentation, market research, market demand forecasting, product pricing, advertising, and promotions, including Web-based marketing. I would pick one recently launched product and one product at an advanced stage of market development to use as objects for the audit. This is a natural grouping of related activities or processes.

- *Sales process.* Sales, including Internet sales, proposal generation, cost estimation, contracting, order-entry, contract maintenance, and customer relationship management are included here. This is a second natural grouping, since they are all interdependent.

The remaining processes will not be broken down into their subprocesses, as most auditors are already familiar with these activities. I would also evaluate all of the subprocesses together as a group during any management system audit.

Product Planning and Design Process

Process	*Customer*	*Strategic*
• Concept development	❏	❏
• Product design and development	❏	❏

Process	*Customer*	*Strategic*
• Design for the environment	❏	❏
• Process design and development	❏	❏
• Equipment specification and safety review	❏	❏
• Supplier selection and long-lead procurement	❏	❏
• Product and process validation	❏	❏

Planning and Production Scheduling Process

Process	*Customer*	*Strategic*
• Product forecasting	❏	❏
• Production planning	❏	❏
• Procurement	❏	❏
• Receiving and storage	❏	❏
• Production scheduling	❏	❏

Production Process (Note we are using our example company)

Process	*Customer*	*Strategic*
• Setup	❏	❏
• Machining	❏	❏
• Heat treat	❏	❏
• OD/face grind	❏	❏
• Race grind	❏	❏
• Assembly	❏	❏
• Final test	❏	❏
• Packaging and labeling	❏	❏
• Implementation and operation of environmental controls	❏	❏
• Implementation and operation of OH&S controls	❏	❏

Distribution Process

Process	*Customer*	*Strategic*
• Storage, including inventory management	❏	❏

Process	*Customer*	*Strategic*
• Implementation and operation of environmental controls	❏	❏
• Implementation and operation of OH&S controls	❏	❏
• Shipping	❏	❏
• Billing and invoicing	❏	❏

Environmental Planning Process

Process	*Customer*	*Strategic*
• Legal and other requirements	❏	❏
• Environmental aspects identification	❏	❏
• Significance determination	❏	❏
• Aspects maintenance	❏	❏

Occupational Health and Safety Planning Process

Process	*Customer*	*Strategic*
• Legal and other requirements	❏	❏
• Hazard determination	❏	❏
• Risk categorization	❏	❏
• JHA maintenance and performance	❏	❏

Analysis and Improvement Process

Process	*Customer*	*Strategic*
• Complaint handling	❏	❏
• Internal audits	❏	❏
• Legal and other requirements	❏	❏
• Regulatory compliance reviews	❏	❏
• Corrective action	❏	❏
• Incidents and accident reaction	❏	❏
• Emergency response and preparedness	❏	❏
• Preventive action, including accident prevention	❏	❏
• Management review	❏	❏
• Objective and management programs	❏	❏

Centralized Support Processes

I focus on the word *centralized* for the following activities since their decentralized components will be subject to review when encountered during each and every other audit performed. Every audit should evaluate the control of documents reviewed during the evaluation. Every audit should verify the availability, legibility, and completeness of records examined as objective evidence. Every audit should examine the competency, awareness, and training of personnel visited during the audit. Every audit should verify the handling, control, and calibration of measurement devices used at the operations examined during the audit.

Even though the outputs from these processes, and therefore information relating to their performance, will be continually reviewed during other audits, there are still centralized functions that may not be examined without a focused review. These audits should focus on these centralized functions only. Time should not be wasted pulling documents from the floor to review revision level control or checking the calibration of production measuring equipment, since these are reviewed adequately during other process-based audits. Because only portions of these activities need to be reviewed, I go into more detail and break these down into subprocesses that should be evaluated during the audit.

Process	*Customer*	*Strategic*
• Centralized document control	❑	❑
– Document review, approval, and issue		
– Maintenance and control of the master list		
– Document retention and disposal		
• Centralized record control	❑	❑
– General record retention, storage, and disposal		
– Legal record retention (environmental and safety)		
• Centralized training	❑	❑
– Identification and communication of competency requirements		
– Training effectiveness verification		
– Identification of *strategic* competencies (not a required action)		
– Employee development		
• Centralized purchasing	❑	❑
– Supplier selection		

Process	*Customer*	*Strategic*

- – Supplier monitoring and development
- – Requisition and placement of purchase orders
- – Expediting (if common in your organization)
- – Communication of ESH requirements and policies
- – On-site contractor training

- Laboratory operations ❑ ❑
  - – Control and conduct of laboratory testing
  - – Control and conduct of calibration
  - – Control of test sets and standards
  - – Actions for failed tests or calibrations
  - – Implementation and operation of environmental controls
  - – Implementation and operation of OH&S controls

- Executive support (management appointee for OH&S) ❑ ❑
  - – Performance monitoring (including customer satisfaction)
  - – Workforce motivation
  - – Resource needs identification
  - – Resource allocation
  - – Strategic quality/environmental/OH&S planning
  - – Management review

- Maintenance and facilities ❑ ❑
  - – Centralized maintenance program management
  - – Maintenance improvement, including objectives
  - – Tooling management
  - – Facility modification, including consideration of environmental and OH&S impacts
  - – Implementation and operation of environmental controls

Process	*Customer*	*Strategic*
– Implementation and operation of OH&S controls		
– Contingency planning		
• Information technology/information systems	❏	❏
– Determination of information needs		
– Database maintenance and security, including the use of error-proofing in database design		
– System reliability and performance		
– Web site accuracy, maintenance, and reliability		

This list includes most of the processes important to the performance of the quality, environmental, and occupational health and safety management systems. Although the list looks intimidating, there are fewer then 20 major processes listed, and by grouping some of these together into value stream audits, the number of audit areas will decrease even more. If you were still performing separate element-based audits of the quality, environmental, and OH&S systems, you would instead be considering 20 quality system elements, 17 environmental system elements, and 17 OH&S system elements. Through integration of like elements, you could knock that number down to maybe 30 or 35, but the sheer number of audits would still greatly exceed the number of audits required to evaluate a management system using process-based and systems auditing.

Although the total number of audits has decreased, the scope of any individual audit has increased, sometimes significantly. This is why the selection and training of auditors is so important. Many companies expect to simply provide training on the new standards and expect auditors to be able to start performing process-based audits. Not so. The transition to an *effective* process-based auditing program requires good people, superior training, and quite a bit of planning and support from the audit program manager. Well-constructed checklists can help if they are used to guide the audit, not restrict it.

Let's take all the information developed thus far and use it to set up a strategy for the audit schedule. Table 4.3 shows the processes just listed and how I would group them together. I also indicate the time that I feel would be required for a well-trained, experienced internal auditor to plan and conduct the audit. All times are given in staff-hours or staff-days. Naturally, these times would need to be adjusted given the level of competency and experience of your auditors and the complexity and size of your processes. Audits of the centralized functions, given their reduced focus, have been grouped together to provide an efficient overall audit scope.

Note also the flow of the audit schedule. We start out with the planning processes, move through the product realization processes, and finish with the improvement processes. I would maintain this flow on the actual schedule. Why? The audit program manager and auditors can take what is learned from previous upstream audits such as planning and apply it to audits of the downstream processes. This is especially important

Table 4.3 Annual audit schedule strategy.

No.	Audit Topic	Scope	Plan Time	Audit Time
1	Market development	Market research to advertising and pricing	1 day	1 day
2	ESH planning	Environmental planning process	4 hours	4 hours
		OH&S planning process		
3	Customer A product realization	Sales process	2 days	3 days
		Product planning and design		
		Planning and production scheduling		
		Production		
		Distribution		
		ESH implementation and operation		
4	Customer B product realization	Sales process	2 days	3 days
		Product planning and design		
		Planning and production scheduling		
		Production		
		Distribution		
		ESH implementation and operation		
5	Customer C product realization	Sales process	2 days	3 days
		Product planning and design		
		Planning and production scheduling		
		Production		
		Distribution		
		ESH implementation and operation		
6	Laboratory, maintenance, and facilities	Centralized activities associated with calibration, testing, maintenance, and facilities	1 day	2 days
7	Purchasing, training, and IT	Centralized components of these systems	1 day	1 day
8	Document and record control	Centralized components of systems	4 hours	2 hours
9	Analysis and improvement process	Complaint handling through audits and review, corrective, and preventive action to objectives and management programs	2 days	3 days
10	Executive support	Top management support for the quality, environmental, and OH&S management systems.	4 hours	2 hours

for the analysis and improvement process audit, since auditors will by that time have a good idea of some of the processes and problems that should be or have been targeted for improvement owing to the conduct of the earlier audits. Assume that the company produces product for three primary customers: A, B, and C.

Using the information in Table 4.3, we can now put together an audit schedule like the one in Table 4.4 that reflects the process and system approach to auditing and the

Table 4.4   Simplified audit schedule.

Audit Topic	Jan	Feb	Mar	Apr	May	Jun	Jul	Aug	Sep	Oct	Nov	Dec
Market development	X											
ESH planning	X											
Product realization Customer A		X						X				
Product realization Customer B			X						X			
Product realization Customer C				X						X		
Laboratory, maintenance, and facilities							X					
Purchasing, training, and IT					X							
Document and record control						X						
Analysis and improvement											X	
Executive support						X						X
Environmental compliance review	X1			X2			X3					X4
OH&S compliance review	X1			X2			X3					X4
Fire and evacuation drill							X					
Tornado drill					X							
Spill drill		X1									X2	
Total planning and audit days	3	5	5	5	2	2	3	5	5	5	5	1

importance of each activity. Relative importance can be determined from the survey presented during the development of the list of processes to be included. Areas of greater relative importance should be evaluated more often than those of lesser relative importance. Note that the overlay of three product realization audits, one for each customer, would, in fact, evaluate common system components of product realization three times, assuming there is some level of standardization of practices across these customer value streams.

Note that we have also reflected planned regulatory compliance reviews and drills on the audit schedule. This is to ensure that these important events occur. The X1, X2, . . . reflect that the overall compliance review is conducted as a series of reviews, with each review focused on a different environmental medium (for example, clean air regulations, water regulations, waste regulations, pollution prevention, and so on) or different safety concern (for example, fire and electrical safety, falls and powered industrial trucks, machine guarding and confined space, personal protective equipment, and so on). Likewise the spill drills may focus on oils and spills to outside storm drains during drill X1 and on actions to respond to a spill of a hazardous chemical during drill X2.

The audit sequence follows the flow discussed earlier, with the analysis and improvement audit coming at the end of the year so that the auditors can use information gained from previous audits to evaluate management actions to correct and/or improve the management system. This audit can also be scheduled to coincide with the organization's management review and setting of objectives and targets, both of which occur at the end of the year in many organizations. Note also that audit of laboratory, maintenance, and facilities has been scheduled for July. In many industries such as automotive, there is a one- or two-week break during this time to allow for vacations, plant maintenance, and facility modifications. This may be a good time to conduct this audit, as there will be heavy activity in these areas during this time. Certain regulatory compliance reviews, such as lockout-tagout, welding safety, and confined tank entry should also be scheduled during this period for the same reasons. The laboratory operations portion may have to be performed before the shutdown begins, however, if the laboratory is shut down during this plant downtime.

The total expected audit days have been tabulated for each month. Indicating the anticipated audit days required each month helps the audit program manager level auditor resources. Note that the audit workload has been reduced during the months of May, June, and July and again in December, since these are heavy vacation months and the audit program manager will have more difficulty securing audit resources, especially if part-time auditors are used. These days do not reflect the time needed to perform regulatory compliance reviews or drills, as these are often performed by outside experts or EHS professionals.

One final note applies to reevaluations of problem areas. It is critically important that the audit program manager consider the need for, and schedule accordingly, reevaluations of areas with significant weaknesses as discovered during other management system audits or through evaluation of customer complaints and performance metrics. Waiting six months until the next scheduled audit is performed is unacceptable when the problems could significantly impact on the company's ability to meet its customer's requirements or regulatory obligations (environmental, safety, and health). The normal practice is to verify completion of the corrective action, primarily through document review. This does not adequately ensure that the actions have been institutionalized and did not create problems in other areas. When significant weaknesses are identified, schedule an additional audit of the problem area after the corrective action has been implemented. Note that this is expected, and may even be required in industries such as automotive and medical device/pharmaceutical, and the failure to do so often is cited by third-party auditors.

SUMMARY

This chapter reviewed some of the key elements that make for an effective audit program. Some of the most important concepts include the use of full-time versus part-time auditors, the role that senior management has in support of the audit program, and developing the audit schedule. The remainder of this handbook will now focus on how to plan and conduct management system audits, beginning with audit planning.

Part II

The Audit Process

P art II examines the audit process in detail, from audit planning through audit execution and ending with audit reporting and postaudit activities. The general flow for this process is shown in Figure II.1. Note that the flowchart shows not only what is done, but also who needs to be involved. Chapters 5, 6, and 7 will expand on the actions shown.

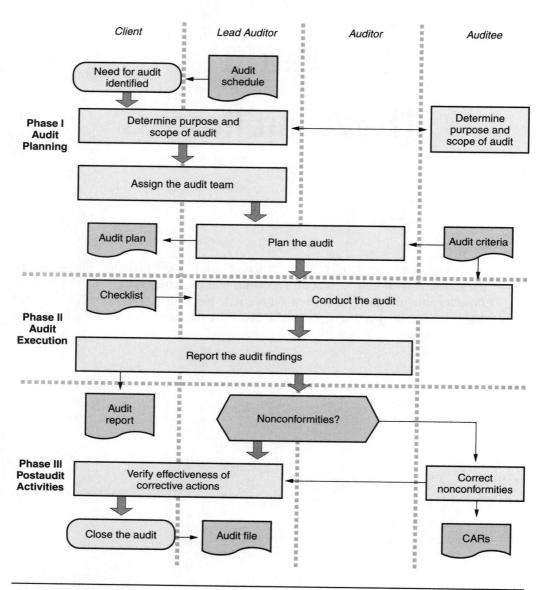

Figure II.1   The audit process.

5

Audit Planning

A s is true in most activities, careful planning is required to ensure that the audit will be successful in finding the weaknesses and opportunities for improvement that exist within the management system. This is especially true for the new or part-time auditor, or for the auditor who is asked to evaluate an area that is well outside his or her normal scope of operations. Unfortunately, planning, more than any other audit activity, is often done haphazardly, if at all. Remember, the primary purpose of the internal auditor is to find weaknesses and opportunities for improvement. To be successful, the auditor must invest some time in planning the audit. The audit planning process is shown in the flowchart in Figure 5.1.

Planning is essential for the following reasons:

- Planning ensures that everyone agrees with the purpose and scope of the audit.

- Planning exposes the auditor to the processes and procedures that will form the basis of the audit.

- Planning allows the auditor to develop a strategy for the audit.

The need for an audit will normally, but not always, be identified by the audit schedule. A detailed discussion on the development of audit schedules is presented in Chapter 4. It is possible that the need for an audit will be identified by a process owner rather than by the audit program manager. An example might be the production manager who wants a production audit prior to a customer review. In healthy audit programs that add value, this should happen routinely.

The basic purpose of any management system audit is threefold:

1. Find any systemic weaknesses that may exist in the process being reviewed.

2. Identify any opportunities to improve the process or system.

3. Identify any best practices that should be shared throughout the organization.

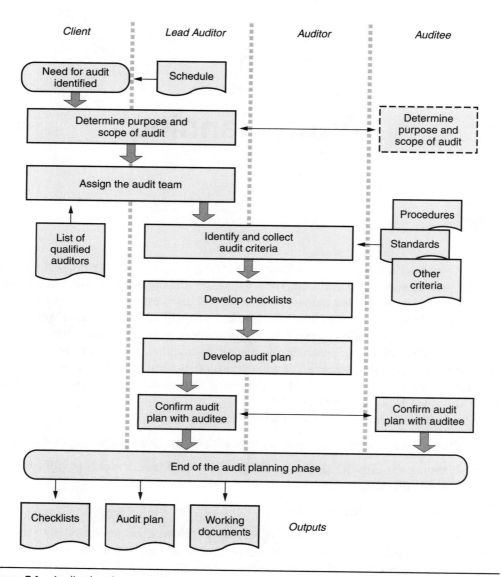

Figure 5.1 Audit planning process.

Beyond these basic purposes, management system audits may be performed to verify readiness to launch a new product, to validate a process, to support strategy deployment, to identify reasons for a lack of demonstrated performance or the root cause of problems, to reevaluate an area or process that had significant weaknesses, or any number of other purposes. Identifying the purpose of the audit is important since it shapes the strategy and focuses the audit on the topics that most need to be addressed to accomplish the purpose.

The audit client establishes the purpose of the audit. The *client* is the individual who is sponsoring, or commissions, the audit. Normally it is the audit program manager who commissions the audit through its inclusion on the audit schedule. In the case of the production audit, the client is the production manager. In other cases it might be senior management.

Once the need for an audit is identified and the purpose of the audit determined, then it is time to set the audit scope. Detailed audit planning starts with the determination of the overall scope. I call this the *macroscope.*

AUDIT STRATEGY—DETERMINING THE AUDIT MACROSCOPE

The audit scope is defined as a description of the extent and boundaries of an audit, in terms of physical locations, organizational units, activities, and processes as well as the time period covered. The scope of the audit defines the boundaries and extent of the audit. As indicated by this definition, the audit *scope* should consider:

- Organizational units, or departments to be audited

- Physical locations or areas to be included in the audit

- Specific activities and processes to be evaluated (the macroscope)

- The time frame (length) of the audit

The most important element of the audit scope involves what processes and/or areas will be included. See Figure 5.2. As noted in Chapter 4 and repeated here, the most effective audits are those that test the linkages and handoffs between related processes. Combining multiple interdependent processes in the audit scope allows the auditor the opportunity to test these linkages.

The most effective quality systems audits are typically those that evaluate an entire value chain, from receipt of order to delivery, for a specific product. For an EMS, an

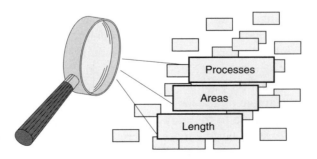

Figure 5.2   The audit scope.

audit that starts with the identification of controls for significant environmental aspects and then tracks the deployment of these controls throughout the organization, the monitoring of the effectiveness of these controls, and their improvement, is more effective than separate audits of their identification, implementation, monitoring, and improvement would be.

The challenge with optimizing the scope is time. To audit an entire value stream might take an auditor two or even three days. Add on an additional one or two days worth of planning time and you can quickly see the magnitude of this problem, which is especially acute when the organization uses part-time auditors. To address these challenges, audit program managers often lessen the scope by splitting larger audits into a smaller number of focused audits. Audit program managers must be careful in this balancing of needs versus resources, since splitting the audit into ever smaller chunks impacts on the ability to test the linkages and alignment between interdependent processes, which is where experience has shown most systemic weaknesses exist.

Another important consideration relating to audit scope is audit efficiency. When the audit scope involves multiple interdependent processes, the auditor normally starts at the front of the process and works forward, or at the back of the process and works toward the start. These basic strategies are called *trace forward* and *trace back,* respectively, and will be discussed in more detail later in this chapter. The important point to note at this time is that the auditor learns more about the system at each workstation or process visited. In other words, there is a building of knowledge about the system and its related processes as the audit progresses. The auditor can bring this increased knowledge to bear during subsequent interviews, allowing for a far more penetrating audit. Because this knowledge is used as it is learned, the audit is also more efficient. The auditor doesn't have to continually relearn the system, as would be the case if the audit was broken up into a series of smaller-scope audits. Overall planning and audit time is therefore much less than if the same processes were evaluated using multiple audits. The bottom line is that an audit of an entire system or value stream is both more effective and more efficient than a series of smaller-scope audits covering the same processes. Other concepts relating to setting the audit scope are discussed in Chapter 4 in the section on audit schedules. Some examples of audits scopes follow:

• This audit will examine the product realization process for DaimlerChrysler, starting with advanced quality planning and continuing through final packaging and shipping. Included in the scope are the processes of contract review, order entry, quality planning, design and development, production scheduling, purchasing, manufacturing, and shipping. Other processes that directly impact on this value stream may also be evaluated to the extent that they support the overall process.

Note: This is an example of a value stream audit for a specific customer. The scope is large and may require three to four days to plan and complete. It would probably be beyond the capabilities of all but the most experienced part-time auditors. It could also be broken up into two audits, one focusing on the contract review, quality planning, and design and development process, the second focusing on the production scheduling through shipping activities. The disadvantage would be the inability to verify proper deployment of the systems developed during quality planning to the manufacturing floor. This disadvantage could be minimized with proper planning, at the cost of some redundancy.

• This audit will examine the implementation and operation of controls used to minimize the impact of our significant environmental aspects, including methods used to determine appropriate controls, the implementation of controls, and the monitoring of their performance.

Note: This is the equivalent of a value stream for an EMS. It focuses on the *doing* part of the PDCA cycle upon which ISO 14001 is based. It could be easily completed in two days by an experienced auditor.

• This audit will examine the methods used to effect OH&S performance improvement, including the internal audit process, corrective and preventive action, the setting of OH&S objectives and management programs, and management review.

Note: This is the equivalent of a value stream for an OH&S management system. It focuses on the *check* and *act* parts of the PDCA cycle upon which OHSAS 18001 is based. It could be completed in one day by an experienced auditor.

• This audit will examine the process used to evaluate, select, monitor, and develop suppliers of production materials and parts.

Note: This is an example of a reduced-scope audit that is commonly found on most organizations' audit schedules. It does examine interrelated processes (evaluation and selection of supplier, supplier monitoring, supplier development), but it will not test the linkage to the manufacturing or planning processes without careful planning. This audit could be planned and conducted in one day.

A final important point worth noting is that the scope of a process-based audit is fluid. By that, I mean that the auditor is free to evaluate any process that directly inputs into or controls the processes being audited. Take for example the product realization process audit scope in the preceding list. The auditor will also evaluate the training and competency of personnel involved in product realization activities. The auditor will also examine document control, record control, and the control of nonconforming product, along with many other requirements found in clauses other than clause ISO 9001:2000, clause 7.0, Product realization. The auditor should only review these items to the extent that they relate to the process being reviewed, however. Reviewing the control of documents examined during the audit is in scope; evaluating documents not related to the process would be out of scope.

RESEARCHING AUDIT AREA STATUS

Armed with knowledge of the audit scope and the purpose of the audit, the auditor(s) can now commence research. This research should start by examining process or system status. Status refers to the current condition of the area. Are there problems with performance? Have there been customer complaints related to any of the processes to be reviewed? Have there been major changes or modifications made to the processes recently? These are important issues since they provide the auditor with the information to narrow the focus of the audit. I call this determining the *microscope*. In any audit the auditor cannot evaluate every possible action or activity. Auditors must be selective. Effective auditors spend the most time evaluating processes or areas that have the worst performance or the greatest potential for weaknesses. The challenge is finding out what these areas are.

The following sources of information can be used and should be reviewed by the auditor to help focus the audit. The audit program manager, quality manager, or EH&S manager should have these sources of information available.

- *Previous audit reports.* Try to obtain and review the last two audit reports for the process being reviewed. Auditors should note areas where nonconformities were noted before. The auditor should review these areas during the current audit to verify that the action taken to address the deficiencies was effective. Second, the auditor should note areas of strength. Less time need be spent in these areas.

- *Previous audit checklists.* If audit checklists are maintained in the audit file, then they should be reviewed for the items just noted. In addition, checklists may provide the auditor with information on areas that were not reviewed during the previous audit and that should be included in the current evaluation. The checklists may also give insight into the strategies used by the last audit team. This could be very useful to the current audit team.

- *Corrective action log.* Auditors should review the last six months of corrective actions to identify any problems related to the processes being reviewed. The auditor should verify that any action taken permanently eliminated the problem during the conduct of the audit.

- *Customer complaints, field returns, and other problem indicators.* These should be reviewed to the extent that they relate to the processes to be audited. A high number of customer complaints or field returns indicate problems in design, manufacturing, shipping, and/or inspection.

- *Communication logs.* For OH&S and environmental management systems, review the communication logs. These may reflect external complaints (for example, for noise or odor) or internal concerns of employees that should be considered during the audit.

- *Current and recent performance metrics.* Review current process performance against established goals. Review the performance trend for the past three to six months. Is performance getting better or worse? During the audit inquire about actions for metrics that are not meeting goals or exhibit sustained trends going in the wrong direction. For OH&S systems this includes the OHSA 300 log and lost workday statistics.

- *Records or logs of accidents, incidents, and/or near misses.* OSHA 300 logs do not necessarily identify the activities where the injury occurred. For this reason many organizations maintain separate logs providing this information. Likewise, ask to view any incident reports for EMS audits. Also in this category are any active or recent notices of violation or citations from state or federal environmental, health, and safety officials. Hopefully this file will be empty. Quality system auditors should note that ISO/TS 16949:2002 requires the consideration of employee safety during the design of processes. A high accident or lost-workday rate in an area may provide an indicator that the organization did not adequately consider worker safety when it designed its processes.

In addition to these noted indicators of current system status, the auditor should also review the following for potential applicability and use during the audit:

- *Documented improvement objectives and related management programs.* If there are formal improvement objectives related to the process being reviewed, then the auditor may want to verify that appropriate personnel are aware of the objectives and that progress is being made toward their achievement.

- *Listing of significant environmental aspects.* For EMS audits, or if a combined audit is being conducted, the auditor should review the listing of significant environmental aspects. Significant aspects associated with the products, activities, or services being reviewed should be noted. During the audit the auditor may evaluate whether the designated controls are in place and are being maintained. The auditor may also want to evaluate employees' awareness of the aspects in their area and the environmental impact they may have if not properly controlled.

- *Job hazard analysis.* For OH&S audits or for combined audits, the auditor may want to review the JHAs of activities that will be reviewed during the audit. The auditor should note significant hazards and the controls used to minimize their associated risks. During the audit the auditor can verify the implementation and use of these controls.

Finally, the auditor should also ask the manager(s) of the area being evaluated if they have any concerns or problems that the auditor should focus on during the audit. There are two reasons to do this. First, the manager will have more knowledge about current problems and may be able to provide information useful in focusing the audit toward areas of weakness. Second, by enlisting their input, the auditor makes the managers part of the audit team. Even if the answer is, "Absolutely not—everything is in great shape!" the auditor is reinforcing the concept that we're all on the same team— I'm trying to provide a service to you.

A review of the sources noted can be accomplished in one or two hours assuming the information is readily available. When part-time auditors are used, I recommend that the audit program manager collect these sources and provide them to the auditor(s) to assist in audit planning. Armed with this information, the auditor is now ready to research the processes and procedures that will be the subject of the audit.

UNDERSTANDING THE AREA TO BE AUDITED

This is the most important part of the planning process, yet many auditors fail to even review the process procedures and instructions prior to the audit. Instead, they just grab a prepared checklist and start auditing. Such audits rarely find weaknesses other than minor administrative errors. Auditors don't have to become an expert on the process, but they do have to understand it well enough to know what questions to ask and to evaluate the adequacy of the responses.

The first step in understanding the process(es) to be audited is to collect and review the procedures that describe how these activities should be conducted. Many companies now use flowcharts to document their processes. These can be an immense aid in helping to understand the process flow and its related inputs and outputs. If a process flowchart is not available, then the auditor should consider generating one. Ensure that key inputs and primary outputs are indicated on the flowchart. The auditor will want to verify these during the audit. During this review, the auditor may want to highlight key requirements that relate to problem areas or that appear to be key to process performance. The auditor will want to include these on the checklist later.

One of my favorite tools for analyzing a process is the suppliers–inputs–process–output–customers (SIPOC) diagram. The SIPOC diagram shows the process flow, key inputs, who supplies the inputs, the outputs from the process, and who gets the outputs. A SIPOC diagram can be created during the procedure review or from discussions with process owners. An example of a SIPOC diagram for a pharmacy operation is shown in Figure 5.3.

Although any auditor should realize that the medication order from the physician is a critical input, the auditor may not recognize the importance that the medication database plays until it is identified on the SIPOC diagram. If this database is incorrect, not updated, or unavailable, then the likelihood of medication errors is amplified. The auditor should plan on spending some time with the IT folks looking at how this database is maintained.

I have modified the basic SIPOC diagram to also provide an area for recording process performance metrics. These should be identified in process procedures or during the initial research mentioned earlier in this chapter. The auditor should highlight those inputs and outputs that are especially important for inclusion on the audit checklist. During the audit the auditor can refer to the SIPOC diagram for additional areas to be examined.

The auditor should consider developing a system SIPOC diagram when planning for an audit of a value stream or system of multiple processes. The focus of this SIPOC is to understand the flow and the system-level inputs and outputs important to system performance. An example SIPOC for a manufacturing system is provided in Figure 5.4.

Several things stand out in the system-level SIPOC. First, production scheduling relies on the production forecast and weekly orders. Rarely is the process used to generate production forecasts evaluated during internal audits. If the production forecast has significant inaccuracies, then production efficiency will be affected. If a review of the throughput metrics showed production efficiency declining, then the auditor may

Suppliers	Inputs	Process	Outputs	Customers
Physician	Med. order	Receive medication order	Information	Pharm. tech
Physician Info. tech.	Med. order Meds d/b computer	Enter order into computer	Information Updated inven.	Pharmacist Pharm. stores
Info. tech.	Meds d/b Printer	Prepare label	Label	Pharmacist
Info. tech. Pharm. stores	Meds d/b Medications	Prepare medication	Medications	Patient
Prior step Pharm. stores	Label Container	Apply label	Labeled meds.	Nurse and patient
Physician Prior step	Med. order Packaged medications	Verify medication	Verified meds.	Nurse and patient
Physician Facilities	Med. order Delivery service	Deliver to prescribing unit	Delivered meds.	Nurse and patient
Process Metrics:				
Cost		**Quality/Productivity/Effectiveness**	**Time/Delivery**	
Administrative cost/order		Pharmacy errors (quantity, dosage, or medication)	Order cycle time, receipt of order to delivery	

Figure 5.3 SIPOC diagram.

Suppliers	Inputs	Process	Outputs	Customers
Production control Sales Production	Production forecast Weekly orders Equip. utilization forecast	Production scheduling	Production schedule	Setup Production
Maintenance Maintenance Prod. control	Tools and dies Setup instructions Production schedule	Setup	First-piece verification	Production QC
Receiving Process eng. Maintenance Downstream proc.	Materials and parts Instructions Equipment Pull kanban	Manufacturing	Work in process Production records Inspection records Finished parts	Production Production QC Final test
Quality control Quality control Engineering Quality assurance	Test equipment Test instructions Acceptance criteria Control plan	Final test	Test records Approved product Failed product	QC Packaging QC
Receiving Engineering Production control Maintenance	Packing materials Packaging specs. Preprinted labels Shrink-wrap mach.	Pack and label	Packaged product	Distribution
Distribution Distribution IT Purchasing	Storage location HiLos Inventory control Trucking company	Material storage and delivery	Inventory records Dock audit records Shipping documentation	Distribution QC Distribution, Accounting
Metrics: Final ppm quality, throughput, overall equipment effectiveness, WIP inventory level				

Figure 5.4 Manufacturing system SIPOC.

want to spend some time evaluating the process used to generate the production fore-cast along with its accuracy.

Second, the auditor may note that first-piece inspection is performed after each setup. The auditor may want to review the inspection results to determine if the setup process is effective (that is, how many setup adjustments does it take to get good parts?). Conversion to small-lot manufacturing, one of the principles of lean, requires efficient setup processes. The auditor may also want to evaluate the setup instructions. In processes like injection molding, it is not uncommon to find that the process settings differ from the setup instructions.

If the auditor noted numerous customer complaints regarding incorrect labeling during the initial research, then he or she would probably target the pack and label operation for detailed review, including an evaluation of the control of packaging specifications and the process used to print and apply labels.

In this example I would probably create a process-level SIPOC for the manufacturing step shown on the system-level SIPOC. The time it takes to create the SIPOC diagram ranges from a few minutes to up to an hour, depending on how detailed the procedures are and how well the auditor understands the processes. Some organizations have revised their system-level procedures to include information contained on the SIPOC, with key inputs and suppliers indicated in the left margin, the process flow in the middle, and outputs and customers in the right margin of the procedure. In this case the auditor may still want to create a system-level SIPOC to tie these processes together and to highlight the key inputs and outputs.

SIPOC diagrams, when combined with knowledge on current system performance obtained through procedure review and the research previously discussed, provide the information needed to determine the areas of focus during the audit, or to use my term, the microscope.

AUDIT STRATEGY—DETERMINING THE MICROSCOPE

The microscope represents those areas where the auditor will focus attention during the audit. In any process-based audit, whether it be quality, environmental, or safety and health, the auditor will find that there isn't sufficient time to review everything in detail. This is normal. Areas that are performing well, as evidenced by solid process performance measures and an absence of problem reports, require less review than areas that are performing poorly. There is a reason why an area's performance is poor and your job as an auditor is to find it. It may be due to poor process design, inadequate resources or support, defective inputs, noncompliance with the process requirements, or a lot of wasteful, non-value-added activities. In essence the auditor becomes a troubleshooter. This is appropriate since in most instances the cause is due to one of the reasons just mentioned, all of which have related requirements in the management system standards.

Only in the situation where the auditor is also seeking out best practices, an advanced topic discussed in Chapter 13, would there be a need to spend a significant amount of time in an area performing well. The microscope, determined through the reviews and analysis previously discussed, defines those areas that require focused review.

As an example, let's look again at the production process in the SIPOC discussion. If the review of performance data and customer complaints indicated that this process was experiencing problems with throughput and labeling, yet product quality was high, then the auditor might plan to spend more time in production scheduling, setup, and packing and labeling. Questions in these areas would go deeper than those in other areas, and the auditor would plan to examine the quality of some of the key inputs into these processes. The other areas would not be ignored, rather they would not be the subject of intense examination unless unexpected problems were noted during their review.

During an audit of an OH&S system, focusing the audit may translate into spending more time in areas that have higher injury or lost-workday rates, or it may mean focusing more attention on certain types of hazards associated with a high level of worker's compensation claims. For an EMS, it may mean targeting areas where environmental performance improvement has been poor.

What do you do if all of the performance data are good and there are no complaints or problems reported anywhere in the process? Celebrate! Then, target areas that you feel hold the greatest potential for error based on your research. The medication database would be one area to target using the pharmacy SIPOC as an example. I instinctively know and can see from the SIPOC diagram that this resource is key to providing the correct medication at the proper dosage. Since it is shown as an input and not as a primary step in the process, I also suspect that it has not been the focus of a detailed review. Therefore, although I will examine each step in the process, I will plan to spend extra time looking at medication database maintenance and support. As auditors gain more experience, they will instinctively know where to focus attention. What is often referred to as auditor's luck is really this instinct. In addition, I will probably also spend more time looking for opportunities for improvement in the form of non-value-added activities and waste, which, if they can be identified, will lead to even higher levels of performance. Remember, the auditor's first responsibility is to find the systemic weaknesses. Focusing the audit helps the auditor do just that.

DEVELOPING AUDIT CHECKLISTS

Checklists have been provided on the accompanying CD to assist in audits of ISO 9001, ISO/TS 16949, ISO 14001, and OHSAS 18801. *Auditors cannot rely on the use of these checklists alone.* These checklists only address requirements from the applicable specifications and standards. They do not address organizational requirements as reflected in local procedures and practices. Nor can they target all of the many different inputs and resources unique to the process being evaluated. They are a starting point, not a complete package. Auditors will need to develop their own checklists, or add to the ones provided, to ensure a complete and sufficient evaluation.

Fortunately, developing an audit checklist is not difficult, assuming the auditor has taken the time to review the procedures and understand the audit areas assigned. In this section we will walk through the process used to develop an audit checklist. Keep in mind that while developing a checklist is not difficult, it does take some practice. No one that I've ever met felt entirely comfortable the first time they tried. Once an auditor has gone through a few audits, he or she will understand what information needs to be on the checklist the next time. A checklist is a somewhat personal tool. It should be seen as a guide and aid to the auditor, not an instruction. Before we begin on the mechanics, let's discuss how the audit checklist can be used to aid the auditor.

Process Awareness

The first benefit of checklist preparation is that it exposes the auditor to the procedures, instructions, and practices that will be reviewed during the audit. You can't build a checklist unless you know what questions to ask. Those questions relate to the requirements, inputs, and practices reflected in process documentation. Developing a checklist forces the auditor to review this documentation. This often overlooked benefit is one of the reasons why I do not always recommend the use of prepared checklists to my clients. Too often auditors in programs that use them simply show up on the day of the audit, grab the checklist, and start asking questions. No planning, no preparation, just do the audit. These audits are virtually guaranteed to produce little in the way of value-added findings. Unless the auditor has extensive experience auditing the same or similar processes, it is a prescription for disaster. Better to do no audit than to mislead process owners into thinking their process is in good shape because an inadequately prepared auditor could not identify the weaknesses that were there. The checklists on the CD are foundation checklists, they are not a substitute for audit preparation.

If the audit program manager chooses to use prepared checklists then he or she must take extra precautions to ensure auditors prepare for the audit. These precautions could include providing copies of relevant procedures and instructions to the auditors (rather than making them find and copy them themselves), having the auditor present the strategy, or reviewing the audit plan prior to the audit.

Structure

One of the greatest benefits of a checklist is that it can help structure the audit. An audit plan provides a macrostructure by identifying the broad areas to be examined and allocating time for each area. A good audit checklist should provide a structure for each individual area or process to be examined. It does this by including questions relating to requirements that need to be verified, in the approximate order in which they will be asked. I say approximate, because the auditor may need to jump ahead or back a little on the checklist to adjust the audit flow to the auditee or the natural process. In general, the questions on the checklist should follow the natural flow of the process. Since most procedures are written this way, audit checklists generally follow the process flow. The presentation of audit evidence may sometimes warrant departing from the natural flow to pursue an area relating to a record, list, or other object.

A good way to test how well your checklist structures the audit is to mentally visualize yourself conducting the audit using your checklist. Does each question flow into the next? Are the questions positioned on the checklist so that the objective evidence presented in response to this question provides the information or objects needed to research the next question? Skillfully constructing a checklist to provide this kind of structure takes experience, but can be accelerated if the auditor visualizes asking the questions, receiving the expected answers, and examining the objective evidence.

Documentation

The best audit checklists not only include the questions to ask and space to document the findings, they also provide areas for comments and information about the samples selected, documents reviewed, and so on. In fact, a well-constructed checklist will also guide the auditor in how to verify the response by providing defined areas for the objective evidence to be examined. A portion of one of the checklists from the CD is reproduced in Figure 5.5 to illustrate. Block arrows show the sections of interest.

This is a portion of a checklist used to evaluate implementation of the OH&S controls to reduce worker risk. Note, the right-hand column provides space to list the risks and related controls for the process reviewed. The auditor could gather this information during initial research (it would be on the JSA for this task) and put it on the checklist. During the audit the auditor knows exactly what to look for and can focus on maintenance and use of the controls. Note how the checklist provides an area where the auditor can list the names of some of the employees observed performing the task to allow for verification of training records in human resources after the interview is complete. This is what I mean when I say the checklist is an *aid* to the auditor.

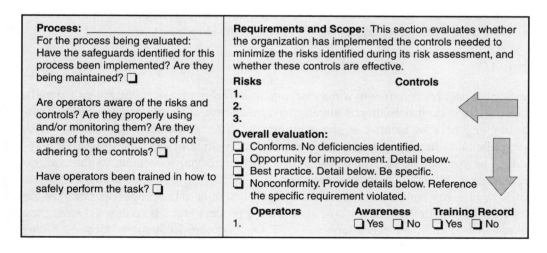

Figure 5.5 Using an audit checklist to document the audit.

| Internal Audit Program
Review the audit procedure and
several internal audits.
Is there a documented audit procedure?
Is it properly controlled?
❏

Does the procedure describe audit
scope, responsibilities, frequency,
methods, and competencies of
auditors? ❏

Does the audit program include all
elements of the OH&S system? ❏

Are previous audits reviewed as part
of audit planning? ❏

Are audit results provided to
management? ❏ | **Requirements and Scope:** This section evaluates the
organization's internal audit process.

Overall evaluation:
❏ Did not check.
❏ Did not apply.
❏ Conforms. No deficiencies identified.
❏ Opportunity for improvement. Detail below.
❏ Best practice. Detail below. Be specific.
❏ Nonconformity. Provide details below. Reference the
    specific requirement violated. |

Audit No.	**Complete/Documented?**	**Independent?**
	❏ Yes ❏ No	❏ Yes ❏ No
	❏ Yes ❏ No	❏ Yes ❏ No
	❏ Yes ❏ No	❏ Yes ❏ No
	❏ Yes ❏ No	❏ Yes ❏ No
	❏ Yes ❏ No	❏ Yes ❏ No

Audit Finding/CAR	**Date**	**Addressed?**
_____	_____	❏ Yes ❏ No
_____	_____	❏ Yes ❏ No

Figure 5.6   Using an audit checklist to show areas audited and not audited.

A good checklist will also allow a subsequent auditor to see what was not evaluated, as well as what was. Good documentation is critical. Auditors must be able to show what was evaluated, how it was evaluated, what specifically was examined, and what was found. This information will be used to assess the thoroughness of the audit and to guide future audit teams when they plan the scope of their audits of the same area or process in the future. In the audit checklist in Figure 5.6 the *Overall Evaluation* section has been modified to include *Did not check* and *Did not apply*. Checkboxes in the left column can be used to indicate specific questions/requirements evaluated.

Now let's focus on the mechanics of checklist development.

Step 1

Review the procedures, SIPOC diagrams, and other information. If you haven't already done this, then do it now. If you already have, then review them again, this time highlighting or otherwise identifying the requirements that you feel are important to verify. Remember, auditors must be selective. You normally do not have time to verify everything. The purpose of the initial research was to equip you to be able to select those areas to focus on. Identify those areas now.

Note also key inputs, resources, and controls essential to the proper operation of the process, along with the primary outputs from the process and where they go to. If they are not identified in the procedure, use a SIPOC diagram. Remember, most problems occur at the interface between processes and their related inputs. It is very important that the auditor verify these key inputs, resources, and outputs.

I recommend printing a copy of the procedure and marking it up to show those items that need to be examined. The auditor can annotate the procedure to add comments and questions identified during initial research. The markup becomes a rough initial draft for the checklist. An example of a marked up procedure is shown in Figure 5.7. This procedure describes the order generation process for a sales and marketing business unit of an international automotive supplier. This business unit receives and administers all of the contracts for its multiple North American affiliates. The auditor is assigned to audit the order generation process for this business unit.

The auditor has done her initial research and understands some of the key performance items and problems that need to be examined. The example shows how she has now gone through the documented procedure and highlighted those requirements she feels are most important to verify. These are shown by the grey highlights in the example. In practice the auditor would probably highlight with a normal yellow or green highlighter. It also shows how she has annotated the procedure with comments to help her develop her strategy. These comments will be transformed into questions and notes on the checklist.

Note particularly the comments on the flowchart. She has noted two documents, the review checklist and the kickoff letter, that are not mentioned in the textual portion of the procedure. This may or may not be an issue, depending on whether they are actually being used. She has commented to verify their use. Many companies are moving toward flowcharted procedures only. Flowcharts frequently contain less information than textual procedures, so more annotation would be expected on the flowchart in these situations regarding what is reviewed, what information is required, and so on.

Finally, note how the auditor has also targeted a brief interview with representatives from invoicing and material control. She wants to get their impression of how well the outputs from this process serve their needs prior to evaluating this process. Information on any concerns they have should be factored into the evaluation. Comments at the bottom of the first page of the procedure indicate material control may not be getting accurate information from sales—this should be confirmed and the impacts noted.

Some auditors stop at this point. They simply use their annotated copies of the procedures to be reviewed as their checklist. While very experienced auditors may be able to get away with this, I do not recommend it and would absolutely not allow it for new or part-time auditors. The annotated procedure is just not a good vehicle for structuring the flow of questions during the audit. In addition, it does not provide any space for the documentation of objective evidence, samples pulled, and so on, during the audit. A well-constructed checklist can do this and much more.

Please note that this procedure is very well-constructed and easy to audit. It shows the key inputs, resources, and outputs, both graphically in the flowchart and specifically called out in the frontmatter of the procedure. It also identifies metrics used to measure process performance. The flowchart shows nicely the sequence and interaction of steps not only within the process but also with other processes. The textual portion expands on and clarifies the steps on the flowchart. Do not always expect to have such nice auditable procedures to prepare from.

WeSupplyIt Corporation	Order Generation	**Issued:** 7/14/01
Approved: *I. McIntyre*	(i) QSP-SAL-02	Revised: 3/7/05

Responsibility: This procedure defines the process WSI-Orlando will use to determine customer requirements and process orders, and to ensure compliance to the requirements described in any legal contracts with potential and existing automotive customers.

Scope: This procedure is applicable to automotive sales, including the following documents, which may be considered as contracts.
- Request for quotations from potential customers
- Supplier agreement or contract
- Letters of Intent
- Purchase orders and EDI releases
- Contract addendums to purchase orders

Responsibility: The Automotive Sales Department and WSI-Orlando management share primary responsibility for implementation of this procedure. Overall ownership for this process is assigned to the VP, Automotive Sales. Other functions within WSI-Orlando will support these responsibilities to the extent noted.

Inputs: Customer request and orders

Resources: Sales contacts from other WeSupplyIt affiliates
Customer requirements
Contract tracking database   *Evaluate how database maintained. Is it current? Is it accurate? Compare info in d/b to info on original contract and amendments.*
Marketing information

Outputs: Accepted contract, agreement, or order, accurately and completely defining the customer requirements, that satisfies WSI's financial or business objectives. This primary output is provided to material control for use in order fulfillment.

Metrics: Sales revenue versus targets, as reported and evaluated during monthly operation meetings
Order accuracy, as indicated by the information review in the order fulfillment process
Proposal effectiveness
Proposal backlog   *Order accuracy info from materials control indicates frequent discrepancies between original customer contact or order and what is entered in customer database. Order accuracy has been running around 84%. Not good!*

References: OG.Form.3.0 Contract Review
OG.WI.1.0 Completion of RFQ Master List
OG.Form.2.0 Request for Quotation/Quotation Checklist
OG.Form.1.0 RFQ Master List

Review of master list show only interior trim has issued local instructions to supplement this. Need to pull and review this instruction QSI-SAL-IT-01,
Procedure: *and have interior trim sales walk us through during audit.*

1.0   General

The general process for order generation is shown in the flowchart embedded within this procedure. This process applies to all orders and agreements between WSI-Orlando and its customers. More detailed instructions may be developed by each sales team (for exampole, interior trim, body, or accessories) if desired to document unique requirements for specific customers, however the essential steps in this process must as a minimum be followed. The following sections provide additional detail to supplement the information contained on the process flowchart.

Continued

Figure 5.7   An example of a marked-up procedure.

2.0 Business Development—Inquiry Review, Presentation, and Proposal Generation

2.1 The cognizant lead salesperson will make the determination as to whether a customer presentation is necessary, considering the nature and size of the potential business and strategic importance of the customer.

Ask how they determine customer requirements

2.2 The salesperson has the responsibility to determine all customer requirements necessary for an accurate quotation. Customer drawings, sketches, functional specifications, or the inquiry or request for quotation are all sources of primary information. The salesperson shall contact the customer to obtain additional information when needed to fully understand the customer's expectations or as needed to complete the quotation. Volumes, delivery dates, and critical milestone dates are important and must be clearly defined in order to quote a job.

Verify this info reflected in each quotation, where did it come from.

2.3 The quotation team (salesperson and supporting groups) has a responsibility to identify and define not only specified customer requirements, but also requirements not specified by the customer but which the WeSupplyIt team knows are required to make the product fit for use. These additional requirements are to be considered during the quotation process and specifically called out in the quote as appropriate.

Ask how they do this. Try to ID obvious rqmts not called out in RFQ or drawings, but reflected in quote.

2.4 *Team Feasibility Reviews* are required for all initial production contracts. Feasibility reviews are performed by the manufacturing site where the product will be produced. The manufacturing site is responsible for obtaining any other support or expertise needed to complete this review. The salesperson will contact the manufacturing site to initiate the review process.

Verify feasibility reviews in file, filled out be manufacturing site. Samples at least 10 recent orders.

2.5 The results of the feasibility review (if required) are provided to the WSI salesperson as a required input into the quotation process. All issues must be addressed, or deemed capable of being addressed, prior to quoting a job. The *Team Feasibility Review* (or equivalent) shall be maintained in the quotation file or feasibility book.

Scan through feasibility reviews in file, ensure all open issues addressed.

2.6 WSI may also receive cost information from the manufacturing plant. Where provided, the manufacturer's base price is indicated on a transmittal to WSI (for example, e-mail, fax, and so on). WSI may build in additional costs (for example, freight charges) as applicable. Price margins will take into consideration the applicable market conditions. Customer confirmation of the negotiated price is reflected by the issuance of a purchase order or nomination document (letter of intent).

2.7 Upon receipt of all relevant information, the salesperson will review the quotation with next-level sales management to ensure that the quotation will meet all of the potential customers requirements, including customer-specific quality requirements. This review must be documented. Documentation may be by signature on the quotation itself, through completion of OG.Form.2.0 Request for Quotation/Quotation Checklist, or equivalent method.

Verify evidence of next-level review

2.8 Each department shall maintain of a listing of quotations received and contract awards to assist quotation follow-up and to assess quotation effectiveness. The exact manner of quotation tracking is up to the individual sales team.

Review log for trends. Is department tracking/ using the trends or backlog don't look good, what action is being taken?

3.0 Contract Award, Review, and Order Entry

3.1 Orders, releases against a previously agreed-to contract, and EDIs are not required to go through the business development steps described in section 2.0 above if their core requirements have already been approved through an existing contract or agreement. These requests enter the order generation process here, after the award announcement.

Verify evidence of review.

Figure 5.7 An example of a marked-up procedure.

Continued

3.2 After a contract has been awarded, a review must be conducted to ensure that the award is the same as what was quoted. Any differences from the quotation must be analyzed to ensure WSI can perform to the modified requirements and that it still meets WeSupplyIt business objectives. In addition, EDIs, releases, or other orders such as those described in section 3.1 above must be reviewed to ensure the right part numbers, quantities, and delivery dates or methods are specified in accordance with contract agreements. Reviews of EDIs and other production orders are typically performed by the manufacturing plants.

Ask salesperson about this role.

3.3 The WSI-Orlando Sales Department serves as the negotiator or mediator between the manufacturing site and the customer for significant contract issues. Any additions or modifications to the original RFQ shall be documented with the customer and the manufacturer. A revised or modified RFQ from the customer shall be filed as an addendum or a replacement to the original RFQ.

3.4 The Sales Department shall notify a customer in writing if the exceptions are not properly documented in the contract. Acceptance of the contract/purchase order/letter of intent, etc. without any exception letter will mean that differences are resolved.

Have sales walk you through how info entered. What info is required? Can it be changed? Do all salespeople have same understanding? Interview several.

3.5 Formal contract review as annotated on the process flowchart consists of completing the blanket or lump sum checklist in the contract tracking database. A part contract will be acceptable if all checklist items are answered "yes." Should an item not be checked (that is, is "no"), the account manager/sales engineer must complete corrective action for the item. This must be done for each item not checked "yes."

* Key!! Spend some time reviewing d/b!

3.6 Additionally, if an item is not checked, the account manager/sales engineer must describe the action taken to resolve the problem and complete the reasoning for recommendation area in the corrective action section.

Verify evidence of review.

3.7 Upon completion of these areas, the account manager/sales engineer should sign or initial the document. A copy of the contract review is provided to material control to trigger the order fulfillment process. The manager of the sales group or another, higher level of sales management will approve the contract. In the event that the account manager/sales engineer is not available for signatures or form completion, another member of the sales staff may perform the contract review. Should the sales member be the manager, approval can be made by another, higher level of sales management.

Continued

Figure 5.7 An example of a marked-up procedure.

Continued

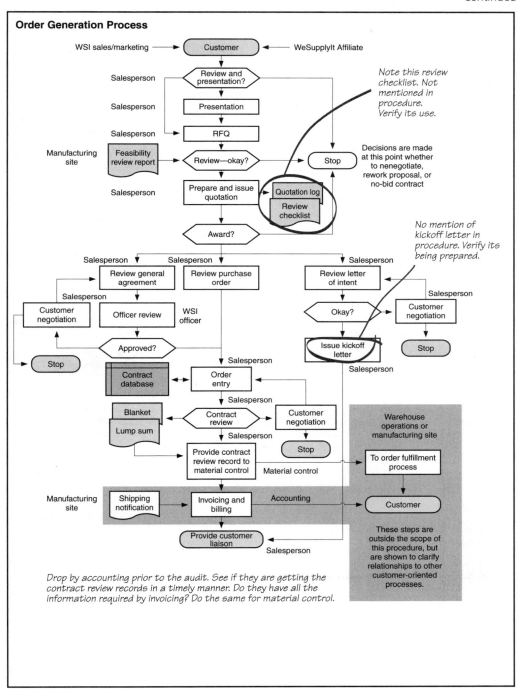

Figure 5.7   An example of a marked-up procedure.

Step 2

Take each requirement you want to verify, and put it on the checklist in the form of a question. Now that you have performed your initial reviews, examined the procedure(s), and identified the areas that need to be evaluated during the audit, you are ready to construct your checklist. The process of developing the checklist is not difficult if you have followed the guidelines presented thus far.

Start with a blank checklist template. I favor the two-column format used throughout this handbook. Other formats are acceptable—the audit program manager should use whatever format his or her auditors are most comfortable with. Consider each requirement or topic you wish to verify and put it on the checklist in the form of a question, as you would ask it. A section of the order generation procedure and the resultant section of the checklist evaluating that section is shown in Figure 5.8.

The auditor continues to add questions to the checklist based on those areas that he or she feels needs to be verified. The initial checklist for this process audit may look like Figure 5.9. I have added the planning page and fields to record sample information in the right-hand column.

2.0 Business Development—Inquiry Review, Presentation, and Proposal Generation

2.9 The cognizant lead salesperson will make the determination as to whether a customer presentation is necessary, considering the nature and size of the potential business and strategic importance of the customer.
Ask how they determine customer requirements

2.10 The salesperson has the responsibility to determine all customer requirements necessary for an accurate quotation. Customer drawings, sketches, functional specifications, or the inquiry or request for quotation are all sources of primary information. The salesperson shall contact the customer to obtain additional information when needed to fully understand the customer's expectations or as needed to complete the quotation. Volumes, delivery dates, and critical milestone dates are important and must be clearly defined in order to quote a job.

Verify this info reflected in each quotation, where did it come from.

Inquiry Review, Presentation, and Proposal Generation	
How are customer requirements determined? What are the sources of information we use? ❑	
Verify as minimum the following reflected:	
❑ Volumes	
❑ Delivery and/or critical milestone dates	

Figure 5.8 Generating checklist questions from the procedure.

Consider the flow of the interview as you populate your checklist. Does one question lead into the next? Can the objective evidence reviewed for this question help you select a sample to use to verify the answer to follow-up questions? Finally, add fields in the right-hand column to help you organize the audit, document samples and results, and, in general, guide you through the interview.

Process Name: Order Generation	
Standard or Process Requirements	**Reviewer Notes and Information**
Planning the Process Audit	
Rough Process Flowchart (Show/list key inputs and primary outputs) **Reference the flowchart in QSP-SAL-02 for process sequence and interactions.** **Primary Inputs:** Customer orders, requests for quotes, contracts Customer requirements documents (specs, drawings, sketches, etc.) Manufacturing feasibility from manufacturing site Cost information from manufacturing site Pricing information from marketing Contracts database, designed by sales and maintained by information systems **Key Outputs:** Proposals and quotes to customers Accepted contracts for manufacturing affiliates Accurate orders to material control, manufacturing affiliates, invoicing	Determine the processes/activities to be included in the scope of the audit. The scope may be provided as part of an audit schedule or plan, or it may need to be developed by the management rep. List the process(es) below: Processes Document No. **Order Generation** **QSP-SAL-02** **Order Entry for Interior Trim** **QSI-SAL-IT-01** Gather information relating to the processes to be examined. The following sources of information should be considered. ❑ Previous audit results of process ❑ Current process metrics **Metric** **Value and/or Trend** Order accuracy 84%, declining Proposal effectiveness Verify during audit Proposal backlog Verify during audit ❑ **Any open or recent corrective actions, complaints** (refer to next page)—None ❑ **Control plans/inspection plans**—NA ❑ **Process flowchart(s)/layouts**—Reviewed ❑ **Operator instructions** (listed above) ❑ **Quality objectives and targets**—None directly related **Objectives and/or targets to review:** 1. 2. **Previous audit findings to verify:** Audit 04-07—Manufacturing feasibility is not consistently received from the manufacturing site prior to proposal issue.

Continued

Figure 5.9 Audit checklist.

Process Name: Order Generation	
Standard or Process Requirements	**Reviewer Notes and Information**
Inquiry Review, Presentation, and Proposal Generation	**Overall evaluation:**

Inquiry Review, Presentation, and Proposal Generation

Do we have a written procedure for this process? Can you show it to me? ❑

Note the revision date and authorization for later verification. Verify compliance to the procedure as the auditee walks you through the process.

Can you show me a list of contract awards we have received this year? ❑

Pick three contracts to use as samples for the remaining questions.

Can you walk me through this process, starting from a request for quote and ending with a contract award? ❑

Use your examples chosen in the last question to verify the auditee's responses.

How do we determine what the customer's requirements or expectations are? ❑

Verify the following information obtained:
Volumes ❑
Delivery dates ❑
Any critical milestone dates ❑

Do we ever have to identify additional requirements not specified by the customer? What are some examples? ❑

Ask how these requirements get reflected in the quotation.

When are team feasibility reviews required? Who does them? What happens if we feel it may not be feasible? ❑

Verify feasibility reviews for the projects chosen are in the file, plus five others. Verify they were completed, open items were resolved.

Overall evaluation:
❑ Did not check.
❑ Did not apply.
❑ Conforms. No deficiencies identified.
❑ Opportunity for improvement. Detail below.

❑ Area of strength. Detail below. Be specific.

❑ Nonconformity. Provide details below. Reference the specific requirement violated.

Projects/Contract Examined

	Requirements Identified?	Feasibility Reviews?
1.	❑ Yes ❑ No	❑ Yes ❑ No
2.	❑ Yes ❑ No	❑ Yes ❑ No
3.	❑ Yes ❑ No	❑ Yes ❑ No
4.	❑ Yes ❑ No	❑ Yes ❑ No

Figure 5.9 Audit checklist.

Continued

Process Name: Order Generation	
Standard or Process Requirements	**Reviewer Notes and Information**

When would it be appropriate to ask the manufacturing plant for cost information? ❏
 	
Increase sample set to include any circumstances the auditor states would necessitate getting cost info, if necessary. Verify information obtained.
 	
How accurate is the information, typically? ❏
 	
This question is only to see if there is an OFI. If typically inaccurate, may want to review profitability of new contracts to see if this is an issue.
 	
Who reviews the final quotation? What do they look for? ❏
 	
Verify evidence of review by salesperson, next level manager. Also verify use of review checklist.
 	
How do we track our outstanding quotations? Do we use this information for anything else? How effective is our quotation process? ❏
 	
Verify quotation log being maintained and updated. Verify information being analyzed/ trended.
 	
How do we track proposal backlog? Have we set any criteria for the backlog? How are we doing? ❏
 	
Verify backlog is being tracked. Review backlog trend. If backlog is significant, or getting worse, ask what's being done.
	Overall evaluation:
	❏ Did not check.
	❏ Did not apply.
	❏ Conforms. No deficiencies identified.
	❏ Opportunity for improvement. Detail below.
	
	❏ Area of strength. Detail below. Be specific.
	
	❏ Nonconformity. Provide details below. Reference the specific requirement violated.
	
	Projects/Contract Examined
	
	                                Quotation **Quotation**
	                                Reviewed? **Tracked?**
	1. ❏ Yes ❏ No ❏ Yes ❏ No
	
	2. ❏ Yes ❏ No ❏ Yes ❏ No
	
	3. ❏ Yes ❏ No ❏ Yes ❏ No
	
	4. ❏ Yes ❏ No ❏ Yes ❏ No
	
	Quotation Process Effectiveness
	      Period 1 2 3 4 5
	Percent
	 Won ___ ___ ___ ___ ___
	
	Backlog ___ ___ ___ ___ ___
	(No.)

Continued

Figure 5.9   Audit checklist.

Continued

Process Name: Order Generation	
Standard or Process Requirements	**Reviewer Notes and Information**

Contract Award, Review, and Order Entry

Assuming we get the contract, what happens then? How is it documented? Can you show me? ❑

Verify a review is conducted after the award. Verify review is documented in Contract database. Examine:

Who can enter information? ❑

Who can access information? ❑

How are changes made if there is an amendment? ❑

Is the data entry form mistake-proofed (for example only certain types of info can be entered into fields)? ❑

Is there any verification of the transcription of information into d/b? ❑

What happens if two people access a record at the same time? ❑

Verify evidence of training on how to use the database. ❑

What happens if there is a contract or order dispute between the plant and the customer? How does it get documented and communicated? ❑

Verify that sales understands their role as mediators. Look for system for recording and communicating resolution.

Also, verify review by manager. ❑

Can you walk me through how we handle a letter of intent? ❑

Follow along the process in the flowchart. Verify that a kickoff letter is used to initiate.

Repeat the above for one or two other salespeople. Assess competency as they walk you through the process.

Reviewer Notes and Information

Overall evaluation:

❑ Did not check.
❑ Did not apply.
❑ Conforms. No deficiencies identified.
❑ Opportunity for improvement. Detail below.

❑ Area of strength. Detail below. Be specific.

❑ Nonconformity. Provide details below. Reference the specific requirement violated.

Projects/Contract Examined

	Entered in d/b?	Final Mgmt Review?
1.	❑ Yes ❑ No	❑ Yes ❑ No
2.	❑ Yes ❑ No	❑ Yes ❑ No
3.	❑ Yes ❑ No	❑ Yes ❑ No
4.	❑ Yes ❑ No	❑ Yes ❑ No

Salesperson	Competent?	Evidence of Training?
	❑ Yes ❑ No	❑ Yes ❑ No
	❑ Yes ❑ No	❑ Yes ❑ No
	❑ Yes ❑ No	❑ Yes ❑ No

Figure 5.9 Audit checklist.

EVALUATING PROCESS EFFECTIVENESS

In Chapter 2, I discussed why it is important that the auditor verify process effectiveness. Effectiveness focuses on results. Historically, auditors have been reluctant to audit for effectiveness. Reasons for this reluctance include:

- Auditors do not know how to audit for effectiveness.

- Auditing for effectiveness is too hard.

- Auditing for effectiveness is too subjective (audit findings should be based on facts, not opinions).

Auditing effectiveness is especially important for quality management system auditors since clause 4.1 and clause 8.2.3 both require action be taken when a process is not producing expected results. Auditors have an obligation to ensure that this requirement is met. With the increased focus on metrics and monitoring in all of the management standards, auditing for effectiveness is not as hard as it may seem. The key to evaluating effectiveness is to base conclusions on facts, not opinions. This section is designed to describe how auditors can plan to do this. Three cases exist.

Case 1—Evaluating Effectiveness to Stated Goals

The easiest situation for auditors is when the process being evaluated has defined criteria and/or objectives. The auditor should evaluate process metrics and compare performance to the defined criteria or objectives. Criteria define current performance expectations. The process is capable of meeting the criteria right now, assuming the process is operated as it is designed. Objectives are improvement goals—they represent desired performance and require dedicated action to achieve. Examples of criteria an auditor could evaluate include:

Laboratory testing criteria. Issue all test reports within 24 hours of completion of the test.

Order entry criteria. Enter all new orders within 30 minutes of receipt.

Customer service criteria. Provide an initial response to all customer service requests within 60 minutes.

Corrective action process. Provide an initial response within five working days.

Air emissions control. Replace exhaust filter media every 60 days.

Chemical hazard evaluation. Evaluate all new chemicals within 72 hours after receipt of request.

Instances where process results are not meeting established criteria should be thoroughly investigated. Inability to determine if the criteria are being met should result in a finding. If there are no records or other data available to assist in this determination, then issue a nonconformance. If records are available, but the criteria are not being actively monitored, then the auditor may want to issue an OFI. It makes no sense to establish criteria if they are never monitored.

Examples of objectives the auditor could evaluate include:

Production process. Reduce the level of scrap by 30 percent from 2004 levels by the end of 2005.

Engineering. Reduce the number of engineering change requests issued within six months of launch to two changes per drawing.

Health and safety management. Reduce the number of lost workdays per 100 employees to 50 percent of 2004 levels.

Environmental performance. Cut overall energy consumption by 50 percent of 2002 levels, normalized for production volume.

All of the management system standards require monitoring of improvement objectives, so the auditor should have little trouble evaluating performance. The auditor must be careful to evaluate only those that directly relate to the area or process being audited. A nonconformance should be issued if the auditor finds that no monitoring is being performed. If monitoring is being performed, but the auditor feels that the frequency of monitoring is insufficient to allow actions to ensure that the objectives will be achieved, then the auditor should consider the issuance of an opportunity for improvement.

It is important to note that it will be the failure to take action when expected results are not achieved that will result in a nonconformance, not the lack of results itself. In a situation where the organization sets challenging goals, it should be expected that there may be instances where goals are not achieved. Issuing a nonconformance solely because of shortcomings to meet an objective could drive managers to set easily obtainable goals. Auditors must base findings on a failure to properly react when expected results are not achieved.

Case 2—Evaluating Performance Where Monitoring Is Performed, but Criteria and/or Objectives Have Not Been Established

In many situations the auditor may find that process monitoring is being performed, but no stated criteria or objectives have been established. Examples include accident rates, the level of scrap for a production process, or the amount of hazardous wastes being generated. In these instances, the auditor must base judgment on long-term trends apparent in the data. For example, if the level of scrap has steadily increased over the past six months, the auditor should investigate whether the process owner has taken any action to identify the causes and to eliminate them. Similarly, a sustained increase in the accident rates within a certain department should trigger action on the part of management. If no action has been taken, then the auditor should consider issuance of a nonconformance. If some action has been taken, but only informally, then an OFI may be warranted. An OFI in this situation will alert the next auditor to the situation so that he or she can determine if action since the last audit has corrected the undesirable situation. The key consideration for the auditor in these situations is that the trend must be in the wrong direction for a sustained period of time, and it must be significant.

Note that rigorous management system requirements for monitoring, such as those contained in the TL 9000 standard, greatly enhance the auditor's ability to audit for effectiveness using process and system metrics.

Case 3—Evaluating Performance When Monitoring Is Not Performed

Although the introduction of ISO 9001:2000 has resulted in the deployment of more robust metrics, not everything is routinely monitored, nor should it be. Auditors can still audit for effectiveness even in the absence of metrics. The key is to first clearly define the purpose of the activity or process. Once the purpose is clearly identified, then the auditor can evaluate whether the activity is accomplishing this purpose. Some examples will serve to clarify.

Example 1: Evaluate the effectiveness of the corrective action process.

Purpose of corrective action process: To prevent the recurrence of problems.

Evaluation statement: The corrective action process is not effective if it is not preventing the recurrence of problems.

Strategy: The auditor will evaluate the past six months of corrective action requests. If the evaluation identifies multiple instances of the same problem or the same root cause, then it will be judged that the corrective action process is not effective in preventing recurrence of problems.

First, note the simplicity of the purpose statement, "To prevent the recurrence of problems." This statement must be clear and simple, and so obvious that nobody, including the process owner, can take exception with the purpose or with its associated purpose statement. Stating the purpose in terms of the requirements in the management standard or in detailed technical terms will dilute this clarity and result in arguments over the purpose of the process, instead of its performance.

Second, note that the strategy requires multiple instances of recurrence. A few instances of recurrence should be expected, since we won't always nail the root cause the first time every time. If this becomes a pattern, however, then action should be initiated to see why our efforts are falling short. If my evaluation of the corrective action program identifies 40 corrective action requests over the past six months, 15 of which are repeat problems, then I would issue a nonconformance against the corrective action process unless it could be shown that the situation had been recognized and action initiated to address the situation. A finding of four or five repeat problems in this scenario would not result in a finding.

Example 2: Evaluate the effectiveness of zone communication boards. These boards are used to communicate important quality, safety, environmental, and throughput performance information to workers in production areas.

> *Purpose of the zone communication boards:* To communicate performance information.

> *Evaluation statement:* The zone communication boards will be considered effective if they are communicating performance information to workers in the areas in which they are located.

> *Strategy:* During the evaluation we will interview operators to assess their awareness of the major quality issue and major safety concern in their area. If they are aware of these issues, we will conclude that the boards are effective.

Again, note the simplicity of the purpose statement. This situation was actually encountered by the author during an audit. A total of 33 operators and supervisors were asked about the major quality and safety issues in their work areas. This information was prominently posted on communication boards located in their immediate vicinity. Only 3 of the 33 interviewed could state what their process's major quality and safety issues were. We issued a nonconformance against the communication boards, citing a failure to take action to correct a situation where a process was not achieving planned results. It might be argued that an OFI would have been more appropriate since prior to the audit no one was aware of the problem, but in this instance the results were so extreme that the auditors felt that corrective action should be required.

Example 3: Evaluate the effectiveness of the internal audit process.

> *Purpose of the internal audit process:* To identify the systematic weaknesses that exist in the management system.

> *Evaluation statement:* The internal audit process is not effective if it is not identifying the systematic weaknesses that exist in the management system.

> *Strategy:* We will compare what external auditors have found against our internal audit results of the same areas. If external audits identified significant, systematic weaknesses in areas where we did not, then we will conclude that our audit process is not effective.

One cannot expect an auditor to identify isolated problems in a management system since the audit is only a sampling. Significant, systemic weaknesses should be captured in the auditor's sample set and thus should be identified during the audit. If they are not, then the audit process needs to be evaluated. Note the use of external auditor's findings as the evidence that weaknesses exist.

As stated previously, findings related to effectiveness must be based on facts, not opinions. In case 1, the facts are clear. There is a goal, our performance is not meeting the goal, and we are not doing anything about it. In case 2, the facts (metrics) should also be clear, but some judgment is required to conclude what represents ineffectiveness. For this reason the auditor should only cite a significant, sustained trend going in the wrong direction. Case 3 is probably the most challenging case to make, and the auditor may want to issue opportunities for improvement in these situations unless the observed results are extremely poor. The auditor's strategy for evaluating the effectiveness of processes and activities should be annotated on the checklist.

DEVELOPING THE AUDIT PLAN

An audit plan is simply a schedule of topics and interviews for the audit. An example was provided in Chapter 3 and is reproduced in Figure 5.10. An audit plan may not be needed for focused internal audits where the auditor will be interviewing only one or two individuals. The value of the audit plan becomes apparent when the auditor must examine many different topics or processes, and conduct interviews with several key process owners. The benefits that an audit plan can provide in these circumstances include:

- The audit plan can help the auditor stay on track. By listing the topics to be covered and about how long each should take, the audit plan can indicate when the auditor needs to pick up the pace or refocus on the key issues.

- The audit plan informs interviewees when they will be needed in support of the audit. This allows them to plan the rest of their day. If they cannot support an interview during the time indicated on the plan, they can notify the lead auditor and he or she can rework the schedule before the start of the audit. It also helps to ensure that your interviewee will be available and prepared when you show up.

- If a key individual is not going to be available during the day(s) of the audit, or if an activity vital to the audit will not be going on, then the audit can be rescheduled. It's better to learn this now, than show up and find that the audit purpose cannot be accomplished. This happened to me once when I took a three-person audit team 300 miles to a supplier's facility to audit its nondestructive testing practices only to learn that there was no product available to test at that time.

- The audit plan can be used to communicate other information to the auditee and serves as the backdrop for the preaudit briefing with the auditee.

- Finally, the audit plan shows important logistical information, the most important being the time allocated for lunch. As the students in my seminars know, Rule Number 1 is always, "*Feed the auditor!*" There's nothing worse than a bunch of hungry, irritable auditors running through your plant. It can get ugly quick.

While an audit plan may not be needed for short, focused internal audits, it should always be prepared when performing an audit outside of one's own facility. This would include audits of a sister division or any supplier audit. The audit plan helps to ensure

Audit No. 9-05	Date: Sept. 6–7, 2005	Auditor(s): Frank Lewis
Audit Scope: Product realization from order entry to shipment		
Audit Criteria: ISO/TS 16949:2002 and local procedures		
Time	**Topic, Area, or Process**	**Interviewee**
Day 1 **8:00–8:30**	**Opening Meeting**	
8:30–9:20	**Order Generation** Quotation to order entry	John Mach, account manager
9:30–12:00	**Advanced Product Quality Planning** Product design and development	Susan Resnick, lead product engineer
12:00–1:00	**Lunch**	
1:00–2:20	**Advanced Product Quality Planning** Process design and development	Tim Brewsky, lead process engineer
2:20–3:20	**Advanced Product Quality Planning** Production part approval	Tien Lei, quality assurance
3:30–4:00	**Production Planning and Scheduling**	Tom Gransky, production control
4:30	**Daily Debriefing**	
Day 2 **8:00–8:20**	**Production Management**	Vicky Summers, first shift production supervisor
8:30–12:00	**Production**	Various
12:00–1:00	**Lunch**	
1:00–2:20	**Production**	Various
2:30–3:15	**Packaging, Storage, and Shipping**	Allen Copeland, shipping and receiving
3:15–4:00	**Auditor Preparation**	
4:00	**Closing Meeting**	
Process owners are requested to inform their employees about the audit and to make arrangements to minimize any disruptions during the interviews. Thank you for your support.		

Figure 5.10   Simple audit plan.

everyone is on the same page and the trip won't be wasted due to the nonavailability of people or processes.

Finally, I normally recommend that the audit program manager review and possibly approve audit plans prepared by new auditors. The two would sit down with the audit plan and the auditor's checklists and discuss the general audit strategy and flow. This review provides an opportunity for the audit program manager to check on the preparation of the auditor, and it provides the new auditors an opportunity to ask questions and confirm their readiness to perform the evaluation. The new auditor gets much more out of this kind of peer review since he or she has already studied the process, its procedures, inputs, outputs, and metrics. Many audit program managers like to spend a few minutes discussing strategy with the new auditor prior to detailed audit planning, and, while I wholeheartedly endorse preplanning discussions, I also strongly recommend a post-planning readiness review.

PREAUDIT COMMUNICATION

The final step in the planning phase is to establish communication with the auditee manager or process owner, typically one or two weeks prior to the audit. The purpose of this communication is to present the audit plan to the auditee and to solicit auditee thoughts on areas that may require additional focus during the audit. For off-site audits, this communication, typically made by phone or e-mail, will also include any logistical support required by the auditors. Logistical support would include:

- Any directions or special instructions on how to get to the facility and where to enter.

- The starting time of the audit or opening meeting.

- A discussion or inquiry on any special personal protective equipment the auditors should bring with them. Companies can normally provide eyeglasses, hardhats, and earplugs, but don't assume they can provide steel-toed shoes or metatarsal guards. It's not a bowling alley!

- Confirmation on any off-site locations to be included in the audit, such as remote warehouse locations that will need to be visited. The auditee may have to make arrangements for such a visit.

- Organizational dress code. The basic rule for auditors is to dress as the client dresses, keeping in mind that a professional appearance is always required. Internal auditors should know what the company's policy on attire is; second- and third-party auditors may not. If the company dress code is shirt and tie, then the auditor should dress in a shirt and tie during the audit. If the company dress code is business casual, then the auditor should dress in business casual. If the company dress code is blue jeans and t-shirts, however, the auditor should dress in business casual to maintain a professional appearance during the audit.

- The need for a conference room or office in which to work.

- The need for access to a set of company policies or procedures related to the activities to be reviewed. If the organization uses electronic document control, then the auditors may require access to a computer terminal. If the auditors do not have the ability to review these prior to the audit, which is often the case, then make sure the audit plan allocates time at the start of the audit to review relevant procedures. In these situations it is best to assign experienced auditors to the evaluation since much of the planning will have to be done in a compressed time frame at the beginning of the audit.

- Confirmation of the audit schedule, as indicated on the audit plan. Ideally the audit plan will be faxed or e-mailed to the auditee prior to any phone call so the auditee will have time to verify the schedule and any necessary rescheduling can be done during this discussion.

Outside of confirming the audit plan, this meeting also allows the auditee to provide input into the audit strategy. I normally ask, "Are there any concerns or issues that you have that we should focus on during the audit?" The purpose of this question is twofold. One, it may provide valuable insight into problem areas that were not identified during the auditor's planning. Such areas or concerns should be noted in the auditor's checklists so that they can be given a closer look during the audit. Remember, the primary purpose of the audit is to find the weaknesses and perhaps the reasons for them. If the organization's auditors typically find *real* weaknesses and *real* opportunities for improvement, and not just administrative nits, and if the organization's management takes action on these findings to improve the processes without punishing the people, then auditors should expect to receive feedback when they ask this question. Process owners don't like having to deal with problems and dysfunctional processes any more than auditors like having to report them.

Second, even if the auditee replies in the negative ("Absolutely not! Everything is working great."), it still serves to reinforce the mind-set that we're all in this together—we're all on the same team. I, the auditor, am here to help you and am willing to look into concerns and issues you have. This is especially important during internal audits and will be reinforced throughout the rest of the audit process. We want to start laying the groundwork for this mind-set here, during the planning stage.

Who do you conduct this meeting with? In the case of a full system audit or off-site audit, normally you would brief with the management representative or quality, environmental, or heath and safety manager. For an audit of a production process, you would normally brief with the production manager. For a review of an area such as shipping and receiving, brief with the area manager. You do not need to brief with every interviewee that shows up on your audit plan.

SUMMARY

This is the end of the planning phase. The auditor has determined both the macroscope (activities and processes to be included) and the microscope (detailed areas to focus on within those activities and processes) based on research related to known problem areas, prior audits, and current performance metrics. The auditor is familiar with the policies, procedures, and operations related to the processes to be reviewed, including the generation of SIPOC diagrams where needed to better understand inputs, outputs, and inter-relationships. The auditor has generated focused audit checklists to facilitate the audit and has identified what processes need to be evaluated for effectiveness. The strategy for doing so is on the checklists. The auditor has developed an audit plan and discussed it with the audit program manager, if needed, and communicated the audit plan to the auditee. Everything is now set to move into the next phase, conducting the audit. In the words of Sherlock Holmes, "Release the hounds!"

6

Conducting the Audit

This chapter provides methods and techniques for conducting the audit. Auditing involves far more than simply asking questions from a checklist. It involves establishing a rapport with the auditee, knowing how to ask questions and how to verify the answers given, recognizing when to dig deeper, and managing the overall audit process. We will explore each of these important skill sets, plus several others. An overview of the audit process as shown in Figure 6.1 serves as an outline of this chapter.

THE OPENING MEETING

Traditionally, audits are kicked off with an opening meeting. The purpose of the opening meeting is to provide introductions, review the purpose and scope of the audit, outline the audit process, and verify the audit plan. Not every audit requires a formal opening meeting, but off-site first- and second-party audits should always have a formal opening meeting. Large internal audits covering multiple systems and processes may also benefit from an opening meeting. Focused internal audits should have an abbreviated, informal opening meeting with the process owner as part of the initial interview. The opening meeting should be conducted by the lead auditor.

I strongly recommend that an agenda be prepared when a formal opening meeting is planned. Items on the agenda mirror some of the items discussed as part of the preaudit briefing with the auditee presented in Chapter 5. An example agenda is shown in Figure 6.2.

The generic purpose of any management system audit can be summed up as follows:

- Find any systemic weaknesses in the processes or system being reviewed.

- Identify any opportunities for improvement.

- Identify any best practices that should be shared throughout the organization.

Some audits may be more focused in their purpose, such as to verify readiness for launch. If so, this would be stated in the opening meeting.

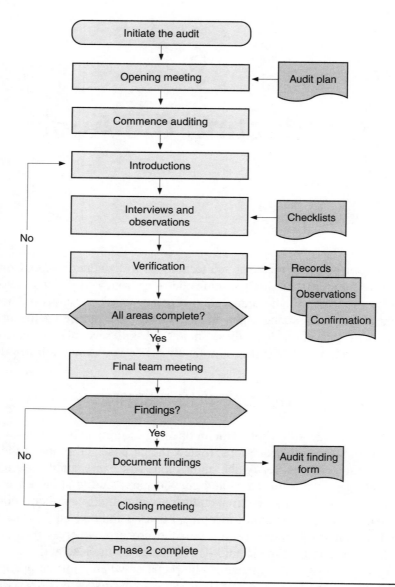

Figure 6.1 Overview of the audit process.

The scope of the audit is the processes, activities, and areas to be included in the evaluation. Unique areas such as satellite locations and back-shift operations and any unique activities such as nondestructive testing or confined tank entry would also be identified during the opening meeting so that any necessary arrangements can be made by the auditee. Confirmation of any special safety considerations, including personal protective equipment, should also be provided. Logistical considerations include verification of the conference room or office the auditors will be working from, availability of organizational policies and procedures, a phone and a phone book, and lunch arrangements.

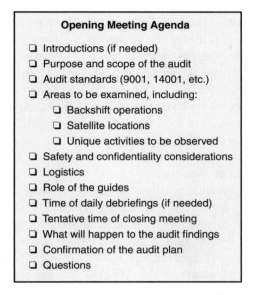

Opening Meeting Agenda

❑ Introductions (if needed)
❑ Purpose and scope of the audit
❑ Audit standards (9001, 14001, etc.)
❑ Areas to be examined, including:
    ❑ Backshift operations
    ❑ Satellite locations
    ❑ Unique activities to be observed
❑ Safety and confidentiality considerations
❑ Logistics
❑ Role of the guides
❑ Time of daily debriefings (if needed)
❑ Tentative time of closing meeting
❑ What will happen to the audit findings
❑ Confirmation of the audit plan
❑ Questions

Figure 6.2 Opening meeting agenda.

Rule No. 1

Feed the auditor!

Although I'm portraying auditors somewhat lightheartedly as being food motivated, there are some issues relating to lunch that do need to be worked out, especially when conducting off-site audits. The foremost of these issues is whether to go out to lunch or have it brought in. Often the auditee will invite the auditors out to lunch. The lead auditor must weigh accepting this offer against the demands of the audit. Most auditors have a working lunch, during which time they discuss what's been found so far, what needs to be reviewed in more detail, and how they may want to adjust the afternoon's schedule. Many also take the opportunity to begin their audit write-ups. None of this can be accomplished when the audit team goes out to lunch. In addition, it may be hard to go out and get back in less than an hour. For these reasons, and a few more to be discussed later on, most auditors prefer that lunch be brought in. Of course, for internal audits the issue is normally moot—the auditor is on his or her own!

Guides (formally called escorts) are traditionally supplied by the audited organization for second- and third-party audits. The role of the guide is twofold. First, guides make sure the auditor gets from point A to point B. Second they serve as representatives of the organization, hearing what the auditor hears and seeing what the auditor sees. They can also provide early feedback to auditee management as to what the audit team is finding prior to daily debriefings or the closing meeting. Internal auditors do not normally need guides. The auditor should insist on a guide when conducting a second-party (supplier) audit. The auditor should point out weaknesses to the guide as they are found during the audit. When a disbelieving manager exclaims, "I can't believe we'd do that!" during a closing meeting, the auditor can turn to the guide for verification.

If guides are needed, the audit team leader should explain their role during the opening meeting. It should also be noted that guides must let the individuals being interviewed answer any questions asked by the auditor. Guides may provide comments after a response has been provided if they need to clarify an auditee's remarks or provide additional information, at the discretion of the auditor. Later we'll examine how to handle situations where the guide wants to answer questions for the auditee, but recognize that prevention is better than correction.

It is traditional to provide daily debriefings to the auditee's management representative during large multiday audits. This debriefing is typically conducted by the lead auditor at the end of the day's auditing. The lead auditor summarizes the findings and potential findings noted by the audit team that day. If there is disagreement over the nature of any of the findings, this is the time to discuss them. In addition, if the auditee's management representative believes there may be additional objective evidence that may mitigate or eliminate the audit finding, this is the time to locate and present it. The management representative is also expected to communicate significant findings to other relevant auditee management, so that there are no surprises at the closing meeting.

The final element of the opening meeting is confirmation of the audit plan. Although the audit was previously reviewed with the auditee at the conclusion of the planning phase, things may have changed since then. Julie may be running late today, or possibly Tom called in sick. If changes to the audit plan are required, now is the time to make them.

Conducting a formal opening meeting at the start of a large audit establishes the lead auditor as being in control of the audit. This can be especially important during audits of supplier facilities. Once the meeting is concluded, it is time to go to work.

INTERVIEWING BASICS

Proper interviewing is more than asking questions. It's knowing which questions to ask, when to ask them, and how to ask them without making the auditee feel uncomfortable or defensive. Good interviewers also understand how to make the interviewee feel comfortable. This section explores these issues, starting with how to establish a rapport with the auditee.

Establishing a Rapport with the Auditee

It is important to establish a rapport, or connection, with the auditee at the start of the interview. Establishing a rapport will make the auditee more comfortable and less nervous. Everyone is a little nervous at the start of an interview, and breaking the ice can really help take the edge off, for both the auditor and the auditee.

Establishing a rapport with the auditee also encourages them to share information. Getting colleagues to share information during an audit may not be easy, since many organizations repeatedly tell their employees, "If the auditor asks you a question, answer it, but don't volunteer any information." This can make colleagues distrustful of auditors in general, or nervous because they must obviously have something to hide (even though they don't know what it is). And unlike the situation during an external audit, during an internal audit *you want* your employees to volunteer information that will help find the weaknesses. Individuals who have been through a number of audits with competent auditors normally do not share this reluctance, but in a large organization that still leaves many who have never been interviewed before or who had the misfortune of getting "Bruno" for their auditor.

So how do you establish a rapport with the auditee at the start of an interview? First, don't start your interview with, "Hi, we're here to conduct an audit of this process. Don't worry, we're not here to audit you, we're here to audit the system." What's wrong with this line? Many auditors use it. The fact that so many auditors use it is one of its problems. It's become a cliché and, as such, comes across as insincere. My natural response when I hear it is to think, "Okay, go talk to the system then and leave me alone!" The second problem is whenever you tell someone not to worry, they start worrying.

So what can you do to establish a rapport with the auditee before launching into the questions on your checklist? Here are a few recommendations:

• *Break the ice.* For most internal audits there is a high likelihood that you know the individual and something about him or her. Ask how her daughter did in the regional gymnastics meet last week. Use some small talk, even if it's about the weather. Just remember, you do have to keep it short, no more than two or three minutes, tops. This means you may not want to ask Fred, the old-timer, how he's feeling today. "Oh, glad you asked! You know my knee's really been bothering me for the last couple of weeks with the rain and all, and my elbow, well let me tell you about that. . . ."

When you're trying to break the ice with someone you do not know well, you can often look around their office or work space and pick up clues as to what interests them. You may see a picture of a boat and ask, "Is that your boat? Do you sail?" Golfing pictures and trinkets are always a good indicator of a topic that can be discussed. Just don't make the mistake one of my students made when spotting a picture of a manager's wife, "Is that your wife? Wow, she's hot!" Not a good ice-breaker.

• *Be pleasant.* One of the most important things that you can do is to be pleasant. You don't have to smile continuously, but you shouldn't have a stern look on you face either. Auditors who are also managers must work even harder at this since they can be intimidating just because of their positional authority over employees.

• *Let them know they are part of the team.* Instead of using the opening line, "Don't worry, we're not here to audit you, we're here to audit the system," say something like this: "We're doing an evaluation of our [blank] process. We're trying to identify any weaknesses in the process or opportunities to improve it. To do that we need your help. We'd like you to walk us through the process and explain how it works. We may need you to answer some questions or show us some of the records generated. If there is anything that doesn't work very well, or improvements that you feel would make the process better, we'd like to hear about those too. If you have any questions, please feel free to ask them. Okay?"

This kind of opening statement sounds much more sincere and truly reflects the role of the auditee. It also makes the auditees members of the audit team, which they really are.

Notice also the use of the phrase *our process*. The words *you* and *your* personalize, and saying something like, "We're here to evaluate *your* process" immediately puts auditees on the defensive by making it clear that if there is a problem, it's their problem. The words *you* and *your* should always be avoided during audit interviews. Also note the use of the word *evaluate* instead of *audit*. The word *audit* will, by itself, make some people nervous, as will the use of the word *nonconformance*. For this reason I use the word *weaknesses*. The use of these simple guidelines should result in an auditee who is not only willing, but enthusiastic about assisting in the audit.

Rule No. 2

Make the auditee feel like a member
of the audit team.

Basic Questions and When to Ask Them

In Chapter 5 we spent a great deal of time discussing audit questions and how to develop them. Auditors need to have a sense of when to ask more basic questions, such as who, when, what, how, and why. During my seminars, students often ask why I even bring up this issue. They know they can always ask these basic questions. The reason I include them in the training is that the right time to ask them may not be obvious. Let's look at some examples.

• *The* who *question.* The *who* question focuses on responsibilities and authorities. Most auditors put the *who* question on their checklists when the procedure or policy states who is responsible or who should take some action. Auditors then verify that the individual cited in the procedure is the one who takes the action. While this is a perfectly valid audit question, auditors need to be aware that it is more important to ask the *who* question when the responsibilities or authorities are *not stated* in the procedure. The likelihood of no one doing an action are much higher when the responsibilities are not clearly defined than when they are. Auditors should be especially vigorous in asking who is responsible, who has the authority, who receives the report, and so on, when it is not clearly defined or when the auditor cannot tell where the responsibility lies from reviewing the procedures. The auditor may find that no one really knows who is responsible or that the action is not being performed consistently.

• *The* where *question.* The *where* question is focused on objective evidence and verification. Rather than just accept the auditee's word on the matter, auditors have an obligation to verify that actions are actually taking place by asking where the records are, where the acceptance criteria are stated, and so on. Verification of objective evidence will be examined in more detail later in this chapter.

• *The* when *question.* The *when* question focuses on frequencies and the completion of scheduled events. It is very similar to the *who* question in that auditors normally put it on their checklists when a frequency requirement is given in the procedure or policy. And while this is an appropriate requirement to verify, it is probably more important to ask the *when* question when the frequency for an action is not stated in the procedure or when the dreaded "waffle words" are used. Examples of waffle words include: as appropriate, when necessary, as applicable, when deemed desirable.

Auditors are often reluctant to evaluate actions associated with waffle words, since they do not have a precisely defined frequency requirement. Auditors must recognize that waffle words are used to provide flexibility, not to avoid any responsibility for action. Auditors can and should inquire, "When would it be appropriate? When would it be necessary? When would it be applicable? When would it be desirable?" They can then audit based on the response they receive. Let me provide an example.

Assume that the procedure for supplier selection and development states that "an on-site audit will be conducted when deemed desirable by the quality manager." The auditor might ask the quality manager when she would deem it desirable to conduct an on-site audit of a potential new supplier. Assume she responded, "I normally consider it necessary to do an on-site audit when the potential supplier is not ISO 9001 certified, and they provide a production part or material other than routine commodity items like bolts and washers." The auditor could then use the approved supplier list to identify new suppliers added during the past 12 months. Assume that there were 15 new suppliers who met the quality manager's criteria—that is, they provided production materials and parts other than nuts and bolts and were not certified. If 12 of these suppliers received on-site audits, I would judge that the organization was generally following its stated policy. I would ask about the other three who did not receive audits, but assuming the answers were reasonable, I would accept current practices as conforming to policy. On the other hand, if I found that only four of these 15 suppliers received on-site audits, I would issue a nonconformance.

The new management system standards do not require written procedures for every process and activity an organization performs. The purchasing process is an example where companies might choose not to develop a documented procedure. In all cases, however, the standards do require that the organization define its processes. Whether the requirements are documented or undocumented, they must be followed. It is up to the auditor to determine what the requirements are when they are not documented in a written procedure by asking questions such as, "When would it be necessary?" If no requirements have been defined in areas where the auditor feels they should be, then he or she can issue an opportunity for improvement. Assume the response by the quality manager in my example was, "Well, we really don't have a formal policy. It's really up to me to decide, based on their response to the survey they send back, if they should receive an audit." In this instance I might generate an OFI recommending the company consider establishing a policy for when an on-site audit of a new supplier should be conducted. Of course, if it had no criteria for selection and evaluation of suppliers I would issue a nonconformance against clause 7.3 of the ISO 9001 standard.

The key to evaluating requirements involving waffle words, or any process without clearly documented requirements, is to ask the process owner to define the process requirements. Asking a quality engineer when we would need to do an audit in this example would be incorrect, since he or she doesn't establish the policy. The quality manager does. If you remember this simple rule, then you can easily evaluate conformance to waffle word requirements.

- *The* why *question.* I like to think of the *why* question as being focused on continual improvement. It is often used when actions just don't seem to make sense, and the auditor is curious why certain things are being done that way. It can often be used to identify non-value-added steps or operations. Auditors must be extremely careful in how they use the *why* question, however, since it can come across as judgmental and opinionated. And, improperly used, or if used too often by the auditor, it can be just that. My recommendation on the use of the why question is this—avoid using the word *why*. Let me provide some examples:

> Bad question: "*Why* do you do a teardown inspection?"
> Good question: "Can you explain the basis for the teardown inspection?"

> Bad question: "*Why* do you print out a hard copy when there's an electronic copy on the network?"
> Good questions: "Can you explain the need for the hard copy?" or "How is the hard copy used?"

The good questions in each of these examples sound more professional and are far less likely to prompt a defensive answer by the auditee. Note that it is the natural overemphasis placed on the word *why* when it is at the start of a sentence that makes it come across as judgmental. For this reason, the auditor can also soften the reaction by taking the word *why* from the front of the sentence and putting it into the middle of the sentence.

Types of Questions

There are three primary types of questions an auditor may ask during an interview. We will examine each of these now. A fourth type will be introduced in the next section.

Closed-ended questions solicit a yes/no response or a specific right/wrong answer. For example, "Do we have a communications log?" will bring either a *yes* or a *no* response. Likewise, "How often do we update our environmental regulations?" will result in a single response such as quarterly, annually, or even "we don't," only one of which is likely to be correct. Closed-ended questions do answer the specific question, but do not provide any information beyond that single issue. Closed-ended questions are most appropriately used to fill in the gaps in an auditee's response to an open-ended question.

Open-ended questions have no right or wrong answer. The auditee is free to respond to the question to a level and depth that he or she feels comfortable with. The auditor gets significantly more information from an open-ended question than from a closed-ended question. Since there are no right or wrong answers, auditees are generally more comfortable with open-ended questions, assuming the questions address a topic or process they are familiar with. An example might be, "Can you show me how we update our environmental regulations?"

A *leading question* is one that provides the expected answer in the question itself, normally in a manner that implies you must be stupid if you don't! For example, the question, "You do update your environmental regulations annually, don't you?" not only makes it clear that the correct answer per the procedure is annually, but also sends a strong message that if you don't, you're incompetent.

Leading questions should always be avoided. They can not only offend, they can also lead to what I call auditor entrapment. Most people will not lie, even when asked a leading question. But they will sometimes rationalize a correct response in the face of such clearly stated expectations. For example, the environmental engineer faced with the leading question might think to himself, "Well, I did update some of the waste regulations" and provide a response of *"Of course!"* even though he knows that he has never bothered to update any of the other regulations that apply to the company. Of course the auditor's next action will be to verify that the regulations have been updated, with the likely result that he or she will discover many of them out of date. You can imagine the uncomfortable situation that would result. As a general rule, avoid leading questions.

The Funnel Approach

Because open-ended questions provide more information, and because they are generally safer to the auditee, I always recommend that the auditor use general open-ended questions that cover broad sections of the topic being evaluated early in the interview process. These early responses provide a wealth of information to the auditor and help to determine areas that need deeper review.

Refer back to the section of the audit checklist shown in Figure 5.9, page 114. You may remember that this checklist was developed for the order generation process. The first two questions set the audit up by retrieving the procedure so that the auditor can follow along and getting a list of contract awards so she can choose samples to use to evaluate the process. The evaluation really starts with question number 3, where the auditor asks, "Can you walk me through this process, starting from a request for quote and ending with a contract award?" This is a good open-ended question to start the audit with. The auditee may, in fact, answer the other questions on the auditor's checklist in the first response to this question. In that case, all the auditor has to do is ask for the objective evidence to verify what she has been told. If something was left out that the auditor expected to hear, then she will follow up with a *clarifying question,* our fourth type of question.

Clarifying questions are designed to fill in the gaps. If, in the auditee's initial response I heard nothing about feasibility reviews, I would ask a clarifying question, "I didn't hear you mention anything about feasibility reviews. Can you explain when we do them, and who does them?" Conversely, I could also ask for clarification in the form of a closed-ended question such as, "Are feasibility reviews performed?" As such, the structure of a clarifying question may be either closed-ended or open-ended, but in all cases its purpose is to fill in the gaps, or funnel down to the missing or suspect information. When used in this manner, the proper use of open-ended, closed-ended, and clarifying questions form a strategy for conducting interviews I call the funnel approach, which is illustrated in Figure 6.3.

The use of the funnel approach leads to an efficient audit that covers the maximum amount of area in the least amount of time. It is also safer to the auditee and allows him or her to warm up to the interview.

Imagine the reaction on the part of an auditee if the first question from the auditor was, "Do we conduct feasibility reviews for new products?" and the answer was, "No." The auditee just crashed and burned on the very first question! The audit will probably go downhill from there.

When developing your audit checklist, I normally recommend that new auditors leave one or two rows blank at the start. This is to provide room for the auditor to come back and inject a general open-ended question to start the interview with. Once you've planned and conducted several audits this will become natural and you will do it out of habit.

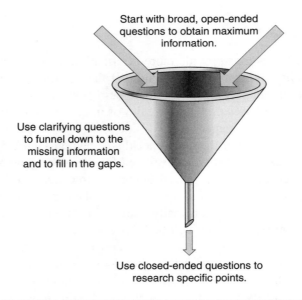

Start with broad, open-ended questions to obtain maximum information.

Use clarifying questions to funnel down to the missing information and to fill in the gaps.

Use closed-ended questions to research specific points.

Figure 6.3 The funnel approach.

Rule No. 3

Start the evaluation by asking general open-ended questions, then use clarifying questions to fill in the gaps.

Active Listening

An often-quoted rule of thumb is that auditors should spend only 10 percent of their time talking and 90 percent of their time listening during an audit. The importance of active listening cannot be overstated. I often provide training in communication skills, including effective listening. One of the most alarming statistics provided by research is that up to 70 percent of all communications are misunderstood. Seventy percent! That's a big number. While many of these miscommunications may have no significant impact during routine interactions, a miscommunication during an audit can have devastating impacts to both the auditee and to the auditor's credibility. Simply stated, auditors must be effective listeners.

Active listening is the use of all of one's senses to focus on the message being communicated by the speaker, including both the emotional and the factual content. Figure 6.4 illustrates the active listening model.

Active listening involves understanding not only the words that are used by the speaker, but also the way the words are used and the nonverbal cues. The words themselves convey only a small part of the message, sometimes less than 10 percent, while the nonverbal cues such as facial expressions, body language, and movements may contain over 60 percent of the overall communication. This is especially true when trying to gauge the truthfulness of a response.

What do I mean when I say *the way the words are used?* Say the following two statements aloud, placing emphasis on the italicized words in each sentence. Are the meanings the same?

Example 1: I do *not* know of any problems with this supplier.

Example 2: I do not know of any problems with *this* supplier.

Although the words are identical in both sentences, the meanings are very different. In the first example the auditee is stating emphatically that this supplier is a good one. In the second instance the auditee is saying this supplier is okay, but there are many others that are not. Just as importantly, he is offering to share his thoughts on these problems with the auditor if she cares to listen. What would happen if the auditor did not pick up on this subtle, but important inflection? She would probably fail to find the weakness, which is her primary responsibility.

As noted, nonverbal cues also provide a significant percentage of information that could be important to the auditor. Referring to Figure 6.4, note that the first thing the auditor should do after asking a question is study the auditee's reaction (that is, nonverbal facial expressions, body posture, and so on). If the auditor sees a look of confusion on the

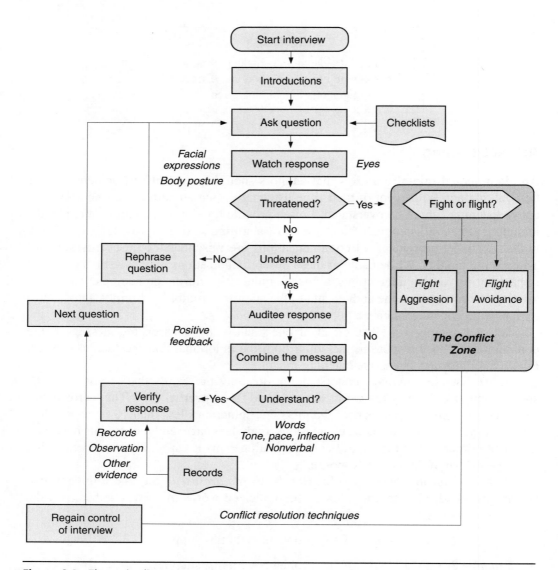

Figure 6.4 The active listening model.

face of the auditee, he or she should immediately rephrase the question or ask if the auditee understood it. You should not leave the auditee standing there in a confused state trying to figure out what you want to know. Similarly, if the auditee reacts by closing his or her stance, crossing arms, and furling his or her brow, the auditor should recognize that something in the question was threatening to the auditee. Knowing this, the auditor can proceed more carefully in the evaluation of the topic, paying particular notice to how questions are phrased. (I will discuss strategies for defusing and managing conflict during an audit later in this chapter.) Finally, if the auditee breaks eye contact and stares at the floor during a response, the auditor might suspect that they're not getting the full story.

Although none of these nonverbal cues prove that something is wrong, they provide indicators that the auditor may need to pursue these areas in more depth. What should the auditor do if he or she feels the auditee is not being entirely truthful or forthcoming? The auditor should tactfully and professionally ask additional questions, look at the evidence more carefully, or increase the sample size of the evidence being evaluated. Remember, the primary objective is to find the weaknesses, and if you have indicators that they exist, it *is* your job to go after them. Just remember to do so professionally and with sensitivity.

When the auditee responds, the auditor must combine the communication pathways. Do the words and the way the words are used match the facial expressions and body movements? If so, review the objective evidence and move on. If not, then dig deeper. The auditor should also encourage the auditee to continue to communicate. There are several ways to do this; some of the more common ones are highlighted in Table 6.1. Auditors should practice their use of these skills. Fortunately, these methods are just as applicable to routine communication settings, and practicing these techniques will improve the auditor's relationships inside and outside of the audit process.

Rule No. 4

Be an active listener.

Table 6.1 Communication methods that encourage dialogue.

Method	Examples	Advantages and Applications
Verbal door openers Short phrase interjected as auditee responds.	"Very good." "Excellent!" "Please continue!"	Short, nondisruptive. Does not stop the flow of information from the auditee, but encourages more information. Should be used liberally during interviews.
Nodding your head	Sorry, you've got to visualize this one.	Same advantages and application as the verbal door openers. Try not to become a bobble head doll, however.
Echoing Short repeat, in the form of a question, of the topic the auditee mentioned that auditor wants more information on.	"MRP system?" "Online learning?" "Universal waste?" "Job hazard analysis?"	Normally causes the auditee to expand on the echoed topic, without causing too much disruption in the communication coming from the auditee.
Reflecting Reflecting back the emotion displayed by the auditee.	"Sounds pretty tough. How has it affected your department?"	Indicates to the auditee that you care, and tests your understanding of their emotions. Especially useful when pursuing resource issues and their impact.
Paraphrasing Summarizing, in the auditor's own words, the content of an auditee's response.	"Let me make sure I've got this straight. . . ."	Somewhat disruptive as the auditee must stop talking while the auditor summarizes. Critical tool for testing your understanding of what you have been told. Should always be done after long responses and to confirm a finding.

As you can see from the table and this discussion, a lot goes on with the asking of a single question. This is another reason why active listening is so important. Active listening helps the auditor stay focused on the auditee and prevents the mind from wandering off or thinking ahead to the next interview. During my seminars I normally give my students this simple quiz and I encourage you to take it yourself.

Question 1. How many words per minute does the average person speak?

❏ 50–100 wpm

❏ 100–150 wpm

❏ 150–300 wpm

❏ 500–800 wpm

Question 2. How many words per minute is the human mind capable of processing?

❏ 50–100 wpm

❏ 100–150 wpm

❏ 150–300 wpm

❏ 500–800 wpm

The answer to question 1 is 100–150 words per minute. The answer to question 2 is 500–800 words per minute. Most people put the answers exactly opposite, but the truth is that our mind is capable of processing information at a rate of two to three times the rate at which words are normally spoken. What does this have to do with audit interviews? Simply this—by focusing your additional mental capacity on the way the words are used, the auditee's facial expressions and body movements, and by comparing what you're hearing now with what you've heard before, you keep your mind focused on the audit and on this interview. Active listening is important in maintaining the mental focus required to spot subtle nuances that can signal more significant problems.

Handling the Difficult Auditee

In this section I want to discuss some common challenges every auditor faces and how you might deal with them when they come up. We are not discussing conflict. These are behavior traits that each of us has to some extent, but which can disrupt the audit if not managed correctly. I will focus on four that I find most commonly.

The Excessively Nervous Auditee. Now, everyone is a little nervous when they are being audited. In fact, so are most auditors. In this case, though, I'm not talking about a little nervous, I'm talking about profuse sweating, shaking, ready-to-run-out-the-door nervous. Is there anything the auditor can do in this situation?

First, the auditor should make sure to carefully follow the guidelines discussed earlier for establishing a rapport with the auditee. This means some small talk to begin the audit and some comments that make the auditee feel like a member of the team. If that doesn't help, the auditor might want to take a little extra time and explain the audit process to the auditee. Often the extremely nervous auditee is someone who has never been interviewed for an audit before. I generally like to ask the auditee during introductions if they've ever been audited before. If they say no, then I spend a little more time explaining what we're doing and trying to get them to feel more comfortable. I also try to take the edge off my voice a little (I tend to talk too fast and can be a little bit too enthusiastic), and I make sure I'm not invading the auditee's personal space.

Some auditors like to tell the nervous auditee, "Don't be nervous. I'm sure you'll do great!" I don't recommend it for two reasons. One, the last thing most nervous people want to hear is that their nervousness is blatantly obvious. This can make them even more nervous. Second, I'm not really sure they will do great, or at least I'm not sure they will feel they did great, and I never want to promise something I'm not certain I can deliver. What I would recommend, is what one of my students said worked for her. Instead of saying, "Don't be nervous," she says, "I can sense you're a little nervous. So am I. Together I'm pretty sure we can get through this okay." The beauty of this statement is that by reflecting the auditor's own nervousness back to the auditee, it creates a bond and reduces the embarrassment being felt by the auditee. I think it's a great idea.

One thing you probably do not want to do with an extremely nervous auditee is to take a break ("Let's go get some coffee or a Mountain Dew."). Most people who are already nervous will become even more anxious if they have extra time to think about it.

So what do you do if, despite your best efforts, the auditee still can't finish a coherent statement? In this situation you may just want to audit someone else, assuming there are others who perform this task. It's not unusual for an organization to have a few people who just can't handle the stress of an interview. As a registrar auditor I even appreciate it when these folks are pointed out to me. The last thing an auditor wants is to have someone break down or go running into the woods. Just make sure it's not the entire second shift production department. I'd be a little skeptical about that.

The Talker. You will run into this individual from time to time. Let me set the stage. You have been assigned to audit the procurement process, managed by Cindy. Now Cindy has just spent the last six months of her life, 12 hours per day, six days a week, putting together the most advanced automated purchasing system the world has ever seen. I mean, this system will do everything. All you have to do is type in the name of the product you want to buy, and the system will scan the online Thompson's Registry, identify suppliers within an economically advantageous area, send out expressions of interest, evaluate the information returned, prequalify the potential suppliers, rank them, and select the most capable vendor. It will then prepare the purchase order, route it for approvals, and set up a history file to track the supplier's performance. This system is slick. And Cindy is dying to tell someone about it. Good auditor that you are, your first question is, "Cindy, can you walk me through our process for evaluating and selecting subcontractors?" You know the rest. For the next 30 minutes you listen to everything you never wanted to know about algorithms, computer coding, and the merits of artificial intelligence.

Some people just love to talk. The challenge with these individuals is not getting them to communicate, it's focusing their communications. The question is, how do you do that without offending them? Some auditors would say to Cindy, "That's nice Cindy, but I really don't have time to get into that now. Maybe some other time," in order to reorient the auditee back to the audit. While I agree with the intent, I would choose a different delivery. The response just provided sends the message, "I'm really not interested." In the case of Cindy, who has really done an excellent job, I do not want to send that message.

My response to Cindy would instead be, "Cindy, I'd love to hear more about the validation rules you set for each of the database fields, but first we need to complete the questions on our checklist. If we have time at the end of the interview, I'd like to learn more." My response does three things. First, and most importantly, it directs Cindy back to the audit. Second, it tells Cindy I am interested, but we are pressed for time and the audit comes first. And third, in case we do finish a little early (doubtful), it puts a time limit on how long I can stay and discuss relational database design. If we get done early and I have five minutes before my next interview, then I'd let Cindy tell me a little more. I might learn something, and I'm building a relationship. Relationship building is always good for the auditor.

As a final thought, I would probably use more closed-ended questions with the talker. They don't get you as much information (not a problem in this instance), but they do focus the question better.

The "Disturbed" Auditee. This is the one that hits my emotional button. You begin to ask the questions from your checklist and the phone rings. Not only does the auditee answer the phone, he takes the call. Five minutes later when the call is over you get back to the audit. Before you can get through the next question there's a knock at the door. Someone needs an approval on a hot requisition right away. This continues through the entire audit. What should the auditor do?

First, the auditor needs to realize who this person is—normally it is a manager or senior executive. You cannot, as one of my students so affectionately suggested, "Just pull the phone cord out of the wall!" You would probably find yourself on the unemployment line if you did. Essentially you have three options, presented starting with the *least* preferred option.

- *Option 3.* Take the auditee away from his office to an open conference room or office. While this may work in some situations, it is the least desirable option for two reasons. One, the auditor will still need to examine objective evidence, most of which is probably back in the manager's office. Two, with today's technology, the manager will probably bring his cell phone, pager, satellite PDA, and who knows what else with him.

- *Option 2.* Ask the auditee if there is a better time to conduct the interview. This sends a strong message that the audit will get done and puts the ball in the auditee's lap to suggest a time when the distractions will not be so great. It's only option number 2 because it does have a potentially serious drawback—

the auditee now controls the time for the interview. You may need to reschedule other interviews if the auditee's quiet time conflicts with another interview. Or consider this nightmare scenario, "Sure Joe, the calls and activity normally die down around 7:00 PM. Anytime after that should be good." Looks like a late night.

- *Option 1.* Ask the auditee to minimize the distractions. In other words, take the issue on directly. Say something like this, "Is there anyway you can have your secretary take your calls during this interview. It should only take about 30 minutes, if we can focus on it uninterrupted." If the auditee responds that no, he has to take the calls ("These are customers, you know.") then you can default to option number 2 and ask when a better time would be. If personal interruptions are the major distraction, then next time you may want to use option number 3. You'll have to go back to the manager's office to review the records at some point, but you can do record reviews while he conducts other business.

The Talkative Guide (or Supervisor). This is also a common situation. Normally for an internal audit you do not need a guide, but you will sometimes have a supervisor or manager who wants to tag along to see how we're doing. You're on the production floor asking an operator if there are any activities relating to this job that could impact the environment and before the operator can answer, the guide or supervisor jumps in with, "Sure. Susan must dispose of the waste solvent, and if it's not done correctly, it could contaminate the ground water." What do you do? For starters, try to avoid the situation in the first place by going over the ground rules with the guide or supervisor before you commence the interviews. Let the guide know that the auditee must answer the question. You may want to note that the guide can add additional comments *after* the auditee has completed his or her response. If you forget to do this prebrief, or the situation arises anyway, then I recommend you take the guide/supervisor to a quiet corner and go over the ground rules again. Do not counsel supervisors in front of those they supervise. If that doesn't work, or if you cannot break away from the interview, then you may want to direct the questions by saying something like this, "Now this question is for Susan . . ." I've had to use this on a number of occasions and it works very well. It also sends a subtle reminder to the guide or supervisor that they need to let the auditee answer the question.

Should an auditor let a supervisor or manager accompany him or her on an audit of their area? Good question. Doing so could intimidate auditees, especially if they view the audit as a test of their abilities. On the other hand, if the supervisor is more of a mentor or coach, then having him or her present may actually make the auditee more comfortable. The auditor must evaluate each situation on a case-by-case basis. If I feel that having the supervisor present would intimidate more than comfort, then I might say something like this, "Bruno, I'd rather you not come along. I know I'd be uncomfortable if my supervisor was present when I was being audited, and I'm afraid your employees might be too. I'd be more than willing to give you a quick debrief when I'm done though." I try not to personalize my objectives by stating that it's a normal reaction to be uncomfortable when your boss is present during an audit—it's not Bruno. Basically I reflect back on myself. I also offer to give him a quick debriefing to maintain his interest in the audit process and to show him respect. Keep in mind, however, that it is his area, and if he still wants to come along, he has that right. The best you can do in this situation is to carefully explain the ground rules before you start.

Handling Conflict During an Audit

If you question almost any auditor and ask them what causes them the most anxiety during an audit, they will probably respond that it is the potential for conflict. We will now discuss some strategies for dealing with conflict should it arise. Please keep in mind that visible conflict during an audit is rare. I've only experienced it a few times in my almost 20 years of auditing. If you follow the guidelines already presented, you may never have to use these techniques, but because the potential for conflict is a major source of anxiety for an auditor, I do present methods for dealing with it so that you can feel prepared.

Note that not all conflict is harmful. When I teach conflict management or team building I always cite research that shows that some level of conflict is necessary if the team is to achieve a high level of performance. Having said that, conflict during an audit is not normally healthy, since an audit is not a forum to develop ideas, methods, actions, or proposals. If auditors find that a debate (a form of conflict) is developing over methods, then they should recognize that they are probably offering opinions on how they think the auditee should do the job. Auditors should not offer their opinions about how an activity should be performed during the audit. In general, conflict, while necessary in other forums, should be avoided during an audit.

Figure 6.5 shows the conflict management model that we will use as the basis for this discussion. Please refer to it as we discuss the process for managing conflict.

Everyone reacts in one of two basic ways when threatened—fight or flight. During an audit, the fight mode is normally evidenced by attempts to intimidate the auditor using the auditee's superior knowledge, position, or length of time with the company as the lever. The flight instinct is normally indicated by attempts to avoid answering the question, either by going off on tangents or by giving only the most minimal of answers. The flight mode, while challenging for the auditor, does not normally result in conflict. The fight mode can.

The first thing that the auditor needs to determine when feeling attacked is whether the attack is personal or just the way this person is. We all have certain behavior traits that we exhibit in given situations. Some of these behaviors can seem very annoying or even a little threatening to others. The auditor needs to ask, "Is Kim really trying to intimidate me, or is this the way she interacts with everybody?" We all know people who are condescending or who talk down to people. Although auditors may find it difficult to talk to such individuals, they need to realize that there is nothing they can do within the time constraints of the audit to change the person's behavior. The auditee is not trying to attack or intimidate personally. The auditor just needs to overlook the behavior and continue with the interview.

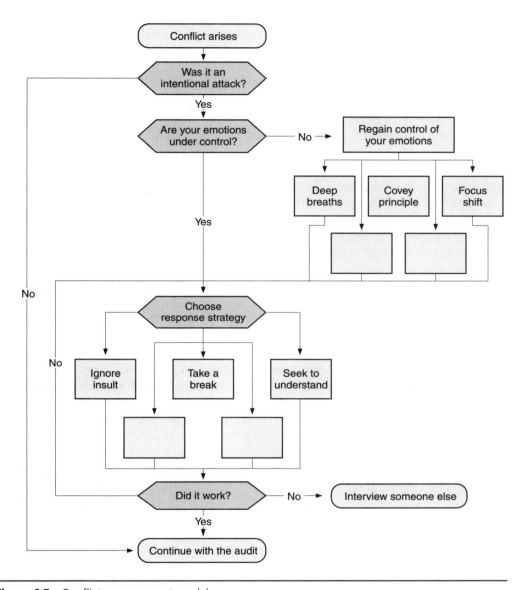

Figure 6.5 Conflict management model.

Assuming the attack was an attempt to intimidate, the auditor must first make sure his or her own emotions are in control before properly responding to the auditee. This can be hard to do. Our emotions usually kick in before our brain does. To avoid the foot-in-mouth syndrome, I recommend that auditors develop a short list of emotional buttons, or behaviors, that get them upset. I previously noted that one of my emotional buttons is the "disturbed" auditee who allows constant interruptions to disrupt the audit. To me this is a sign of disrespect for the auditor, which is why I find it upsetting.

The important thing is that I know that this is an emotional button for me, so when I'm in an interview and the phone rings I can automatically kick in my emotional control strategy before I get too upset. I can engage the brain before the heart gets carried away.

Do you know what your emotional buttons are? If not, don't worry, someone will punch one sooner or later! When they do, I recommend you make a note of what got you upset on the back of your checklist. Consciously noting it will help you retain it and later recognize it when it is pushed again during a later audit.

Once you recognize that someone has pushed an emotional button, then the next step is to apply your emotional control strategy. Everyone needs to have at least one strategy to help them stay calm when they are upset. I have listed three here. The first is the pretty well-known strategy of taking a couple of deep breaths before you respond. It sends more oxygen to the brain, but, more importantly, stops you from providing a knee-jerk response. During the deep breaths you instead think of the proper and professional way to respond to the intimidation.

Another method involves the Covey approach. Steven Covey, in his popular book *The Seven Habits of Highly Effective People,*[1] notes that all of us are in control of our own emotions. If we get upset, it's because we have allowed ourselves to become upset. We can also choose not to become upset. Now, this sounds pretty rational, but it's not so easy to do. I can, however, apply the Covey approach when I feel I'm being intimidated by using the following line of thought, *"Kim is trying to throw me off my game through her intimidation. If she does, she wins. I am not going to let Kim win. I will maintain my emotional control and continue with the audit."* Because I am competitive by nature, I can use the Covey approach to reinforce my need to stay calm. It works for me.

The last approach is to momentarily shift your focus away from the emotionally charged situation to something more calming. A friend and peer of mine uses this technique. When he feels himself getting upset, he shifts his focus to an upcoming skiing vacation in Sun Valley. It helps him put the audit and the current situation in perspective. While important, in the grand scheme of life, it's not worth getting upset about. In effect, he goes to his "happy place." If you need to go to your happy place for a few moments to regain emotional control, then do so.

You may note that I put two additional blank boxes in Figure 6.5. They symbolize other techniques auditors can use to maintain their emotional stability. The key is that you select one and then apply it whenever you recognize that someone has pushed your emotional button.

Once you have your emotions under control, you can turn your attention to how you want to handle the auditee. I will present three basic strategies. Which one you use depends on the situation and your comfort level with each one.

- *Ignore the insult.* Let me set the stage. I'm talking to Ken, the purchasing manager. I ask Ken to walk through our process for monitoring and developing our suppliers. Ken's response is, "Sure, Joe, I'll walk you through our process. I've been here 25 years, so I know how things should work. And, I'll go real slow so *even you* can understand." Now, I may not be a rocket scientist, but I think I can recognize Ken's response as an attempt to intimidate. A good way to respond would be to say, "Okay, Ken, please do.

And don't worry about going too fast, I'll slow you down if I need to." In essence I ignored Ken's insult, or at least pretty much did, and asked him to continue. This works most of the time because most people will stop trying to intimidate if they see that it isn't working.

• *Seek to understand.* This strategy is probably the hardest to accomplish, but it's usually the best option. The auditor reflects back the emotions displayed by the auditee and attempts to surface the reasons behind the frustration, fear, or anger. It is based on the assumption that there is no real reason to be angry with the auditor. Auditors don't write the procedures, they don't make the decision to implement the management system, they aren't trying to tell anyone how to do their job, and they certainly aren't going to tell anyone how to fix their problems. The auditor's job is simply to evaluate whether the procedures are being followed and if they are getting results. It might sound something like this, "Ken, I can sense you're not comfortable with the audit process. Can you help me understand why?" If Ken says it's true, and that he doesn't need anyone trying to come in and tell him how to run his department, then you can explain that you can't and won't try to tell him how to run his department. You can explain what the auditor's role really is and hopefully address the root cause of Ken's hostile reaction during audits. The advantage is that it not only will stop the intimidation for you, it will also eliminate the intimidation of other auditors who must interview Ken.

The risk in seeking to understand is when the reason for the auditee's anger or frustration is rooted in something the auditor cannot address. For example, suppose Ken's response was instead, "You're right, Joe, I don't like audits. Every time you guys find some little nonconformance someone gets fired!" And it's true! Not too much you can do there. My rule is that seeking to understand is the best strategy, as long as you know there is no valid reason for someone to be angry with the audit process.

• *Take a break.* This last option is always available and may be the best option if the auditor was not able to completely control his or her emotions and things got a little heated. Taking a short break, getting some coffee, or even starting fresh after lunch may be a good decision, as it lets everyone cool off and think about their behavior. Most people know it's inappropriate to lose control during an audit, and they will compose themselves better when you recommence. It can be disruptive to take a break, so I recommend it only when you find you really need to let things cool off.

Note that I've left a couple of blank boxes on the diagram to indicate other methods that may work. The key is to have a strategy, and use it when you find yourself in conflict. If none of your strategies work, you may have to interview someone else. In this situation, you need to let the audit program manager know what happened after the audit is over so that he or she can speak with the individual and hopefully resolve it for future audits. Allowing such behavior to continue can damage the internal audit program or result in serious consequences to the organization if it is exhibited during customer or registrar audits.

Now that we have examined the basic interviewing techniques, we are ready to move into some of the more technical skills and strategies for the audit.

MANAGING THE AUDIT FLOW

Audit flow refers to the sequence of interviews and topics to be reviewed during the audit. The auditor needs to structure the flow so that the information learned from one interview can be applied to the next interview. Normally this can be accomplished by following the natural sequence of a process, starting at either the beginning (trace forward) or the end (trace back) of the process. During the audit, the auditor will follow the process illustrated in Figure 6.6.

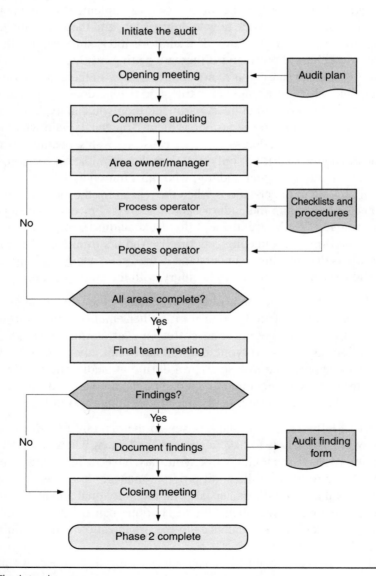

Figure 6.6   The interview process.

Figure 6.6 is very similar to Figure 6.1, except that we have expanded the interview section to show the interview flow of area owner or manager, then process operator, then next operation process operator, and so on.

Interviewing the Process or Area Owner

When you go into a new area, the first interview should be with the owner of the area or process. Often this will be the department or area manager. The goals of this initial interview are as follows:

1. Establish the level of manager involvement and support. Managers should be actively involved in the operation and improvement of processes they are responsible for. This can be done by asking questions relating to process metrics, current process performance, and objectives.

2. Clarify key requirements. As noted in our discussion of waffle words, there are certain requirements that only the process owner can clarify. These include: When would it be appropriate? When would it be desirable? When would it be necessary? There may be other areas where the auditor noted that the requirements were unclear or ambiguous. These should be clarified during this initial interview.

3. Determine what concerns, issues, or problems exist, from the area owner's perspective, that should be researched more extensively during the audit. I always like to ask for input from process owners and operators to involve them in the process and to reinforce the concept that we're all on the same team. If you barely get a response to this question, try asking, "What are your greatest challenges in operating or improving this process?" People who are reluctant to discuss problems are often willing to discuss challenges, even though in practical terms they may be one and the same.

4. Finally, the auditor will want to verify conformance with any requirements directly related to actions conducted or carried out by the process owner or area manager.

A checklist for conducting this initial interview may appear as shown in Figure 6.7. I previously noted that a formal opening meeting is not often conducted for focused internal audits. Rather, an informal opening meeting is held as part of the initial interview, since the first interviewee is typically the area owner or manager. In this case the auditor would briefly review the following before launching into the questions on the checklist:

- Purpose and scope of the audit.

- Areas to be examined.

- The tentative time for the closing meeting and where it will be held. Note that the closing meeting may simply be a report-out to the area manager on the audit findings at the completion of the audit.

- Confirmation of the audit plan, if one was prepared.

Standard Requirements	Reviewer Checks
Area manager/owner audit questions	
Ask the area manager or owner to describe the major activities performed in the area under review. During this discussion, ask: 1. **How are these activities monitored?** Have process metrics been established? Include monitoring of activities relating to significant environmental aspects. ❑ 2. **How are these processes performing?** Review the metrics, both for current performance and for trends. Probe into about any questionable areas. ❑ 3. **How is this information (process performance) communicated to the workforce?** Is there a method or process? ❑ 4. **What are the manager's/owner's most important concerns or problems with the process?** Ask about current or recent process issues, equipment issues, product problems, etc. Get as much info as you can about these issues. You will try to determine reasons for problems during the audit. ❑ 5. **What improvement projects or objectives are currently underway that affect this process?** Improvement projects/objectives may be related to process, product, or cost. Consider also any environmental objectives or targets. Ask how these align with corporate objectives and/or the quality policy. It helps to have reviewed the corporate objectives prior to this interview. ❑ 6. **What is the performance on achieving any objectives and/or targets that have been set?** Are they being monitored? Is the manager/owner knowledgeable about performance in achieving these objectives? ❑ 7. **What would you consider to be the group's best practices?** Research any areas that the process owner feels are superior. If the best practice encompasses an entire process you may want to use the best practice checklist. 8. **Is there anything we should look at closely while we are out on the floor/in the area?** Is there anything we can do to address concerns the manager/owner may have with the process? Most likely these will be associated with the answer to question 4. ❑	**Basic Process Information:** Name of process: _____ Manager/owner: _____ Metrics: _____ Performance: _____ Metrics: _____ Performance: _____ Metrics: _____ Performance: _____ Metrics: _____ Performance: _____ Concerns/Problems: _____ Concerns/Problems: _____ Objectives/CI: _____ Performance: _____ Objectives/CI: _____ Performance: _____ Best practice: _____ Performance: _____ Best practice: _____ Performance: _____ **Overall evaluation:** ❑ **Conforms.** No deficiencies identified. ❑ **Opportunity for improvement.** Detail below. ❑ **Best practice.** Detail below. Be specific. ❑ **Nonconformity.** Provide details below. Reference the specific requirement violated. **Full description of NC/OFI/BP** (use back if necessary)

Figure 6.7 Checklist for interviewing the process or area owner or manager.

The time it takes to do this informal opening meeting is brief—typically three or four minutes. Reviewing these basic items at the start of the interview ensures that everyone is still on the same page, and is highly recommended.

Evaluating Process Operations

After leaving the area owner, the auditor will turn attention to the individual operations that make up the process. The best way to evaluate most operations is to use a trace forward or trace back approach. These two well-known audit strategies are shown in Figure 6.8.

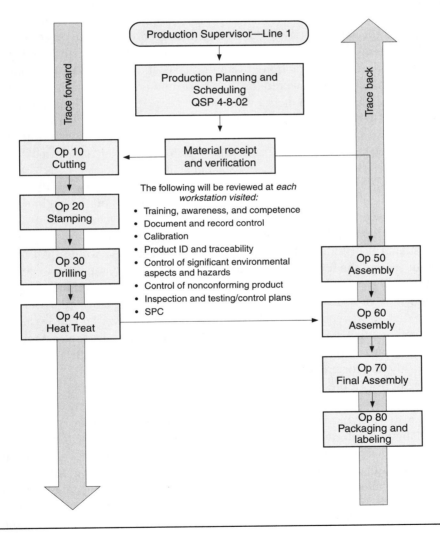

Figure 6.8 Trace forward and trace back.

In trace forward, the auditor starts at the front end of the process and follows the natural process flow until arriving at the end of the process. In our example, the auditor might begin by selecting a part currently being run on the production floor. He might then gather the control plan, process FMEA, and process flowchart for this part and begin the audit by interviewing the line 1 production supervisor who is the process owner. Next, he might evaluate the production scheduling process using the part(s) selected as his sample. The auditor would then move onto the production floor to begin the evaluation of the production process itself.

Using a bill of material for the component part, he might start in receiving where he would verify proper verification, storage, and labeling of incoming materials. He would then move to operation 10; followed by operation 20, stamping; operation 30, drilling; and so on until he had reached operation 80, packaging and labeling. At each station the auditor would verify document control, record control, control of any non-conforming product, product and material identification, the calibration and handling of any measuring devices, completion of required inspections and tests, and conformance to the work instructions. He would also verify through observation the competency of process operators, along with their awareness of the quality, environmental, and (possibly) safety and health aspects of their work. The auditor may also choose to audit whether required environmental and/or health and safety operational controls are in place and being maintained, assuming the organization is also certified to the ISO 14001 and OHSAS 18001 management system standards.

Trace back is essentially the same concept as trace forward, except that the auditor starts at the back end of the process and moves upstream toward the beginning. One of the very talented auditors from whom I had the privilege to learn always liked to start her audits of a supplier facility on the shipping dock. She did this because she wanted to see firsthand the products that the company produced. She would then pick one of those products that she felt represented a reasonable level of complexity to be her object for the audit. She obtained a traveler (list of production and verification steps) for the object and then traced backward until she reached the engineering department and the original contract requirements. By the time she got there, she had learned enough about the product that she could tell at a glance whether all of the contract requirements were properly incorporated into the final assembly. The choice of trace forward or trace back is mostly auditor preference.

By tracing forward or back through the process, the auditor is able to use the information and knowledge gained during earlier interviews at subsequent workstations. The auditor is also verifying the handoffs and interactions between processes such as production planning, material receiving, and production. He or she is automatically verifying the primary inputs and outputs for each subprocess since they are the subject of earlier or subsequent evaluations. By examining many of the critical inputs, resources, controls, and enablers for the process, this strategy embraces the concept of process-based auditing described in Chapter 3. The use of trace forward and trace back results in both an effective and efficient audit and is the method of choice for professional auditors.

Because the auditor has so many things to examine, in addition to compliance to work instructions, it is very helpful to provide a checklist that includes those things that should always be confirmed at each workstation. This is especially important for production process audits, where the number of processes linked together may be large. An example of such a checklist is shown in Figure 6.9. The auditor would print a copy of

Standard Requirements	Reviewer Checks
Basic producion process audit questions	

Have the operator walk you through/discuss the process being performed. During the discussion, verify the following items:
 	
1. **Is there a procedure/instruction at the workstation?** Is it current? (Note the rev. # for later comparison to the master list.) ❑
 	
2. **Is the procedure being followed?** Follow along as the operator walks you through the process. Ask the operator if the procedure is adequate. Note any deficiencies or inadequacies. ❑
 	
3. **Are material and parts properly identified?** Can everything be identified? How? ❑
 	
4. **Is the inspection status for materials and parts identified?** Ask the operator how to know the incoming product is good. ❑
 	
5. **Are the inspections required by the control plan or inspection plan being performed?** Are they at the right frequency? The right sample size? The right measurement device ? ❑
 	
6. **Are the measurement devices used at this workstation calibrated?** Are they being properly handled and stored when not in use? Verify calibrations/MSAs later. ❑
 	
7. **Are environmental controls being followed for any significant aspects?** If environmental monitoring or recording is required, is it being done? ❑
 	
8. **Are the operator(s) properly trained?** Check training records later. Are operators aware of the importance of their actions to the QMS/EMS? Are they aware of any significant environmental aspects?
  • Competency ❑
  • Awareness ❑
 	
9. **If SPC is used at this station, is it being properly conducted?** Is it effective? Review the charts for out-of-control conditions. ❑
 	
11. **Is nonconforming product control acceptable?** Do operators understand how to handle it? ❑
 	
12. **Other items** (list) ❑
	Basic Process Information:
	
	Name of workstation/activity: _____
	Operator(s): _____
	Procedure/instructions: _____ Rev: _____
	Gage/device type: _____ Serial #: _____
	Control/insp. plan # _____ Rev:_____
	
	Overall evaluation:
	❑ **Conforms.** No deficiencies identified.
	❑ **Opportunity for improvement.** Detail below.
	❑ **Best practice.** Detail below. Be specific.
	❑ **Nonconformity.** Provide details below. Reference the specific requirement violated.
	
	Full Description of NC/OFI/BP (use back if necessary)

Figure 6.9 Production operation checklist.

this checklist for each production workstation that's visited. He or she would then complete the checklists during the audit. Additional checklists would be completed, if desired, to account for known or suspected process problems, auditor or area owner concerns, or at audit program manager direction. Compliance to work instructions would be verified using in-place documentation at the workstation. This compromise between a completely unique checklist developed from scratch and a prepared checklist generated by the audit program manager works well for production processes where the sheer number of operating instructions may make it difficult, if not impossible, to prepare for each operation individually.

USING THE AUDIT CHECKLISTS

Now is a good time to discuss how to use the audit checklists provided on the CD. There are 18 quality management system checklists—nine based on ISO 9001:2000 and nine based on ISO/TS 16949:2002. An organization would use only the set that applies to the standard or specification they are certified to. There are five sections on the environmental management system checklists based on ISO 14001:2004 and five sections on the health and safety management system checklists based on OHSAS 18001.

Each checklist is process-based in that it focuses on one or more of the core processes that make up the management system as defined by the appropriate standard. The checklists include requirements from a number of different clauses within the standard where these requirements serve as inputs, resources, or controls to the process defined by the checklist. Each checklist also includes questions focused on process performance—is the process getting results?

The bundling of processes that appear on any given checklist was chosen to (1) group natural processes together and (2) provide for an efficient audit that could be completed by one or two auditors in a day. Naturally, the time it would take to complete any individual audit varies significantly depending on the size of the organization and the complexity of the process, but the checklist groupings attempt to strike a balance between audit efficiency and the elimination of redundancy.

The Quality Management System Checklists

ISO 9001 and ISO/TS 16949 each have six core checklists and three product realization audit checklists. The structure of the checklists varies slightly between the two standards to allow for more efficient audit groupings. The core checklists contain all of the requirements that apply to the processes contained on the checklist, no matter where in the standard they are found. As an example, requirements relating to training and document control will be found on every checklist, since they apply to every process. The core checklists represent complete reviews of the process to the requirements of the standard or specification. Two of these, the quality planning and design and production checklists, focus on the product realization processes that form the heart of any quality management system. These six core checklists and the processes they address are identified in Table 6.2.

Table 6.2 Quality management system core checklists.

Checklist	Processes Addressed
Quality planning and design (9001 and 16949)	Customer-related processes including order generation, quality planning, design, and development (APQP and PPAP for 16949)
Production (9001 and 16949)	Product and service provision including all manufacturing operations
Production support (9001 only)	Servicing and the centralized activities associated with calibration and testing, tooling and facility management, and maintenance
Monitoring, measurement, and improvement (9001 and 16949)	Continual improvement, analysis of data, and customer satisfaction monitoring (and internal audit, corrective and preventive action for ISO 9001)
Resource and support processes (9001 and 16949)	Purchasing and centralized activities associated with training, document, and record control
Management responsibility (9001 and 16949)	Management responsibility, including overall management system planning, quality objectives, communications, strategic resourcing, and management review
Audit and Corrective Action (16949 only)	Internal audit, corrective and preventive action

Note the use of the phrase *centralized activities* in a number of the processes addressed in the checklists. Centralized activities represent those requirements that would normally *not* be evaluated during an audit of one of the other core processes. For example, the control of documents will be an evaluation item on every audit checklist for each process reviewed. Since the availability, legibility, revision status, and adequacy of documents will be continuously reviewed during each audit, there is no need to perform a separate evaluation for conformance to these requirements. There are, however, some centralized functions associated with document control that may not be evaluated during other process-based audits. These include tasks associated with the preparation, review, approval, and issuance of documents, maintenance of the master list, and the control of obsolete or archived documents. These activities are normally centralized within the department or the organization and are the subject of the focused document control audit. Similarly, the performance and effectiveness of preventive and predictive maintenance will be evaluated during each production audit, but the management of the maintenance system, scheduling of maintenance, setting and achievement of maintenance objectives, and control of key replacement parts needs to be evaluated at some frequency as part of a focused audit.

A word of caution is in order. These checklists only capture requirements from the applicable standard or specification. They do not capture all of the additional requirements from your customers or that your organization calls out in its detailed procedures and instructions. They also do not adequately display all of the important inputs, controls, and resources for these processes that are unique to your company. They serve as a solid foundation to prepare from, not as a ready-made, complete checklist that an auditor can just pick up and use. The audit program manager and lead auditors should modify these checklists to include these additional internal requirements and inputs using your procedures, SIPOC diagrams, and flowcharts. These internal requirements should replace some of the generic requirements on the checklist.

Perhaps the greatest value of these checklists is in their use as a guide for structuring your audit program. They are organized around natural processes like order generation and order fulfillment. They combine related activities into natural groupings that can or should be audited together. They include requirements from other parts of the standards or specification that serve as important inputs, resources, or controls and which should be evaluated during the process audit. When used in this manner, and when customized to address your internal requirements, they can serve as the backbone of your internal audit program.

In addition to the six core checklists discussed earlier, each quality management set also has three product realization audit checklists. These would be used when evaluating the production to delivery process. They are designed to simplify and facilitate production audits. Normal checklists don't work too well on the production floor because the nature of the production audit requires visiting multiple workstations and evaluating each against a fairly long list of requirements. Trying to wade back and forth through the 20-page core production checklist at each workstation visited would be extremely cumbersome and is just not practical. To simplify the conduct of the production audit, while capturing the value of the checklist, streamlined versions have been developed that can be used when doing a manufacturing audit. Two of these have already been presented in Figures 6.7 and 6.9. The third covers handling, packaging, labeling, and storage to delivery activities. These checklists would be used in place of the core production checklist during the audit and are summarized in Table 6.3.

When used in this manner, the core production checklist becomes more of a planning and support tool, identifying additional items that might be evaluated if there is a need and providing additional and more probing questions if the auditor finds weaknesses that need more thorough evaluation. Note the parenthetical references next to the requirements on the simplified product realization audit checklists on the CD. These numbers represent the page number of the corresponding topic on the core production checklist. If the auditor feels a need to probe into an area, he or she can go to that page on the core production checklist and use any of the additional questions to dig deeper.

Individual pages from the core production checklist can also be provided to the auditor if the audit program manager wants to target a specific area such as training

Table 6.3 Product realization audit checklists.

Checklist	Scope	Application
Area owner or manager	Area or process owner awareness, involvement, and inputs into the audit. Process performance and improvement.	One checklist for each process or area evaluated.
Production operation	Conformance to core process requirements and to other generic requirements that apply to any production operation.	One checklist for each workstation visited.
Preservation	Handling, packaging, labeling, storage, preservation, and delivery of product.	One checklist for each product evaluated.

during a particular audit. This blended approach of using simplified checklists for the audit, supplemented by the core production checklists, attempts to balance audit thoroughness and practicality. Many of my students who have adopted this approach have written to say that use of the checklists has improved the quality of their audits while reducing the time required for planning.

Environmental Management System Checklists

There are five sections to the environmental management system checklists. They represent the three primary processes of environmental planning, operational control, and environmental performance improvement, and two primary support processes, monitoring and corrective action and centralized support activities. The processes that each address are shown in Table 6.4.

These core checklists mirror the checklists developed for the quality management system, which allows easy integration if combined quality and environmental management system audits are performed. The discussion provided for the quality management system checklists applies equally to these EMS checklists with the exception that the abbreviated production audit checklists are not needed for an EMS review. The control of significant environmental aspects and operator awareness of the same should be added to the production operation audit checklist if desired.

Occupational Health and Safety Management System Checklists

There are also five OH&S management system checklists. Similar to the EMS checklists, they represent the three primary processes of OH&S planning, operational control, and OH&S improvement, and two primary support processes, monitoring and corrective action and centralized support activities. The processes that each address are shown in Table 6.5.

Table 6.4   Environmental management system audit checklists.

Checklist	Processes Addressed
Environmental planning	Environmental policy, environmental aspects, legal, and other requirements
Operational control	Operational control, environmental monitoring for individual activities, emergency preparedness, and response
Improvement	Management responsibility, including overall management system planning, environmental objectives, communications, strategic resourcing, and management review
Monitoring and corrective action	Internal audits, nonconformances, corrective and preventive action, compliance reviews, environmental performance measurement for the overall EMS
Support activities	Purchasing and centralized activities associated with training, document and record control, maintenance, and calibration

Table 6.5 OH&S management system audit checklists.

Checklist	Processes Addressed
OH&S system planning	OH&S policy, hazard identification and risk assessment, legal and other requirements
Operational control	Operational control, OH&S monitoring for individual activities, emergency preparedness, and response
Improvement	Management responsibility, including overall management system planning, OH&S objectives, communications, strategic resourcing, and management review
Monitoring and corrective action	Internal audits, incidents, nonconformances, corrective and preventive action, compliance reviews, OH&S performance measurement for the overall management system
Support activities	Purchasing and centralized activities associated with training, document and record control, maintenance, and calibration

These core checklists mirror the checklists developed for the quality and environmental management systems, which allows easy integration if combined OH&S and EMS or combined quality, environmental, health, and safety audits are performed. The discussion provided for the quality management system checklists applies equally to these OH&S checklists with the exception that the abbreviated production audit checklists are not needed for an OH&S management system review. The control of significant workplace hazards and operator awareness of the same should be added to the production operation audit checklist, if desired.

OBTAINING OBJECTIVE EVIDENCE

Up to this point this chapter has focused on interview techniques and audit strategies. Now we will turn our attention to verification of the auditee's response. As any experienced auditor knows, verification through the use of objective evidence is required. Auditors must not blindly accept the words of the auditee. Most auditees will not outright lie to an auditor, but as previously pointed out, they may rationalize a correct response. The auditor must review objective evidence to confirm conformance to system requirements and to identify weaknesses that the auditee may not even be aware of. Knowing when to ask for evidence, how much evidence to review, and how detailed of a review to perform are skills that can make or break the audit.

Forms of Objective Evidence

Objective evidence can come in many different forms. These include:

• *Management system records.* Records include approval records, meeting minutes, inspection and testing records, reports, or any other document that provide an historical account of a prior event. Records are the most common form of objective evidence and should be examined whenever they exist. Formal records are normally identified in a records matrix and/or in the boilerplate of management system procedures and instructions. Certain records, such as training records, internal audit reports, and records of management reviews are required by the management system standards. Others are defined by environmental, health, and safety regulations. Still others are defined by the organization itself as a means of ensuring the proper operation and control of key processes. Records provide evidence that past actions were conforming.

- *Operational data.* Operational data may be used to verify conformance, even if they are not formally controlled as a management system record. They are normally short-term in nature and would only be useful to verify current conformance.

- *Performance metrics and trend charts.* As explained in Chapter 5, this information is very important for audit planning and for verifying process effectiveness. Performance information is a type of record, since it is historical, but unlike other records, it may change over time. An example is a performance chart that shows the level of scrap over the past 12 months. Every month the first month in the series will be replaced by the last month's performance.

- *Lists, matrices, indices.* These items represent real-time compilations of information. I am hesitant to classify these items as records, since their real-time nature precludes their use to verify historical conformance. They are often used to provide evidence that we have a current system in place and to select samples for more thorough investigation. Some common examples include the approved supplier list and competency matrices.

- *Procedures, instructions, and other documents.* Documents provide evidence of current system controls and practices and may be used to verify that the system design conforms to the requirements of the applicable standard or specification.

- *Personal observations.* One of the best forms of verification is seeing an activity performed with your own two eyes. Personal observation is the best way to verify competency, but it should be combined with record reviews whenever possible since auditees sometimes have a habit of performing an activity correctly when the auditor is around and taking shortcuts when the auditor isn't. Personal observation can be used to verify that an operator knows what to do; records are then used to verify that it is done consistently.

- *Collaboration by the auditees.* Although it is always desirable to have a record or other hard evidence that an action was performed, there will be instances where records just don't exist. Let me give you an example.

Suppose you want to confirm that operators on a production process are being trained on revisions to an operating instruction. You pose that question to the production supervisor who replies, "Absolutely! We have a short pre-shift meeting each day. I cover any procedure changes that impact operations during this meeting." You ask whether any records exist for this training and he replies no, they maintain records of initial training and on new procedures, but not for every procedure change. Now you have a choice. You can cite them on a nonconformance to ISO 9001 clause 6.2.2, which says that you must maintain appropriate records of education, training, skills, and experience. Alternatively, you could note a recent revision and go out on the line and question some operators to see if they are aware of the change. I would recommend the latter. If all of the operators were aware of the revision, then that provides sufficient evidence that the supervisor is in fact conducting training on procedure revisions and that it is effective. Giving them a nonconformity in such a situation would increase the already prevalent mind-set that ISO 9001 is nothing more than an administrative exercise that doesn't add real value. While I would expect to find records of initial training and essential competency attainment for operators, I would not expect to find records of all of the ongoing training that goes on continuously in a progressive organization.

Sample Size

How many records should an auditor review in order to confirm conformance? That depends. If the auditor is using a trace forward or trace back strategy and has picked one or more parts to test the system, then the auditor should review records associated with those parts. In some circumstances the auditor may not have an object for the audit or may want to expand the sample beyond the objects selected.

Auditors rarely pull more than four or five samples. The reason is that the audit is primarily trying to find systemic weaknesses, not isolated occurrences. If the deficiency is systemic, then the auditor can expect it to show up in a sample size of four or five, assuming the samples were randomly selected and representative of the general population. This is an important assumption, however. Sample selection is more important than sample size.

Assume the auditor is evaluating the order generation process. The procedure says a manufacturing feasibility review will be performed prior to quoting or accepting any orders for new products. The auditor wants to verify that these reviews are being performed. The reviews are coordinated by the account manager and maintained in the contract file. Assume the company has three account managers. In order to get adequate representation of the overall population, the auditor would want to select two or three samples from each account manager's portfolio. Choosing five samples from one account manager's portfolio would not represent the overall population.

Two important points need to be made regarding sample size and sample selection. First, completely random samples are not always appropriate. If account manager number 2 has a history of noncompliance, then the auditor should select more samples from account manager 2's portfolio. Second, two or three samples may be adequate, if there is no indication of a problem. If the auditor finds deficiencies, however, then the sample size should be increased. The auditor will need to determine if the deficiency is systemic or if it is an isolated occurrence. This information is important to the auditee manager who will have to respond to the finding.

As a final comment, it was noted in Chapter 3 that auditors may need to ensure that product is being properly verified per customer, regulatory, and/or internal requirements through some type of overinspection. In these situations sample size may take on statistical significance. Auditors in these unique situations should be familiar with statistical sampling tables and plans, the thrust of which should be incorporated into the organization's normal inspection plans.

Verification Strategy

The verification strategy used by the auditor is normally fairly obvious. In the example just cited, the obvious way to verify that manufacturing feasibility reviews are being performed is to sample a number of accounts, ensuring that there is a record of a feasibility review for each new product. In some instances, however, the verification strategy may not be so apparent. Assume you've been assigned to audit the purchasing process and one of the requirements states that any receipt of nonconforming material will result in a supplier corrective action request (SCAR) being issued to the supplier, with a copy of the SCAR and response being placed in the supplier's history file. How would you verify that the SCARs are being issued as required?

Many auditors would ask the purchasing manager for examples of where a supplier had provided nonconforming product. This allows the auditee to select the samples, which is never a good way to find the weaknesses. A better strategy would be to stop by the receiving department on the way to purchasing and note several instances of incoming product problems using the receiving department records. When the auditor wants to verify this requirement during the purchasing manager interview, he or she can then specifically ask to see the history files for the suppliers noted during the visit to the receiving department.

Auditors should examine each question on their checklists and ask themselves, "How will I verify the auditee's response? Do I know what to ask for and how I will choose the samples?" If the answer isn't evident, then the auditor should develop a verification strategy and add it to the checklist.

Rule No. 5
Never let the auditee pick the samples.

Determining the Consequence of the Finding

One of the things that sets apart the superstar auditors from their peers is their ability to tie findings to real consequences. They have the ability to transform the finding from a technical violation into a problem that is affecting the organization now. They get management's attention. They also get management's support.

Auditors should *never* be content with the discovery and citation of a nonconformity. They should *always* attempt to determine if this deficiency is having an affect on the organization and, if so, by how much. Let's take a look at one of our previous audit findings—the communication boards in the production areas. You may remember that our auditors found that they were being maintained, but were not effectively communicating to the area operators as evidenced by the fact that 30 of 33 individuals interviewed could not state what the major quality or safety issue was in their area. The audit finding received a negative reaction from the plant manager when it was reported. Let's assume that the auditors took the time to do a little research into the impact of this failure to communicate. What if they discovered that in each of the areas evaluated, the major quality issue (missing parts, foreign material, incorrect assembly, and so on) had not only remained the same, it had actually increased every month over the past six months? Or that the accident or lost workday rate had steadily increased? What if they were able to put a dollar figure on the cost of repair or rework due to the major quality issue? This information may very well prompt a different reaction from the plant manager.

Here are some more examples. You decide which audit findings would most likely prompt a more supportive reaction from management and more assertive corrective action.

Finding 1a: The control plan being used in final assembly for part BD459-X2 was obsolete in violation of clause 4.2.3 of the ISO 9001 standard and section 4.6 of QSP-QA-02.

Finding 1b: The control plan being used in final assembly for part BD459-X2 was obsolete and did not contain all customer required inspections in violation of clause 4.2.3 of the ISO 9001 standard and section 4.6 of QSP-QA-02. It was further noted that 400 units of product BD459-X2 were rejected by the customer in March for the attributes that were missing on the control plan. The direct costs associated with resolution of this problem were in excess of $200,000.

Finding 2a: The roll-off scrap steel container located outside of rollup door number 4 was not covered as required by ESP-FA-004.

Finding 2b: The roll-off scrap steel container located outside of rollup door number 4 was not covered as required by ESP-FA-004. It was noted that a failure to cover a roll-off scrap steel container was cited as the root cause of a 2001 release of oil to the creek that runs behind the plant. This incident resulted in a notice of violation from the state and a fine of $60,000.

Finding 3a: The protective guard on label machine number 3 was not installed in violation of the job hazard analysis and health and safety policy.

Finding 3b: The protective guard on label machine number 3 was not installed in violation of the job hazard analysis and health and safety policy. It was further noted that the plant experienced three instances of worker injury due to inadequate or removed machine guards in 2004, which resulted in a total of 17 lost workdays.

The auditor may have to spend an extra 30 minutes to track down the consequences, but it's definitely worth the extra time. Always attempt to determine if the deficiency has had any real effect on the organization or is likely to based on past occurrences. Always attempt to put a dollar figure to the consequence if you can. Money is the language of management. This applies to opportunities for improvement and best practices as well as to nonconformities.

One client institutionalized this concept by adding a cost section to the bottom of the corrective action forms. Using a few standard costs that the auditor had worked up with accounting, the company routinely applied a cost of poor quality dollar amount to every corrective action generated. You'd be amazed at how much better the response was from management when it could see how much money their nonconformances were costing them.

Rule No. 6

Always try to identify any real effects of your findings—use dollar values where available.

Auditee Confirmation

Auditors should always share their findings with the auditee before they leave. There are several reasons why this is important. It is critical when you think you have a nonconformance.

Sharing findings avoids invalid findings generated because of miscommunication. If you remember, I started this section by noting that 70 percent of all communications are misunderstood. A well-trained auditor who practices active listening can significantly improve upon that percentage, but the fact is, sometimes we just don't understand what the other person is trying to say, or they don't understand us. Sometimes we think we have a nonconformity, but we really don't. Let me give you an example.

Assume your procedure for supplier evaluation and selection requires joint agreement between both purchasing and quality assurance before a new supplier goes on the approved supplier list. You previously asked the purchasing manager to walk through *our* process for evaluating and selecting suppliers. She replied throughout her response, "*I* do this . . . *I* do that . . . *I* check this . . ." Never once did she mention any quality involvement. You decide to write up a nonconformance to the procedure requirement for QA participation in this process. When you get to the closing meeting you present your nonconformance, at which time both the purchasing manager and the quality manager jump up and exclaim, "Quality's involved!" You respond by noting that never once did the purchasing manager mention quality's involvement, to which she responds, "I didn't know you wanted to know what everybody did! I only thought you wanted to know what I did!" At this point you slink down in your chair and in your best Emily Litella (Gilda Radner, *Saturday Night Live*) impression meekly say, "Never mind." Sharing the finding with the auditee before you leave, or even as it is identified, gives the auditee the chance to correct any misconceptions that could lead to an invalid finding. It protects you, the auditor.

Sharing the finding allows the auditee to get a jump on an action plan to correct the deficiency. Auditees may even be able to correct it before the audit is over. It will still be reported, but you can also report the status of actions, which will put the auditee in a better light or lessen the administrative burden needed to handle and track the deficiency until it is closed. Note that complete closure of a nonconformance prior to the completion of the audit should be fairly rare, since root cause identification must be performed prior to determining action that must be taken and this alone usually takes longer than the time available for the audit.

Sharing the findings reinforces the concept that both the auditor and the auditee are on the same team. The auditor should be willing to share the findings with the auditee as a sign of courtesy and respect.

Rule No. 7

Always confirm your findings with the auditee.

AUDIT DO'S AND DON'TS

As a final review of interviewing techniques, consider the following lists of audit do's and don'ts. The first two rules in the do list are particularly important when auditing in teams. Auditor 1 should complete all questions in his area before auditor 2 starts asking questions in her area. Do not tag-team the auditee.

- Do ask one question at a time.

- Do conclude one topic before going to the next.

- Do make the auditee feel like a member of the team.

- Do be a good listener. Try to spend no more than 10 percent of the time talking. Listen actively.

- Do explain the purpose of any note taking to the auditee. Auditees will assume you are writing a negative comment. Let them know at the start of the interview that you will be taking notes. If you must record their name, let them know why.

- Do stay within the scope of the audit.

The last item on the list used to be easy. Auditors were assigned elements such as document control, which meant the scope of the audit was document control. Anything else was outside the scope. With process-based audits it may not be so clear. An audit of a manufacturing process could include document control, training, calibration, maintenance, record control, product identification, and the control of nonconforming product in addition to conformance with the process instructions. It may even include the control of significant environmental aspects and job hazards. Anything associated with the process being reviewed would fall within the scope of the audit.

What would be outside the scope? Assume the auditor found some deficiencies with the training records of one of the process operators. As a result, the auditor starts to examine the overall training program, including how competencies are identified. The auditor is now going outside the scope of the audit. This can be a problem for several reasons. First, the training coordinator was not informed that an audit of this program would be conducted and may feel blindsided by the review. Second, the auditor hasn't prepared adequately for a review of the training program and is likely to miss a lot. Third, time spent auditing the training program is time not spent on the assigned audit.

Now that we've covered what auditors should do, let's look at what we shouldn't:

- Don't use emotional words or opinions. Emotional words and opinions include *you, you're,* and *I,* all of which can put the auditee on the defensive. Everything should be *we* and *ours. Why* can also be an emotional word and must be used with care.

- Don't ask unsafe questions. Questions asking an auditee to pinpoint problems with another person or another individual's process should be avoided.

- Don't argue. The auditor is not there to defend the management system. Do not allow yourself to be drawn into an argument.

- Don't offer opinions. Stay away from the *I* word during the audit. If the auditor has recommendations about how a process could be improved, then save them until after the audit or carefully cite them as opportunities for improvement.

- Don't feel confined to asking only questions on your checklist. Although much of this chapter has focused on the use of checklists, the auditor must never feel constrained to only asking questions from the checklist. The checklist is a tool, not a standard.

- Don't write up nits. What's a nit? A nit is any finding that is administrative in nature and could never have any real impact on the performance of the management system. Examples of nits are obvious typographical errors, fields not marked NA when blank and there is no requirement to do so, and administrative oversights that are obvious and easily correctable.

Let me give you an example. During one auditor training session, a student came to me with a complaint about the audit program manager. Since I had worked with the audit program manager in the past and knew her to be a good auditor, I was very interested in what the student's complaint was.

"Well, the audit program manager conducted our last quality audit. We have one report that we file every month, and the procedure states that we must staple any attachments to the report prior to filing it away. During the audit the audit program manager noted that, while all the attachments were with the reports and they were all located where they were supposed to be, the attachments were binder-clipped to the reports instead of being stapled. She gave us a nonconformity to the procedure. I couldn't believe it!"

Now technically, the audit program manager was within her rights to issue an NC. After all, the procedure does say "stapled." In the real world, however, this finding was a nit. The practical impact was that the auditor lost credibility in the eyes of the auditees. She may have found several other valid, important weaknesses and they wouldn't hear her. All they kept seeing was this nit that she wrote up.

Since nits are sometimes violations to the requirements, even if trivial, how does an auditor avoid writing them up? The short answer is, *don't go looking for them.* The purpose of Chapter 5 is to give you insight into how to plan an effective audit because auditors never have enough time to look at everything. Focus on significant requirements. Focus on problem areas. Focus on performance. Do not focus or even look for nits. If an auditee points one out to you, it's often best to ask them to fix it and move on. You gain credibility in the eyes of the auditee when you overlook the nits and stick to things that matter.

Rule No. 8

Don't go looking for nits.

PREPARING FOR THE CLOSING MEETING

Preparation for the closing meeting includes determining the category of each finding and writing up what the auditors have found. This is normally done during the final team meeting. If you're auditing by yourself, then take heart—consensus shouldn't be too hard to reach!

Final Team Meeting

During the final team meeting the auditors will want to classify their findings and assign and complete write-ups. If the team had working lunches, much of this may already have been completed.

The team should be in agreement on what the nonconformities are. Remember, a nonconformity is a violation of a requirement. Every nonconformity should be traceable back to a chapter and verse of a procedure, instruction, stated policy or practice, or to the relevant management system standard. If the auditor(s) cannot trace the violation back to a requirement, then it's not a nonconformance. It's just that simple. If the linkage is not sufficiently clear that a team of experienced auditors, trained on both the standard and its interpretation can all agree, then you may be better off citing it as an opportunity for improvement. In instances where there is disagreement, but the finding is considered significant, then the lead auditor makes the call. He or she is in charge of the audit.

Once agreement has been reached on the nature of the findings, then the lead auditor should make assignments on who should write up what. This is where the one-liner form discussed in Chapter 4 comes in handy. Unless there is good reason to do otherwise, group all similar findings together and cite them on one nonconformance report.

Do not issue nine nonconformance reports citing failures to properly update and locate current revisions of documents on the production floor. Issue one NCR citing all nine instances as examples. This does two things: first, it reduces the number of NCRs that have to be generated, tracked, completed, verified, and closed; and second, it provides a bigger picture of the scope of the problem. When looked at this way, the single NCR may warrant an assignment as a major nonconformity, as will be discussed.

Classification of Nonconformities

I am not a big fan of calling nonconformance major or minor. I've seen too many instances where the auditors and the auditees end up fighting over semantics instead of focusing on the problem itself. Since registrar auditors and many internal audit programs use the designations, though, I do address them in this section.

In general, a finding will be considered to be a *major* nonconformance in the following situations:

- There is a complete or total failure to address a requirement in the standard.

- Although there is a system to address a requirement, the high number of failures identified by the auditors clearly that indicate that the controls are not working and thus constitute a failure of the system. This would be the case in our example of nine separate instances where auditors found obsolete, outdated documents in use on the production floor.

- The violation has a high probability of resulting in nonconforming product getting out to the customer. An example might be inspection to a control plan that is two versions out of date and does not reflect current customer-mandated inspections.

Similarly, the finding will be considered to be a *minor* nonconformance if it doesn't meet the preceding conditions. For example:

- Work instructions were occasionally absent in areas that clearly required such documents.

- A few failure(s) of document and change control in various areas of the company had been observed.

- Inspection status on a few products or their associated documentation was absent in one area.

Note that the definition and classification of findings will vary from one organization to the next. Some organizations provide additional categorization of findings to provide insight into the significance or promptness of the response required in reacting to the problem. Internal auditors, in particular, must be familiar with their organization's definitions and classification system for audit findings and must use these definitions when citing audit findings.

Audit Write-Ups

All audit nonconformities must be documented. The following information is normally provided in a nonconformance report:

- Description of the nonconformity

- Reference to the requirement that is being violated

- Background information needed to understand the finding:

    - Form or report numbers or other specific identifier

    - Number of deficiencies and the size of the sample

    - Location or area where identified, as appropriate

    - Any other pertinent information that the auditor feels would be useful to the auditee

An example of an audit nonconformance report and write-up is provided in Figure 6.10. The following items typically do not belong in an audit nonconformity write-up:

- Employee names (although functional titles may be acceptable)

- Opinions as to the cause of the deficiency

- Recommendations on how to correct the deficiency

The auditor must always remember who the nonconformance report is for—it *is not* the audit program manager, it *is not* the other auditors. It *is* for the auditee manager who will have to take action to correct the deficiency. He or she may not have been present when the deficiency was found. This means the write-up must be clear and directly traceable to the requirement that was violated. The description of the deficiency must leave no doubt as to what the problem was or why it is considered a violation. By including information relating to the number of deficiencies, sample size, and so on, the auditee manager can determine whether the violation was an isolated occurrence, in which case the action will be to correct it, or a systemic weakness that warrants significant effort for root cause determination and elimination.

I cannot overemphasize the importance of developing clear and actionable audit write-ups. The best audit in the world serves no purpose if the auditee takes the wrong action because he or she does not understand the basis for the finding. One of the best ways to ensure that your audit write-up clearly conveys both the requirement being violated and the reason for the nonconformance is to write the description of the nonconformity as a negative of the requirements itself. As an example, assume you are citing a failure to update and maintain emergency response procedures in accordance with ISO 14001 clause 4.4.7, which reads, "The organization shall periodically review and, where necessary, revise its emergency preparedness and response procedures, in particular, after the occurrence of accidents or emergency situations."

A solid write-up might be the following:

Finding No. 02-17	**Audit Finding Form**
Date: Nov. 19, 2005	☑ Nonconformity
	☐ Opportunity for improvement
Auditor: R. Tubbs	☐ Best practice

Finding: Management reviews do not consider all of the relevant inputs required by ISO/TS 16949:2002, section 5.6.1.

Description: ISO/TS 16949:2002, section 5.6.1, requires that management reviews consider customer feedback and process performance during the management review. One management review has been held since the QMS was upgraded to the new requirements. No evidence could be provided that these essential inputs were considered during the management review, and these items do not appear on the current agenda form.

_____	_____
Auditor	**Cognizant Manager**

Requirement Violated: ISO/TS 16949:2002, section 5.6.1

Root Cause:

Management Action to Be Taken:

Estimated Completion Date of Action: _____

Date Action Completed: _____ **Action Taken By:** _____
| | Cognizant Manager |
Verification of Action:

_____	_____
Auditor/Verifier	Management Representative

Figure 6.10 Example audit nonconformance report.

Emergency preparedness and response procedures are *not* being reviewed and, where necessary, revised in accordance with ISO 14001 clause 4.4.7.

ISO 14001 clause 4.4.7 requires periodic reviews and, where necessary, revision of emergency preparedness and response procedures, in particular, after the occurrence of accidents or emergency situations. A site emergency was declared on December 14, 2003, in response to a fire in injection molding line 3. Evaluations of the post-emergency incident review and interviews with the emergency response coordinator found no evidence that either the site emergency response plan or general fire and evacuation plan were reviewed for adequacy or necessary revisions. It was further noted that no documented evidence of any reviews of these procedures could be located and that no modifications to these procedures have been made since their issuance in October of 1998.

The first statement clearly lays out the core requirement and the fact that it is not being met. The following paragraph describes in more precise detail exactly what the auditor found and provides context and support for the auditor conclusion. The auditor might have to spend a couple of extra minutes to fill in the extra detail provided in the second paragraph, but compared to the effort required to identify and pursue the deficiency, this time is very short and is well spent.

Now let's look at some audit write-ups that could be improved. Spend a few minutes and jot down how you might improve each one before looking at the discussion that follows.

Audit Write-Up 1

Description: The control of measurement devices was found to be inadequate.

Objective evidence: Several calipers in the plant were noted to be out of calibration, and some did not have any serial numbers on them.

Audit Write-Up 2

Description: Quality audits are not effective.

Objective evidence: Three of the seven internal audit reports for 2003 did not find any nonconformities. Two of the remaining four only found a few minor administrative deficiencies.

Audit Write-Up 3

Description: The audit found that the control of quality-related documents was really swell.

Objective evidence: This area appeared to be very much improved over the last audit.

In audit write-up 1, there is no reference to the requirements being violated. Although calibration is certainly a requirement in the standard, serializing gages is not. Is it a violation of a local procedure? If not, is the issue really that there is no way to verify calibration status? If this is the issue, then the auditor should cite it as such. Second, where were the gages being used? Calibration of product acceptance gages is certainly required, but what if these gages were being used in the training department? Also, if the gages were being used to accept product, then an evaluation of the impact of the out-of-calibration gage on the product should be immediately initiated. The auditee will also have to retrieve the gages to ensure they were calibrated, and it may be difficult to do without any serial numbers or locations. Also, how many gages were found to be out of calibration? "Several" leaves a lot to be desired. Was it two? Three? Four? And out of how many? Three gages out of 150 sampled is one thing, three out of four is something else altogether. Finally, have there been any recent incidents where customer notification and/or reinspection were required because of the use of out-of-calibration gages? What were the costs associated with these occurrences?

The audit finding in write-up 2 was not substantiated based on the evidence presented. Maybe there were no systemic weaknesses to be found. There has to be a standard, goal, or basis for comparison to make a determination relating to effectiveness. The basis for comparison could be external audit results or recent and significant adverse events in the areas the internal audits examined, but there must be some means of comparison.

In audit write-up 3, shouldn't the auditor give credit where credit is due? Yes, but not like this! Superior performance should always be noted by the auditor, especially when it represents best practice. But the rule for doing so is, be specific! It is critical when giving praise that you pinpoint the specific practices that are praiseworthy. Rarely will an auditor have sufficient time to completely and in great depth be able to evaluate an entire system or process to the point of being able to say the whole thing is really swell. Instead, indicate exactly what you found to be superior. Maybe it was the control of electronic documentation or the methods used to communicate changes to document users. I guarantee that the first time you make an alligator statement like the one shown in this example, the next week the system will crash and you'll be explaining to a senior department manager that you really didn't look at *that* part of the system, you really meant *this* part. Too late.

Rule No. 9

Provide sufficient background information in your write-up to allow the auditee to understand both what was found and what the requirement is.

Rule No. 10

When citing areas of strength, be specific.

THE CLOSING MEETING

Now you're ready for the closing meeting. While the closing meeting for a small internal audit may be rather informal, some presentation of the findings is required. This discussion applies equally to both formal and informal closing meetings, with the only difference being the level of formality and whether an agenda is used.

I still remember George Smith, my mentor in the Naval Nuclear Propulsion Program and still one of the best auditors I've ever known, discussing the importance of the closing meeting. "The closing meeting is the only time when you know you have the auditee management's attention. They may choose not to read the audit report, but you've got them at the closing meeting." Don't waste this opportunity.

The purpose of the closing meeting is as follows:

- Present the audit findings:

  - Best practices and positives

  - Nonconformities

  - Opportunities for improvement

- Ensure auditee understanding of findings.

- Provide the audit conclusions.

- Provide clarification as to what will happen next:

  - Report distribution

  - Process for responding to findings

  - Timing of actions

The audit team leader conducts the closing meeting, with input from other auditors as necessary. No matter what the level of participation from other members of the audit team, it is still the lead auditor's meeting. A flowchart for conducting this meeting is shown in Figure 6.11.

Let's look at some of the highlights from the flowchart. First, I always recommend an agenda for a formal closing meeting. Not only does it help you structure the meeting, it also reinforces that this is your meeting. Although dialogue is allowed and even encouraged at some points, as discussed a little later, you need to be able to control the tone and the direction of this meeting. Having and quickly reviewing the agenda to kick off the meeting helps you do that.

Second, I included an audit summary in the flowchart. An audit summary is the overall conclusion of the auditor or audit team regarding the overall level of performance of the process based on all of the findings. Consider it to be auditor spin. The audience for the summary or conclusion is senior management. It's like an executive abstract. Do senior managers need to take the time to delve into this audit report or can they just glance through the summary? Consider the following two short summary statements:

Summary 1. This audit found several serious deficiencies, which if not corrected, could lead to shipment of nonconforming product to the customer. Most importantly, nonconforming product was found mixed with good product and obsolete control plans were found in use in the final inspection area. A total of 12 nonconformances were issued and are detailed in the body of the report.

Summary 2. This audit found minor administrative deficiencies relating to document and record control and the administration of training records. A complete description of these and other deficiencies is included in the body of the report. A total of four nonconformances and two opportunities for improvement were reported.

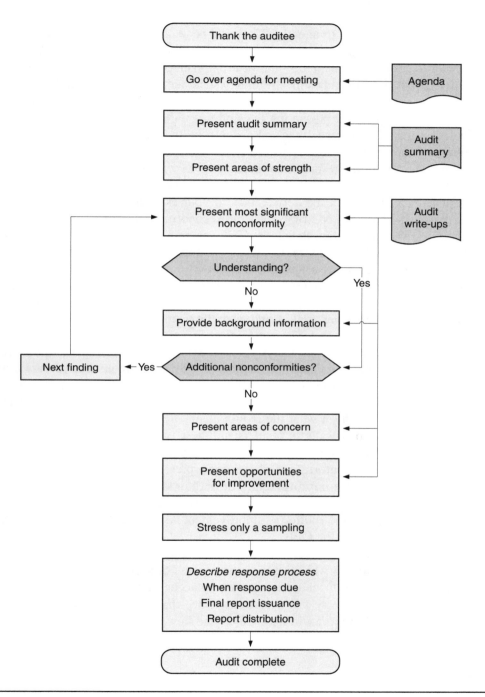

Figure 6.11 The closing meeting.

Which one would get your attention? It would be ideal if senior management always reviewed every audit report in great detail, but it doesn't work that way. The audit summary provides a mechanism to signal your top management team when it should get involved. I always recommend using a summary statement after supplier audits to inform senior supplier management how its customer (you) views its overall performance.

Note how I recommend presenting the findings. First present the best practices or positives. It lets the auditee see that you are fair and balanced and makes them more receptive for what's next. Note, in particular, how I recommend presenting the nonconformances. Most auditors present them in the order in which they were found, in other words, NC-1 followed by NC-2 followed by NC-3 and so on. I strongly recommend against that. Instead, present the deficiencies in your estimated order of significance. Present the most important NC first, then the second most important NC, and so on. Why? Because you want to get the auditee management's attention right away! If you bore them right off the bat with three or four minor administrative deficiencies, you may lose them before you even get to the real zinger.

Some auditors like to save questions until the end. I like to invite questions after each NC is read. Keep in mind, the purpose of the closing meeting is to present the findings, background into how they were found, and what the requirements are that they relate to. It is *not* to debate whether they are nonconformances. The time for that debate was during the audit and the daily briefings. Once the closing meeting starts, the findings are the findings. I always explain this at the beginning of the meeting prior to laying out the agenda. I also tell the auditees that if they disagree with a finding, they can so note it in their response to the NC. It may also be noted in the audit report, but the point is that the auditee is allowed to question what the requirements are and what exactly the auditor found. If the auditee manager doesn't understand these two items, then the chances that he or she will take effective corrective action is greatly diminished.

Once all of the nonconformances have been presented, the auditor is ready to present the opportunities for improvement. The auditor should make it clear that action on OFIs is not required. They do not violate any requirement; instead they are areas where, in the judgment of the auditor(s), improvement is possible. Once that's said, then the auditor can run through the OFIs.

Finally, the auditor should stress that the audit is only a sampling and there may be, and probably are, additional weaknesses in the process or system reviewed. This standard warning is necessary to guard against complacency and is especially important when the audit has found very few violations. Once that's said, the auditor normally goes over how the audit report will be handled and how the auditee should respond to the findings.

Recommendations for Action

What should the auditor do if, during the closing meeting, he or she is asked for recommendations for fixing the problem? Historically, auditors have always been trained to resist providing such recommendations, for good reason. The three most important are:

1. Providing recommendations on problem correction can transfer ownership from the auditee to the auditor. When the auditor comes back next time and finds the same problem, the auditee might respond, "We did what you told us to do!" Although the auditor should not accept this response, it's too late now. The problem wasn't fully investigated and the cause eliminated because the auditee considered the problem resolution to have been transferred to the auditor. Now the company will have to try again after another six months or so of living with the problem.

2. The auditor rarely knows the audited process well enough to provide insightful recommendations on how to fix the problem. The auditee is the process expert, not the auditor. Any recommendations the auditor provides have a high likelihood of being wrong.

3. It is premature for anyone, including the auditor, to consider corrective action prior to determination of the root cause. This is how Band-Aid fixes get implemented. As mentioned earlier, it is highly unlikely that the root cause of any significant problem can be identified prior to the completion of an audit.

Having said all that, when I performed and led audits for the Naval Nuclear Propulsion Program (NNPP) I always provided recommendations for action when I thought they were essential. The only actions that I considered essential were those related to product and to immediate actions to determine the scope of the problem and to contain it. Let me give you several examples.

Example 1. During the audit you identify three out of eight gages in use on the production floor that had exceeded their prescribed calibration interval. At this point we appear to have a systemic problem, but we do not know its extent. I would provide a recommendation for action that included immediate verification of all remaining gages in use, immediate calibration of any gage that was found to be outside its calibration interval, and investigation of the impact on product for any gages found to be out of calibration. I would accept nothing less on the auditee's initial response five or 10 days later. Why wait five to 10 days to find out the auditee didn't do it? By that time a large amount of suspect product may have been shipped.

Example 2. During an environmental management system audit you find several barrel of waste without proper identification. The auditee indicates that the labels fell off the drums. Similar to example 1, I would recommend that a review of all remaining waste barrels be conducted, the integrity of their labels inspected, and any unlabeled barrels be characterized for the wastes contained.

Example 3. During a health and safety management system audit you discover several machines where the machine guards had been permanently removed to make it easier for workers to stick their fingers into the conveyor mechanism to clear jams. I would recommend an immediate evaluation of all remaining machines and replacement of any engineering safeguards pending the determination of root cause and permanent corrective action.

Example 4. During an audit of a production process you note that product was being accepted to the wrong inspection criteria. I would recommend immediate containment and reinspection of product still in the facility and an immediate investigation into the impact of the error on shipped product.

In each of these examples, the focus is on containment and immediate action. If the auditor knows there are actions that must be taken to control the problem, then he or she may want to note this in the audit report, if it is within organizational policy to do so. Keep in mind that when I was performing audits for the NNPP I was in the role of second-party auditor. I was the customer and I was stating that the customer would accept nothing less than the recommended action in the supplier's response. The same principle applies to internal audits, however.

Note that none of the examples provide recommendation for long-term action to identify or eliminate the root cause. Reasons 1 through 3 at the start of this section apply to these actions, and I recommend that requests for auditor recommendation for long-term action be declined for these reasons.

Sometimes an auditee may remark, "You're always telling us what we do wrong, but you're never willing to help us fix it. I thought we were a team here!" If the auditor gets this response after declining to provide recommendations for action, then I recommend the auditor recite the three reasons listed previously, and offer assistance outside of the framework of the audit. In other words, I might reply that I would be happy to be a member of the problem-solving team once the audit is complete, but I cannot as an auditor provide recommendations for long-term action in that it may compromise my independence as an auditor. Clearly establishing the boundary between independent auditor and problem solving team member helps to ensure that ownership stays where it belongs—with the auditee.

The ANSI/ISO/ASQ QE19011S-2004 guidance document on auditing notes that recommendations may be provided by the audit team if specified by the audit objectives. It also notes that auditors performing second-party audits must be particularly careful not to lead the supplier to believe that any recommendations are extensions of contract requirements or represent binding directions. This is another reason to limit recommendations for action to immediate and containment actions only.

AUDITOR ETHICS

The final topic in this chapter is auditor ethics. I've saved it for the end because it really infuses all phases of the audit. Auditors must be ethical. Ethics goes beyond accepting bribes and gifts. You won't become rich being an internal auditor anyway, believe me. It also applies to auditor independence, auditor impartiality, and freedom from bias.

Keep in mind that the standard we must subscribe to is not just freedom from bias, it's freedom from even the appearance of bias—a much higher standard.

If there is an appearance of bias in the audit, the auditee may not accept the auditor's findings. Review the following situations, and consider whether you would be comfortable with the auditor's findings:

Situation 1. An auditor evaluates a department where his spouse is the manager. He finds no deficiencies.

Situation 2. An auditor evaluates a department where her ex-spouse is the manager. She finds tons of problems.

Situation 3. An auditor evaluates a department where he used to work, but transferred out of six months ago. The reason for the transfer was that the auditor and the department manager couldn't stand each other. The auditor finds numerous deficiencies in the department's operations.

The auditors in each of the above situations may have, in fact, performed an impartial and objective audit. It doesn't matter, since the appearance of bias was present in each. The appearance of bias may not impact the results of the audits, but it may seriously impact the credibility of the audit program and the enthusiasm of the auditee to implement effective corrective action.

The difficult thing with the appearance of bias standard is that it may be hard to control. While the audit program manager should be aware of situation 1, she may not be aware of situation 2 and probably wouldn't be aware of situation 3. It is up to each auditor to stay aware of situations where the appearance of bias could be questioned and to note such instances to the audit program manager. This means training all auditors on the standard of appearance of bias.

When we turn our attention to second-party audits, the appearance of bias considerations become more important. Contracts and thousands, if not millions, of dollars of business can be affected by the results of an audit. What may be acceptable during an internal audit may not be acceptable during a second-party audit. While the same issues of prior or current personal involvement apply, some additional concerns can come into play.

Auditors should not accept gifts in any form during audits of a supplier. Gifts include golf clubs, food, or entertainment. My earlier joke about feeding the auditor is thus modified to read, "Feed the auditor—unless you're doing a second-party audit." The supplier is under no obligation to pay for your meals during an audit and to accept food may result in an appearance of bias. Some might argue that I'm going too far. Surely lunch isn't going to bias an auditor. I may agree that a boxed lunch or pizza brought in by the supplier at the request of the audit team probably wouldn't affect the audit results too much, but what about an expensive lunch at the country club the supplier has a membership to?

I still remember when we would arrive on-site to perform an audit of a supplier's facility when I was in the Navy doing audits for the NNPP. We always had to fork over $4.50 each for the box lunch we would have the supplier order and $1.25 to cover the coffee we were likely to drink. Why did we do that? To avoid *any* appearance of bias. Now I'm not recommending that auditors pay the supplier for the coffee they drink, but I am recommending that each organization set standards for conduct to use during supplier audits to ensure there is no appearance of bias.

Some of my students in my auditing classes have raised the issue, "Well Joe, if the auditor shouldn't accept food from the supplier during the audit, how come our registrar allows us to buy his lunch and take him out to dinner? Couldn't that be an appearance of bias issue?" While it's a very good question, the short answer is no. During a third-party registration or surveillance audit you are contractually obligated to pay for the auditor's reasonable expenses, which include meals. Therefore there is no conflict or bias. You'd have to draw the line, however, at post-dinner entertainment. You are not obligated to pay for that, and any such offer could be seen as attempts to influence or bias the auditor.

SUMMARY

To summarize this section, we started with the opening meeting. We said that a formal opening meeting is not always required for an internal audit, but even then an informal review of the purpose, scope, and audit plan should be performed during the first few minutes of the opening interview with the process owner or manager.

We then examined different types of questions, and when to ask them. Most important were the *who* and *when* questions. We also discussed how to ask the *why* question without making the auditee defensive. We examined different types of questions and their application to the funnel approach, which is an interview strategy that starts with broad open-ended questions to obtain maximum information followed by open-ended or closed-ended clarifying questions to fill in the gaps.

We discussed difficult auditees the auditor might face and strategies for handling these challenges. Strategies for handling conflict were also presented.

We then launched into a discussion on managing the audit flow using trace forward and trace back, and how to use the checklists provided on the CD accompanying this handbook to guide the actual conduct of the audit. We discussed the different types of audit evidence, how to select it, and how much to select.

We examined some important do's and don'ts for auditors, including the need to avoid audit nits, which can damage the credibility of the auditor. We discussed the preparation for and conduct of the closing meeting, including how to write up audit findings and how to handle requests for recommendations for ideas on how to fix the problems. Finally, we finished up with a discussion on auditor ethics, and the need to maintain freedom from an appearance of bias.

The first two phases of the audit are now complete. We'll close with the list of the ten rules for conducting an audit:

1. Feed the auditor!

2. Make the auditee feel like a member of the audit team.

3. Start the evaluation by asking general, open-ended questions, then use clarifying questions to fill in the gaps.

4. Be an active listener.

5. Never let the auditee pick the samples.

6. Always try to identify any real effects of your findings—use dollar values where available.

7. Always confirm your findings with the auditee.

8. Don't go looking for nits.

9. Provide sufficient background information in your write-ups to allow the auditee to understand both what was found and what the requirement is.

10. When citing areas of strength, be specific.

7

Postaudit Activities

This chapter addresses the final phase of the audit process. In this section we will discuss what should be in the final audit report, how to evaluate actions proposed by the auditee, how to track these actions, and how to verify that action was taken and was effective in eliminating the cause of the deficiency. We will close this chapter with a short discussion of the audit file.

THE AUDIT REPORT

A final audit report should be prepared to document the audit. Either the lead auditor or the audit program manager, depending on organizational policy, may prepare the final audit report. The audit report provides a complete record of the audit. There is no set format for the report, but whatever format is used should be used consistently. The following items should be included in the audit report:

- The purpose and scope of the audit.

- Dates of the audit.

- Auditors, including identification of the lead auditor.

- Identification of the organization, processes, or areas audited.

- The audit criteria, including the standard or specification that formed the basis for the audit. I recommend recording the number and revision date of each system-level procedure associated with the core process being evaluated. I do not recommend listing each instruction or support system procedure that was evaluated unless they are associated with a nonconformity.

- A complete description of the audit findings (nonconformities, best practices, opportunities for improvement), including what was found, what was in violation, where it was found, how many were found, and so on.

- Audit report distribution. This is especially important for external audits of suppliers. It may not be necessary for internal audits.

- Any unresolved diverging opinions between the audit team and the auditee. If the auditee management disagreed with a nonconformance, then it should be noted in the audit report.

The following items *may* be included in the audit report:

- Listing of key personnel contacted during the audit. I recommend using functional titles versus names. I also do not recommend listing hourly worker names, unless there is an overriding reason to do so. An overriding reason might be in a citation for a best practice, where someone who wants to benchmark and adopt the practice needs to know who to contact.

- Statement of the confidential nature of the audit report contents. This is normally boilerplate for environmental and health and safety audits. It is also important for audit reports of supplier operations.

- Recommendations, if part of the organization's policy. I normally discuss these within the audit summary statement or in the body of the audit findings.

- Any agreed-upon action plans. This may be appropriate when the organization does allow recommendations for immediate and containment action or could be used in lieu of such recommendations. It is especially useful during supplier audits, when it is important to take quick action to protect customer (in other words, your) product.

- An audit summary or conclusion statement. Again, not required, but a good idea for outside audits and audits of the entire management system or a large portion thereof.

The audit report is more than just a record. It is a communication tool. Use it to benefit the company. Check to ensure that the format you use serves the needs of its audience. Who is the audience of the audit report? Some potential users are listed, along with how they might use the report:

- *Senior management.* Top management will want to know the results of the audit and how the organization's management system is performing. To make it easier for them to digest, consider adding a summary or conclusion section to the report.

- *Auditee management.* Auditee management must take action to correct the deficiencies. Unfortunately, many audit nonconformance reports or corrective action requests only provide minimal background information on what was found, where it was found, how many were found, and so on. You can use the audit report to provide this information.

- *The audit program manager.* The audit program manager will use the audit report both to document the audit and as a reference for future audits. He or she can also use the report to track corrective action in certain instances. We used to do that with supplier audits. Instead of issuing eight or nine corrective action requests that would have to be tracked individually, we issued the audit report to the supplier quality representative. The audit report was formatted to include the findings, background, any recommendations for immediate or containment action, and a place for the supplier to respond with the action taken. We asked the supplier to provide us with bimonthly status reports on each of the nonconformances identified in the report until all were closed out. This system worked extremely well and avoided the administrative burden of handling hundreds of corrective action requests. Note, it may not work quite as well in an internal audit where you have multiple action assignees (to whom do you issue the audit report?).

- *The next audit team.* As I noted in Chapter 5, previous audit reports will be one of the tools the audit team will use to prepare for the audit. A well-written audit report that contains the information already cited can help the audit team quickly assess the nature of previous findings and areas they may want to focus their attention on.

- *Outside auditors.* Although we should not structure our audit report just to satisfy outside auditors, we do need to recognize that they will use the report to determine if our audits are thorough and complete. Give them a good impression of your audit program.

As I mentioned, there is no prescribed format for the audit report. Some organizations simply slap a cover page onto the audit nonconformance reports or corrective action requests and call it the audit report. If this works for your intended audience and the cover page contains the essential information cited, then go with it. If this doesn't work, consider one of the following formats.

The first format, shown in Figure 7.1, is an example of a generic audit cover sheet that could be attached to the front of the audit nonconformance reports or corrective action requests. Together with the corrective action requests, it would provide a history of the audit itself. Coupled with the completed corrective action requests, it would provide a history of both the audit and the action that resulted. This cover sheet would be prepared and issued by the audit program manager within a few days of the audit. Alternatively, it could be prepared and issued by the lead auditor at the closing meeting, in which case the auditee manager would normally sign instead of the audit program manager.

This audit report format is fairly simple and serves the basic purpose of the audit. The weakness in this approach is that it lacks a place to document the opportunities for improvement and best practices. To provide a forum to document these, the auditor

---

Audit Report Form
February 8, 2005

Date of Audit February 4, 2005   **Audit No.** QA05-2

Audit Team: Thompson (Lead), Cranick

Purpose: To evaluate the effectiveness and implementation of the supplier selection and monitoring process.

Scope: This audit examined all aspects of supplier selection, monitoring, and development.

Audit Criteria: ISO 9001 and QSP-PUR-01

Key Personnel Contacted:

    Tom Browers, manager, purchasing

    Kim Delanney, buyer

    Ralph Beres, buyer

    George Tines, manager, QA

Summary: The audit found several significant weaknesses in the processes used to select and monitor supplier. Most significantly, the audit found that the documented process used to evaluate potential suppliers is not being followed consistently and that routine monitoring as required by the procedure is not being performed. In addition, it was found that follow-up action is not being pursued after the issuance of corrective action to the supplier as required by the procedure. It was noted that this deficiency has the potential to impact the quality of product provided to our customers.

Other deficiencies are noted in the audit finding forms attached to this report. Corrective action requests (CARs) Q04-12 through Q04-17 were issued to address these findings. An initial response to these CARs is requested by March 4, 2005.

       _____   _____

          Audit Team Leader   Audit Program Manager

1

Figure 7.1 Example audit report format.

must either put these on an audit finding form, such as that shown in Figure 4.3, page 70, in lieu of a corrective action request, or a summary table should be included, as shown in Figure 4.6, page 73. The examples in these figures provide a means for documenting the OFIs and best practices.

The format shown in Figures 7.2 and 7.3 provides more flexibility and more information than did the report format in Figure 7.1. By providing a space to document opportunities for improvement and best practices, it alleviates the need to use a separate audit finding form or table. This facilitates use of the corrective action program and the CAR form as the primary process to track audit nonconformities. It also requires more effort to prepare. Figure 7.2 is the first page. It summarizes the audit and is targeted for the organization's executives. Figures 7.3 and 7.4 provide an example of the main content of the report.

Internal Audit Report	**Audit #** QA05-2 **Audit Dates:** 2/4/05

| **Audit Purpose:** To evaluate the effectiveness and implementation of the supplier selection and monitoring process. ||

| **Audit Scope:** This audit examined all aspects of supplier selection, monitoring, and development. ||

Audit Team: Thompson (Lead), Cranick	**Key Auditee Personnel Contacted:** Tom Browers, manager, purchasing Kim Delanney, buyer Ralph Beres, buyer George Tines, manager, QA

| **Audit Criteria:** ISO 9001:2000 and QSP-PUR-01. ||

| **Section I Executive Summary:** The audit found several significant weaknesses in the processes used to select and monitor suppliers. Most significantly, the audit found that the documented process used to evaluate potential suppliers is not being followed consistently and that routine monitoring as required by the procedure is not being performed. In addition, it was found that follow-up action is not being pursued after the issuance of corrective action to the supplier as required by the procedure. It was noted that this deficiency has the potential to impact the quality of product provided to our customers.

Other deficiencies are noted in the audit finding forms attached to this report. Corrective action requests (CARs) CAR-04-12 through CAR-04-17 were issued to address these findings. An initial response to these CARs is requested by March 4, 2005. ||

CARs generated as a result of this audit: CAR-04-12, 13, 14, 15, 16, 17	**Initial Response Requested By:** 3/4/05

_____ Audit Program Manager Date	_____ Lead Auditor Date

Figure 7.2 Example audit report format.

If it were desired to use the audit report itself to track corrective action, then the form in Figure 7.3 and Figure 7.4 could be modified to include a section entitled Description of Action Taken under the Description of Nonconformance. Sign-offs and verification could be added to the right column. I would only recommend this for supplier audits where there is a central point of contact for problem resolution.

You may have noted that I have included a new category of finding in Figure 7.4 called a *Concern*. This category is not recognized or used in any of the traditional audit schemes, but I favor it nonetheless because it does provide the auditor a place to document findings that do not fit well in any of the other three categories but could be important. A concern would be a practice that, while not a violation of any requirement currently, is likely to result in a violation in the future if action is not taken. Like an OFI, a concern does not require action on the part of the auditee, but it does draw attention to the situation and tells the next audit team that it may want to confirm that no deficiencies exist because of the practice. If the audit program manager agrees that this would be a useful category of finding, then he or she should include it in the audit

Section II Nonconformances	Page _2_ of _7_
Finding: Suppliers are being added to the approved subcontractor list with outstanding audit corrective actions. **Description of Nonconformance:** QSP-4.6-01 states that an audit may be conducted to confirm a potential supplier's capability to satisfy contract requirements. It further states that any corrective action resulting from such an audit must be corrected before the supplier can be added to the ASL. The audit found four instances in the last year where vendors were added to the ASL prior to their completion of corrective action. In three of the cases, the corrective action is still outstanding. Reference audit reports for: ABC Company WeProvideIt WidgetsRUs Rust and Bust, Inc.	**NC Number** NC-01 --- **Reference** QSP-PUR-01 section 4.3.2. --- **CAR Number** CAR-04-12
Finding: Purchasing and QA are not jointly reviewing the capabilities of potential new suppliers. **Description of Nonconformance:** QSP-4.6-01 requires that both Purchasing and QA jointly review information regarding a potential supplier's capabilities prior to placing the vendor on the approved subcontractor list. Discussions with the managers of purchasing and QA indicated that this review is not being performed. It was stated that QA is only contacted if there is a unique quality requirement that may require special consideration.	**NC Number** NC-02 --- **Reference** QSP-PUR-01 section 4.3.1. --- **CAR Number** CAR-04-13

Figure 7.3   Example audit report format, page 2.

procedure and train auditors in its use. Auditors would normally massage their concern to fit within an OFI in instances where concern is not a valid category of finding. Finally, note that this audit report also has a section where the auditors can list any areas that are part of the process or area evaluated that were not audited. This can be important to the next audit team.

TRACKING AUDIT FINDINGS

The audit is not complete until actions have been taken to address the audit findings and the actions have been verified. In my almost 20 years of auditing, I have written up more audit programs for failure to take timely corrective action on audit findings than for any other reason. The best audit in the world provides no value if appropriate action is not taken to address what the audit finds. The flowchart in Figure 7.5 diagrams the essential steps in tracking and verifying auditee actions.

Section III **Opportunities for Improvement and Best Practices**	Page <u>7</u> of <u>7</u>
Description of Observation or Improvement Opportunity During the audit it was noted that requisitions travel from the requestor (department head) to the purchasing manager, then to the cognizant buyer who selects the candidate vendor, back to the requestor who approves the vendor selection, and finally back to the buyer for PO issuance. Discussion with cognizant personnel indicated that it may be possible to eliminate several of these reviews by providing requestors access to the approved supplier list (ASL), which identifies vendors by product and the buyer who handles the commodity/product.	**Obs. Number** O-1 **Reference** NA ☑ **OFI** ☐ **Concern** ☐ **BP**
Description of Observation or Improvement Opportunity The audit identified that both electronic and paper copies of the ASL may be in use at any given time. The electronic version is maintained current real-time, while the paper copy is updated once a month. Although this is in accordance with current procedures, the audit team is concerned that it could lead to nonconformities in the future as a result of having two separate, but potentially different ASLs in existence at one time.	**Obs. Number** O-2 **Reference** ☑ **OFI** ☐ **Concern** ☐ **BP**
Description of Observation or Improvement Opportunity	**Obs. Number** **Reference** ☐ **OFI** ☐ **Concern** ☐ **BP**
Areas Not Audited: None. All components of the subcontractor selection and monitoring process were examined.	

Figure 7.4 Example audit report format, last page.

Every audit program needs a system to track actions taken to address the audit nonconformities. Some audit program managers also like to track the response to opportunities for improvement, best practices, and (where used) concerns, even though these do not require a response. If the organization only tracks actions taken to address audit nonconformities, then I recommend that the existing corrective action process be used. All nonconformities arising from the audit would be cited on corrective action requests, logged into the corrective action log, and tracked as would any corrective action.

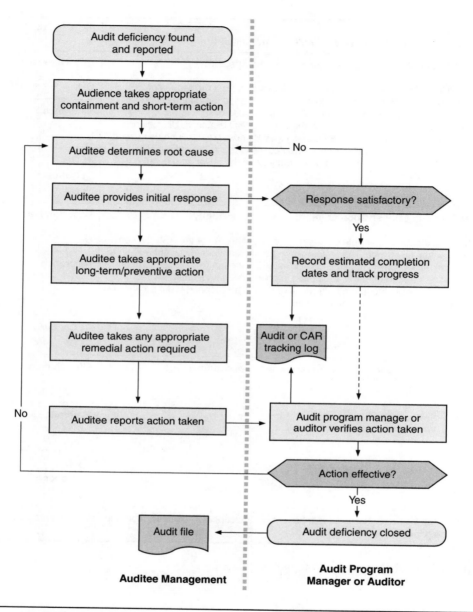

Figure 7.5 The verification process.

If the organization wants to track the response to OFIs, best practices (BPs), and concerns, then it will need to use an audit finding form such as Figure 4.6 and create a separate log to follow the action. The point is, the audit program manager needs a system to help follow up on nonconformance resolution. A log (hard copy or electronic) is essential. The log should include the following fields:

- *CAR number* (or audit finding form number).

- *Date issued.*

- *Action assignee*—person the CAR was issued to.

- *Short description of the finding.*

- *Initial response due date.* Organizations often require an initial response within five or 10 working days.

- *Date initial response received.*

- *Estimated completion date for long-term action.* I recommend this date be assigned by the auditee and communicated in their initial response.

  Note: I do not like mandatory time frames for permanent corrective action such as 30 days, 60 days, or 90 days after receipt of the CAR, since every problem is unique and requires a different timeline for action. Some problems had better be permanently fixed within 10 days. Others might require extensive training and may require four months. I recommend letting the auditee fix the date. He or she is the one who has ownership of the problem. As long as it's a reasonable date and is responsive to the situation, then let them set it. If the date is unreasonable, then negotiate with the auditee. If this is continually a problem, or if the auditee continuously misses estimated completion dates, then go with the mandatory 30-, 60-, or 90-day requirement for closeout.

- *Actual date action completed.* This is normally based on a report from the auditee assigned an action.

- *Action taken* (optional). This can ease review of actions since you don't have to go back to the individual CARs returned by the action assignee. Adding this also takes up more space in the log. I recommend it when the log is in an electronic format.

- *Date the action was verified.* Verification is normally performed by the audit program manager, the auditor who found the deficiency, or the next audit team.

- *Root cause category* (optional). Although not normally found in action logs, this field can be very useful when tracking the effectiveness of corrective action. If you maintain your log electronically where you can easily sort your records, consider using it.

Most of the leading management system software packages contain this information in relational databases. These can significantly ease the task of data entry by taking information from the corrective action request or audit finding form and using it to populate the tracking log. If the audit program manager doesn't have one of these systems, then he or she can simply cut and paste. Hopefully you don't have so many deficiencies that this becomes a real burden.

Once the audit findings are entered into the log, then the audit program manager needs to track progress in completing the assigned action using the due dates. The action assignee should be contacted any time a due date is missed. If the reason for the delay is reasonable, then the audit program manager and the action assignee should negotiate a new realistic due date. If the reason is not valid or if the action assignee misses the new estimated completion date, then the action assignee's upper level manager should be contacted for help in resolving the issue. Some organizations change the action assignee to the upper level manager in these circumstances. This often has the desired effect of prompting action.

The audit program manager should review the planned actions and estimated completion dates provided by the action assignee in the initial response. If the planned actions or estimated completion dates are completely unrealistic or indicate that the auditee really did not understand the nature of the problem, then the audit program manager should contact the action assignee and negotiate new actions and/or estimated completion dates. Keep in mind, however, that the responsibility for action rests with the auditee management, not the auditors, so any such intervention should only be pursued when considered absolutely necessary.

It is also vitally important to report on corrective action, especially overdue corrective action, during senior manager staff meetings and reviews. This allows top management to get involved if action is lacking in correcting audit deficiencies in a timely manner.

One final comment on audit tracking systems. Although I normally recommend using the organization's existing corrective action program to track audit nonconformances, I have noted a tendency in many companies to *only* issue CARs in response to an audit finding. In other words, when I review the corrective action log, I find that all of the CARs were the result of internal audits. This shows a lack of awareness of the purpose of the corrective action process, which is to serve as a method of responding to any problem that requires corrective action, not just those identified during internal audits. Problems noted because of a customer complaint, a missed launch date, excessive scrap, equipment failure, a safety violation, or any other source should also be documented and addressed through the corrective action process. If the tendency is to only issue CARs after an internal audit, then you may want to create a separate action tracking system to highlight this weakness. When the quality, environmental, or health and safety manager looks at the corrective action log and sees that it is blank, it sends a powerful signal that he or she is not doing a good job of using the corrective action process to respond to organizational problems.

VERIFYING AUDIT CORRECTIVE ACTION

Verification that the planned action was taken and that it was effective should be completed before the audit is considered closed. Action may be necessary on any of four levels: immediate, short-term, long-term, and remedial. The focus of each of these levels, and examples for each, follow:

1. *Immediate or emergency action.* The focus is to contain the problem and mitigate any quality impact.

   Example. The production process was immediately shut down. All suspect product was contained and inspected.

2. *Short-term or temporary corrective action.* The focus is to allow operations to continue through a Band-Aid fix.

   Example. One-hundred percent inspection was immediately implemented.

3. *Long-term or preventive action.* The focus is to eliminate the root cause and permanently correct the problem.

   Example. The cause of the instability was determined to be a malfunctioning sensor. The sensor was replaced and the process capability confirmed. Online process monitoring and control was implemented on this and similar lines.

4. *Remedial action.* The focus is to recover from the effect of the problem and clean up the mess.

   Example. Examination of process records indicated that one shipment of suspect product was shipped. The customer was immediately notified and a team was dispatched to inspect the delivered product. All nonconforming product was contained and replaced.

Now we'll take a look at an example from an environmental management system audit.

1. *Immediate or emergency action.* The focus is to contain the problem and mitigate any environmental impact.

   Example. The electrostatic paint line cleaning operation was immediately shut down.

2. *Short-term or temporary corrective action.* The focus is to allow operations to continue through a Band-Aid fix.

   Example. A temporary catch tank was connected to the system to contain the hazardous rinse water until the wastewater treatment system could be restored.

3. *Long-term or preventive action.* The focus is to eliminate the root cause and permanently correct the problem.

   Example. The wastewater treatment system was restored to full normal operation. Additionally, a daily system check was added to the preventive maintenance schedule to verify proper system operation.

4. *Remedial action.* The focus is to recover from the effect of the problem and clean up the mess.

   Example. Monitoring of the ditch and creek downstream of the plant was immediately performed. No effluent escaped the plant. All residue inside the plant was cleaned up and appropriate reports filed.

Verification normally focuses on the long-term action taken to eliminate the cause. Verification may also be appropriate for immediate and short-term action, if the problem directly impacts product or is otherwise especially significant. Verification of remedial action may be appropriate when regulatory or customer issues are involved.

Verification that the action was taken can be accomplished through a review of revised documents, by examining new forms, or going to the process and visually sighting the new controls or talking to process personnel. You can use the same methods you use to evaluate the process during the audit. Verification that the action was effective can only occur after some history has passed without the recurrence of the problem. This will be indicated by records or other objective evidence. It uses the techniques discussed in auditing for effectiveness.

Verification is normally conducted by the audit program manager, the auditor who found the deficiency, or the next audit team assigned to review the process. The audit program manager normally decides who should perform the verification and whether they are verifying that the action was taken, whether the action was effective, or both. It is common for the audit program manager or auditor to verify that the action was taken, and for the next audit team to verify the effectiveness of the action. Keep in mind that the next audit will probably not occur for some time, and you may not want to wait six to 12 months for the next audit to see if the action was effective in eliminating the problem. In instances where the audit found several significant issues, common practice is to reaudit the area shortly after the actions have been implemented.

The audit program manager can close the audit once the actions taken by the auditee have been completed and verified. Closure doesn't really involve any new actions other than maybe signing off on the audit report and verifying the audit file is complete.

AUDIT FILE

Audit records must be maintained. Although all you really have to maintain is your audit report, I recommend you maintain the following for each audit completed.

- Audit report, including documentation on all audit findings.

- Checklists use to conduct the audits. Although the audit report contains a summary of what the auditor found, it does not reveal what the auditors looked at, what the auditors did not look at, how they structured the audit, or the strategy they used to conduct the audit. A well-constructed checklist such as those we have used in this handbook should provide all this information. This information will be used by the next audit team assigned to audit that process or area to help them prepare and plan their audit.

- Auditee responses to any audit nonconformities. You will need to provide evidence that actions were taken to address the deficiencies cited. If you only include the initial audit finding forms given to the auditee at the closing meeting, you may not have the documentation in the file to show that action was taken. You need to include the completed audit finding forms that show completion of action and verification. If you use the corrective action program to track your audit findings, then you should not have to worry about this since you should have records of completed CARs in that system that you can refer to.

- Records of verifications of deficiency correction. This can be reflected on the CAR, audit finding form, or action tracking log.

- Any other working documents that the auditors or client feel would be useful to the next audit team. Only keep those items that you feel would be invaluable to the next audit team. Everything else should be referenced on the checklists.

Retention times should be established for the audit report. As a minimum, it is recommended that you keep your audit reports for a period of three years.

SUMMARY

This phase completes the audit process. We have now issued the audit report and verified that the action proposed by the auditee was accomplished and was effective. We have closed the audit, including putting together the audit file. If you've made it this far, congratulations! The rest of this handbook will focus on the unique aspects of quality, environmental, and health and safety audits.

Part III

Specific Audit Instructions

Previous chapters focused on the mechanics of auditing. The remaining chapters will present specific strategies for conducting quality, environmental, and health and safety management system audits. Combined audits will be discussed in Chapter 11. Auditing the automotive core tools will be presented in Chapter 12. The final two chapters, 13 and 14, present advanced audit techniques. Chapter 13 discusses how to identify and evaluate best practices. Chapter 14 examines how to ensure that the management system is aligned with and supporting the execution of the organization's strategic plan.

8

Conducting Quality Management System Audits

T his chapter will build on parts I and II, applying these concepts to the performance of audits of quality management systems based on the ISO 9001:2000 standard.

ISO 9001:2000[1] AND ISO/TS 16949:2002[2] REVISITED

As noted in Chapter 1, the ISO 9001:2000 standard, and its automotive variant ISO/TS 16949, are based on five primary clauses as shown in Figure 8.1. The primary value stream in the diagram is the product or service realization process. It is this process that interacts with customers, determines their requirements, designs the products or services needed to meet those requirements, and then carries out the manufacturing or service activities needed to produce the product or deliver the service, with the result, we hope, being satisfied customers.

The processes and activities relating to the quality management system, resource management, and management responsibility clauses support the primary product and/or service realization processes by providing critical inputs, resources, or controls to each other and to the activities directly tied to producing customer value. The measurement, analysis, and improvement process monitors and measures the outputs from the system, including its products, services, and processes, its overall management system, and customer satisfaction, and takes action to correct or prevent problems or make improvements where needed. An understanding of these core processes and how they interact is important in that they provide structure for developing the audit strategy and scope.

Figure 8.2 expands the generic model of Figure 8.1 by showing how the processes addressed in ISO 9001 and ISO/TS 16949 might appear in a typical manufacturing organization. The activities of a typical service organization could be visualized by replacing the term *product* with *service* and replacing the manufacturing activities with activities unique to your services. For example, for a hospital, order generation and quality planning might become initial patient assessment and treatment planning. Production would be replaced by delivery of patient care, and the activities within this grouping modified to

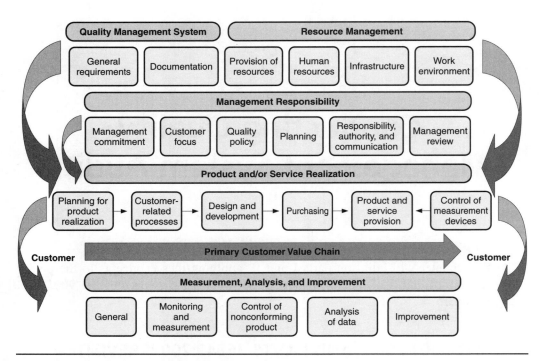

Figure 8.1 ISO 9001 and ISO/TS 16949 quality management system model.

include patient education, primary care (anesthesia, radiology, surgery, physical therapy, and so on), post-treatment care, and discharge planning. Production support activities would become treatment support and could include areas such as pharmacy operations, facilities and equipment maintenance, and nutrition planning.

The primary benefit of Figure 8.2 is that it provides a generic model that almost any organization can use to plan an audit strategy. The model should be expanded to include other important processes that may not be directly addressed by the standard, but which the organization has determined must be controlled because of their importance in providing value to the customer or supporting activities that do. Examples might include information management and technology, new idea generation, and call center management. This expansion would be appropriate given the ISO 9001 standard's requirement in clause 4.1 to "identify the processes needed for the quality management system and their application throughout the organization." The model should closely mirror the organization's macro-flowchart, if it has developed one, but the groupings might be different.

In this model, the customer value stream, or product realization, is represented by the order generation and quality planning and production activities. These processes start with the customer and end with the customer and are the most important activities to control in that they are the main determinants of customer satisfaction. The other activities are important in that they provide critical inputs and resources, as in the case of the production support and resources and support processes, or they provide the

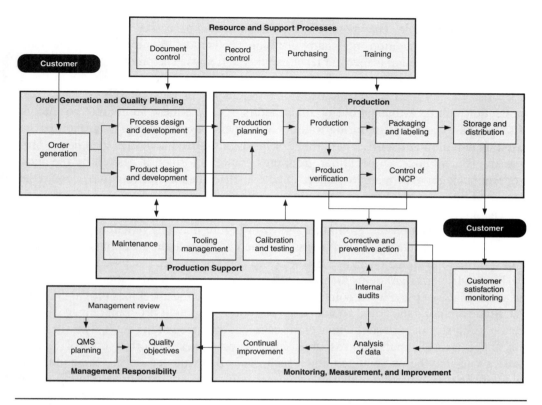

Figure 8.2 ISO 9001 activities.

infrastructure for management, measurement, and improvement of the products and processes that make up the system. They also must be properly managed and controlled in order to avoid the garbage in–garbage out principle. As noted in Chapter 1, an organization may have multiple customer value streams, depending upon the customers and products and/or services it provides. Identifying these value streams is important to the auditor in that the goal of the process-based audit should be to evaluate as much of the value stream as possible during the audit.

Finally, consider that it may be more convenient to group the internal audit and corrective and preventive action processes together into one audit, and to combine customer satisfaction monitoring, analysis of data, continual improvement, quality objectives, and management review into another audit grouping. The audit program manager should determine which grouping leads to the most efficient and effective audit.

AUDIT SCOPE

The model shown in Figure 8.2 attempts to group activities that have a high degree of interdependence and thus form *natural* audit flows to allow for the most effective and efficient audit possible. They represent *systems* of related processes. This is particularly true for the order generation and quality planning, production, monitoring, measurement, and improvement, and management responsibility activities. The production support and resource and support processes are grouped primarily for convenience. Audits of these processes will be focused on the centralized elements of these activities since their application will be evaluated during other audits. As such, these audits will be smaller in scope than was the case during traditional element-based audits. The groupings are based on assembling a sufficient number of these centralized activities together to provide an efficient audit scope. Other groupings could be formed if desired by the audit program manager to provide for a more effective, efficient audit, taking into account the status and importance of the organization's activities.

The checklists discussed in Chapter 6 and provided on the CD accompanying this handbook are based on the groupings shown in Figure 8.2. The remaining sections of this chapter will discuss key audit points for each of these audit groupings. The reader may want to refer to the checklists as these key audit points are discussed.

Key audit points are items that the auditor should pay particular attention to during the audit. Many of these audit points are incorporated into the checklists provided on the CD. Some are not, but should be added at the auditor's or audit program manager's discretion. Each section will start with a clarification of the scope of the audit, a key description of the critical inputs and resources into the processes, important controls and/or metrics that may be encountered and which could be evaluated during the audit, and some of the primary outputs that the process should deliver. Questions relating to the inputs, resources, controls, and/or metrics should be added to the organization's checklists to the extent that they apply.

KEY AUDIT POINT: ORDER GENERATION AND QUALITY PLANNING

The order generation and quality planning process starts with the business development process, includes all activities needed to understand the customer's needs and requirements, and flows through the design, development, and planning to meet those needs. It includes the activities of proposal generation, contract review, order entry and confirmation, product design and development, process design and development, and all related planning activities needed to support readiness for production launch or service delivery. It may also include marketing and advertising, Web site maintenance, and sales forecasting to the extent that these provide information to the customer about the organization's products and services or provide critical information for production realization planning (for example, capacity planning). Customer relationship management, complaint handling, and call center operations may also be included, as could the new idea generation and commercialization processes. The order generation and quality planning process flow has been expanded in Figure 8.3 to provide additional detail into the activities that may make up this system of processes.

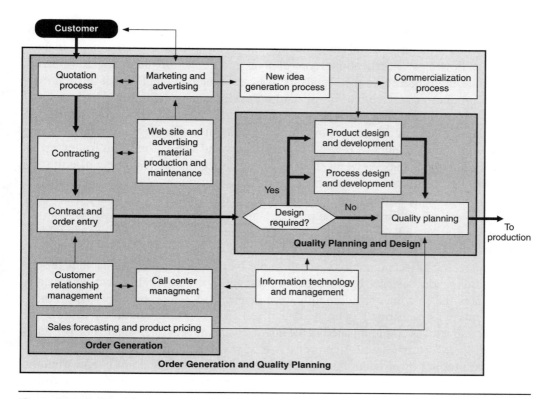

Figure 8.3   Order generation and quality planning.

The primary flow through this process is shown by the heavier lines. Activities in the primary flow also have specific requirements for their operation and control in ISO 9001:2000 and ISO/TS 16949. Activities that support this primary flow and can greatly influence the quality of outputs from the order generation and quality planning process are also shown and should be included in the evaluation to the extent to which they apply and are included in the scope of the quality management system. Including these additional activities transforms the quality management system into an integrated business management system.

Audit Strategy

A common strategy for conducting an audit of order generation, quality planning, and design control is to pick one or more current contracts and then follow those contracts (and their related records) through the inquiry, contracting, and quality planning phases. If the organization also performs product or service design and development, then at least one, and preferably two contracts that included design and development should be chosen as objects. One of these two contracts should be in production, allowing the auditor to examine the order entry process and the final documents used to translate customer requirements identified during the contract review, planning, and design and development activities to the production environment. These final production documents include final design drawings, specifications, control plans and inspection plans, operator instructions, and failure mode and effects analysis. It is recommended that one of the contracts include a product or service that is still under development, preferably a later stage of development, to allow more complete evaluation of the quality planning and design process. Particularly important is how the development project is managed, including the scheduling and conduct of reviews, verifications and validations, and follow-up on actions arising out of these reviews. Evaluation of project management is difficult for a product or service that has already been launched since many of the project management tools such as the timing plan or project management plan may be discarded or only available in their final form after the project launches.

The interviews will normally begin with the account manager for the contract(s) selected as the objects. As an alternative, the auditor can wait until commencing the interview to select the objects (contracts) for the audit by examining a list of recent and open contracts being administered by the account manager. The auditor should systematically evaluate how the customer requirements were determined, how capability to meet these requirements was confirmed, who was involved in the determinations, and how the accepted contract was communicated to the quality planning and/or design team. The auditor should look for early involvement of those who will have to design, plan, or manufacture the product or provide the service. A key element at this point is confirmation that the company can manufacture the product or deliver the service prior to confirmation of the contract with the customer. Often this is done by sales without the involvement of those involved in actually fulfilling the contract, leading to late deliveries or products and services that cannot fully meet customer expectations. The auditor should also evaluate the order entry process for releases against the contract, ensuring that the minimum required information is received, confirmed, and entered into the order handling system per local procedures. The auditor may want to depart from use of a specific contract object to do this part of the evaluation, relying instead on observation of order entry as it is being performed in real time, as opposed to record reviews.

For companies that provide standard catalog products, the interview may commence with the salesperson or product manager responsible for the products or commodities selected as objects. In this situation more attention should be focused on ensuring that the catalog, technical data sheet, and/or Web site is accurate and up to date. The auditor may want to focus on the timeliness of order entry, verification of inventories, confirmation of price, delivery destinations and routing modes, and the process for placing orders on backorder. Company procedures should detail these tasks. If not, the auditor will have to spend more time with the process owner finding out how they should be performed prior to conducting the evaluation. Design and development in these organizations is typically for the general market versus a specific customer. As such, the auditor will focus on how market data, forecasts, focus groups, and historical information for current similar products were or are being used to determine customer expectations. The commercialization and new idea generation processes may also warrant specific attention.

For providers of services, the auditor will focus on the development of a scope of work that details the services that will be provided or its equivalent. For a hospital, a patient care plan would be the equivalent to a scope of work. The focus is on how the customer's needs were determined and the organization's ability to satisfy those needs assessed, culminating in the agreed-upon scope of work.

The auditor will then interview the lead engineer or planning team member, still using the objects selected at the start of the audit to test the system. The focus of this interview will be on how the requirements defined during the order generation phase were translated into product and service requirements suitable for production and/or service delivery. The activities to be evaluated depend on the organization's design, development, and quality planning processes, which are typically documented in local procedures and/or quality plans. In the automotive industry, these activities are spelled out in more detail in the ISO/TS 16949 specification and in customer reference manuals such as the *Advanced Product Quality Planning and Control Plan Reference Manual.* The auditor should systematically evaluate these activities and their outputs in the form of drawings, specifications, pilot studies, FMEAs, and inspection plans. Especially important is the completion of all customer- and organization-defined verification and validations. Timing, and whether the design and planning process met customer or internally targeted launch dates, is also important.

During the audit, the auditor should pay particular attention to the inputs, resources, controls, and outputs noted in the next section, to the extent that they apply to this organization.

Key Inputs and Resources

This section contains some of the key inputs and resources that support order generation and quality planning. Auditors should consider these inputs and resources when planning their audit and include those that are most important for ensuring high-quality outputs and/or process effectiveness and efficiency. *Items marked with an asterisk should always be considered for inclusion.*

Information

Collecting, analyzing, and communicating information about customer and market needs and expectations is critical. The following sources of information will be derived from the activities shown in Figure 8.3. The auditor should check to see that not only is the information complete and accurate, but also whether it is made available to and used by those involved in the planning and design of products and services. It is this critical linkage between what is known and what is used that dictates that order generation and quality planning be evaluated together during the audit. The auditor must verify that the information gathered by sales and marketing is communicated to those involved in product and service development.

• *The results of customer interviews, focus group studies, and market analysis.* These are especially important for suppliers to the general mass market.

- *Information used by the customer to determine if the company's products and services will meet its needs and requirements.** This is especially important for providers of standard products and services, where the customer often determines whether a product or service is suitable based on a catalog or Web site, without assistance from a company representative. Examples would include company catalogs, technical data sheets, and Web site. These items form part of the organization's offering and should be evaluated for accuracy and completeness.

- *Information on specific customer requirements and expectations.* Often called the voice of the customer, this information will be gathered from the following sources and should always be reviewed:

  - Contract or order requirements*

  - Customer-specified standards, specifications, or drawings

- *Historical information relating to similar products or services.* This includes:

  - Lessons learned*

  - Customer complaints*

  - Field failures, returned product analysis results

  - Competitive product analysis

  - Reliability studies

- *The organization's business plan and/or marketing strategy.* This may provide valuable information on pricing, market segmentation, or production investments planned. For companies producing products for the general market, this information may be particularly useful. Market planners and product developers should be aware of this information when they plan for new products.

- *Sales forecasts and/or market estimates.* This information affects product pricing and production capacity planning. The auditor may want to evaluate to what extent sales forecasts accurately reflect actual sales after launch.

Human Resources

Human resources include the availability of adequate personnel as well as their training, competency and understanding of their roles, responsibilities, and authorities. Auditors should evaluate:

- *The training and competency of personnel.** The auditor should always evaluate the training and competency of personnel involved in the operation of any process evaluated. Competency can be evaluated by questioning auditees about the process being evaluated and by watching them perform specific tasks. The identification of required competencies, a requirement of ISO 9001, should be confirmed by noting some of the unique and important competencies required to perform the activities and then reviewing the job description, competency matrix, or training plan to verify that these competencies were identified. Ask the process owner or auditee, "What would a new employee have to know to be able to perform this activity correctly?" Failure to identify core competencies can lead to inconsistent process operation and quality problems. The auditor can then verify that training was provided or competencies obtained through a review of training records and plans.

• *Individual roles, responsibilities, and authorities.** Auditors should identify key decision points in the operation of the process and should ask questions to evaluate whether a consistent understanding of who has the responsibility and authority to make these decisions exist. Key decision points may be contained in procedures, job descriptions, and flowcharts or they may be provided as an element of the training process. Where they are documented, the auditor can verify whether the auditee's understanding is consistent with the procedure. Where they are not documented, the auditor can question the process owner during the first interview. Pay particular attention to responsibilities and authorities associated with contract and order reviews, approvals, and amendments. For design and development, focus on design reviews and readiness reviews.

• *General quality management system awareness.** General awareness includes how the auditee contributes to and supports the quality management system and policy, awareness of any quality objectives affecting the process, and awareness of how well the processes are performing. Improvement is difficult if those involved in the operation of processes are not aware of the problems or goals associated with the process.

Infrastructure

Infrastructure requirements include computer systems, technology, software, standards, and databases needed to properly perform the activity. Each will now be examined in more detail.

• *Computer systems and databases.* Much of the information used in order entry and product development resides in computer systems and information databases. Where this information is critical, the auditor may want to evaluate how the information is maintained current, how it is protected (for example, backup and security), and the extent to which it is available to those that need it. It is not uncommon to find that information in a product database is different than the information provided in the company catalog, or that information about customer interactions is not being maintained even though this may be critical for good customer relationship management. The availability of product information may also be important to personnel working in a call center responding to customer problems or concerns. The auditor may find that the database of lessons learned does not allow keyword search and is cumbersome to use, leading to its nonuse during new product development projects.

During one audit, I discovered that a database for order entry was prone to unintentional modification due to inadequate safeguards when editing orders. This resulted in frequent discrepancies between what was in the order database and what was required in the hard-copy customer order, which resulted in frequent problems with delivered orders. Poor performance as indicated by process metrics may point to the need to evaluate computer systems and databases. The auditor may also want to question the auditee about information that is not provided in the database that would improve process performance if it were.

• *Technology availability and reliability.* Just because a company has a computer system or a database of information doesn't mean it performs as needed. The auditor may want to ask the auditee questions regarding system reliability and availability. I remember one audit where the information needed to evaluate a process was available on the company intranet. Accessing and using this information was a central part of this activity. The problem was that it took five to 10 minutes for the page to load every time it was accessed. I asked the auditee about this and she replied that this was typical and that it greatly impacted her productivity and efficiency. It can also lead to reliance on memory instead of reliable information, which can lead to quality problems. The company's information needs had outpaced its information technology infrastructure. Such instances can be noted as opportunities for improvement.

• *Standards and specifications.** It is not unusual for a contract to call out industry or customer specifications and standards in the contract. Unfortunately, it is also not unusual to find them unavailable to those that design products or services. When called out in customer documents, they become mandatory inputs and must be available. Auditors should always spot-check the availability of standards and specifications called out in contract documents.

• *Software.* Although it may not be necessary that engineers have the latest version of AutoCad, it may be a problem if engineers are all working with different versions. This is especially important where customized software has been developed for the organization. Normally, revisions to such software are only made when needed, due to the high cost of modification. If the modifications were needed, then everyone should be using the latest version.

Controls

The following controls are always potential areas for evaluation and should be included on the auditor's checklist.

• *Document control.** The auditor should always verify that the documents in use are available as needed and of the current revision level. For electronic documents, verify that auditees know the file path and can access the documents they normally use, or should use, during the conduct of their work.

• *Record control.** The auditor should verify that the records required for the process are properly completed and maintained. The auditor should evaluate legibility and traceability to the activity or account that generated them. If retained locally, the auditor should verify that they are being maintained for the required length of time and that they are protected against damage or loss. This may involve backup and security for electronic records. Pay particular attention to records of contracts, amendments, feasibility reviews, design reviews, and verification and validation results.

Primary Outputs

The primary outputs from the order generation and quality planning process are identified in this section. Auditors should evaluate the quality and timeliness of these outputs since they are necessary inputs into other activities and will affect the quality of the product or service if they are incorrect or provided at the wrong time. Auditors may want to interview the downstream users of the output to gain an understanding of how well they are meeting their needs. The quality and timeliness of outputs provided to the final customer are almost always evaluated, those provided to internal customers often are not. Recognizing that the output from one process becomes the input to the next process is at the heart of the process approach to management and evaluating the adequacy of these internal outputs should be a priority of every audit.

Order Generation

• *Accurate quotation.** Accurate quotations include not only what the organization can do to meet the customer's requirements, but also how much its products and/or services will cost as reflected by the price. Products that fail to meet profitability goals often do so because of inaccurate cost estimates generated in support of the quotation. Auditors can use product profitability versus projected profits as an indicator that the cost estimation process needs to be improved. If the market for resources and materials is highly variable, leading to inaccurate cost estimates and unprofitable product introductions, then this fact should be recognized and methods for incorporating this variability should be worked into the estimated costs. More thorough review of the pricing and cost models and assumptions about the resources markets (that is, critical inputs) may be warranted in these situations. Excessive variation between estimated and actual costs or profitability should be noted as an opportunity for improvement, however, and not as a nonconformance. Auditors should also verify that all the necessary approvals were obtained before the quotation was issued, possibly including those responsible for designing or manufacturing the product or providing the service.

• *Approved contract or order and subsequent amendments.** A properly reviewed and approved contract or order is a primary output from the order generation process. Auditors should verify that the appropriate reviews and approvals were obtained on the contract or order. Auditors should also verify that any changes or amendments were communicated to those who should be aware of those changes, such as those in purchasing, manufacturing, and logistics, depending on the nature of the change.

• *Customer requirements, needs, and expectations.** This item was previously discussed under key inputs and resources. As an output, the auditor may want to verify with the engineering or quality planning team that the information it receives from sales and marketing meets its needs. If the sales team fails to obtain information needed to design the product or service, or to understand the customer application environment, then there is a high likelihood that what the customer receives will not be what the customer expects or needs. If the engineering team is responsible for obtaining this information, then verify that it is in fact obtaining it and not assuming it understands the customer's requirements.

• *Marketing materials, advertising materials, and company Web site information related to products and services.* This information was discussed in the previous section. As an output, it may be used by the customer to help decide whether an organization's products and services meet its needs. The auditor should verify the accuracy of the materials.

• *Up-to-date customer database.* An important output of the order generation may be a complete and accurate customer database. Information relating to customer preferences, repurchase rates, and buying behaviors can be key to an organization's marketing strategy and is especially important to organizations following a customer intimacy strategy. The auditor may want to question the sales and marketing manager to find out what information should be entered into the customer database prior to the audit or during the initial interview. The auditor can then assist the manager in evaluating whether the sales staff is consistently obtaining and entering the required information.

• *Up-to-date and accurate order database.* Information from the order database is often used to trigger production planning and/or material requirement planning and purchasing. The auditor may want to spend a few minutes with the production planners during the audit planning stage to inquire about the accuracy of this key information source.

• *Satisfied customers.** The ultimate output of this, along with all of the other value-stream processes, is a satisfied customer. Satisfaction surveys, customer report cards, and other customer and industry metrics that indicate that the organization's products or services lag behind competitor's offerings or otherwise don't meet their needs reflect potential weaknesses in the order generation and quality planning process. Evaluation of the other inputs, resources, and outputs described in this section may discover what these weaknesses are.

Quality Planning and Design

• *Product/service development quality and project plans.** An intermediate but important output is the quality plan or project plan. Some type of plan should be generated that indicates what has to be done (including verifications and validations), when it should be done, and who should do it. This plan may or may not be retained after the product or service is launched. In the order generation, quality planning, and design checklist, we recommend that the auditor choose as an object at least one product still in development. The auditor should evaluate the quality plan and/or project plans developed for this product.

• *Drawings, specifications, bill of materials.** A primary output of the design process will be the design records, or drawings, specifications, and other documents that describe the product or service. The auditor should evaluate these to ensure they were reviewed and approved before they were issued, and that any changes are properly controlled.

Configuration control of drawings for large projects in particular can be challenging and is the source of many quality deficiencies in the final product.

• *Verification and validation data, including records of design reviews.** The auditor should verify that all of the verifications and validations, including design reviews, material testing, product testing, and environmental testing, called out in the quality plan or project plan were completed and the results reviewed. The auditor should also verify that any open issues arising from these verifications and validations were addressed. Verification and validation applies equally to services, where trial runs or pilot tests may be necessary.

• *Process flowcharts and layouts.* Process flowcharts and layout drawings may be developed to show the product flow through the production process and to plan for an efficient or lean manufacturing process. The auditor may want to verify that these outputs are being updated as the design evolves.

• *Equipment, tooling, and gauging plans.* For manufacturing organizations, important outputs include the equipment, tooling, and gauging plans used for the acquisition and/or deployment of the organization's manufacturing assets. Where equipment, tooling, or gauging must be procured, the auditor may want to verify that the specification of requirements is completed and provided to purchasing with sufficient lead time to ensure that it is obtained and can be verified before it is required for production. The auditor may also want to verify that these actions are reflected on the quality or project plan. Finally, for companies certified to the ISO/TS 16949 specification, the auditor may want to inquire whether health and safety considerations were factored into any equipment specifications. The 16949 specification requires consideration of employee safety during the design of manufacturing processes. That consideration should begin with equipment acquisition. Where equipment is already available within the organization, the auditor may want to question whether manufacturing capability was evaluated during equipment assignment. This can be especially important in products with tight manufacturing tolerances.

• *Operator instructions.* If new operator instructions will be needed, then the auditor can verify that these outputs contain the information that will be needed by production operators. Production operators and supervisors can provide feedback for this review. Equally important is whether the format can be understood by those who will have to use it. It is not uncommon to find all operator instructions in English in plants where the majority of production workers speak a different language. The auditor may want to question the quality planning team about what arrangements have been made to communicate the necessary information to those who do not speak English. Visual instructions are often used, but other methods have been successfully applied such as bilingual production line leaders and qualification/certification programs.

• *Purchasing information.** Drawings, specifications, the bill of materials, and project plans all contain information essential to purchasing. The auditor may want to visit with the purchasing representatives prior to the audit to determine whether the information provided by the quality planning team/design engineers consistently meets their needs in relation to content and timeliness. If not, ask them to describe typical deficiencies and then incorporate questions relating to these areas into your checklist.

• *Setup instructions and process parameter information.* The quality planning team should prepare setup instructions, process data sheets, and other information needed to properly set up and control the manufacturing process. These could be reviewed by the auditor for content and completeness if historical information shows this to be a problem. Similar to operator instructions, process operators and supervisors could provide feedback on the general adequacy of setup instructions and process parameter sheets.

• *Inspection plans with acceptance criteria.** The auditor should verify that a process is in place and is being used to identify necessary product and/or service inspections, verifications, and tests that will be needed once the product or service is launched. These should be reflected in operator instructions, inspections plans, or by some other method. During the production audit, implementation of these plans will be confirmed.

• *Satisfied customers.* Of course the ultimate output is a satisfied customer. The same indicators noted for the order generation process (satisfaction surveys that indicate that the organization's products or services lag behind competitor's offerings or otherwise don't meet their needs) can be used to evaluate the quality planning and design processes.

Auditors within the automotive industry should note that the inputs and resources listed in this section do not address all of the items required by ISO/TS 16949, such as FMEAs and measurement system studies. These additional items are called out in the advanced product quality planning process and are discussed in Chapter 12.

Process Performance Indicators and Metrics

The following list of performance indicators include those commonly used to monitor and measure the order generation, quality planning, and/or design and development processes. The auditor should never expect to see all of them in use—most organizations use only one or two primary measures for each core process. The auditor should be aware of those that are used and should evaluate them to determine if the process is achieving its desired results. The auditor may want to recommend consideration of others as an opportunity for improvement, *if it can be demonstrated that current metrics do not evaluate an important process or that current metrics are inconsistent with current strategic goals and priorities.* The auditor must keep in mind that it is the responsibility of the process owner and senior management to determine how the process should be monitored, not the auditor. Auditors can evaluate the effectiveness of processes, even in the absences of metrics, by using the techniques presented in Chapter 5.

• *Sales and marketing*

- Gross sales (productivity)

- Sales from new products (productivity)

- Repurchase rates (customer loyalty) (productivity)

- Promotions—new leads generated (productivity)

- Promotion costs/new lead generated (cost)

- Bid success rate (won/lost) (quality)

- Quotation cycle time (efficiency)

- Order entry accuracy (quality)

- Quoted versus actual costs (cost)

- Customer satisfaction (quality)

- *Customer service/customer relationship management*

  - Contacts per service rep (productivity)

  - Average cycle time, customer contact to final solution (efficiency)

  - Average customer wait time (quality)

  - Customer satisfaction (quality)

  - Percent solutions first call (productivity, quality)

- *Research and development*

  - New product sales (productivity)

  - New product margins (productivity)

  - Percent projects successfully commercialized (quality)

  - Number of new patents (productivity)

  - R&D costs/two-year returns (cost)

  - Project cycle time, conception to launch (efficiency)

  - Customer satisfaction (quality)

KEY AUDIT POINT: PRODUCT AND/OR SERVICE REALIZATION

The product and/or service realization process starts with the outputs from the quality planning process and ends with the product's transfer to the customer or delivery of the service. The product and/or service realization process flow has been expanded in Figure 8.4 to provide additional detail into the activities that may make up this system of processes.

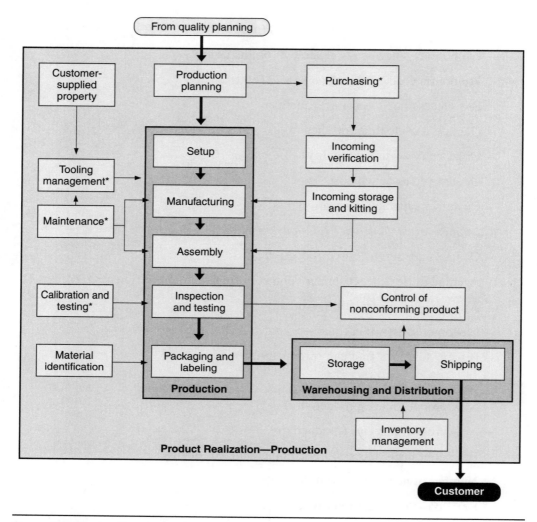

Figure 8.4 Production process.

The primary flow through this process is shown by the heavier lines. Service providers would replace the production-related activities with those needed for service realization. These may include service scheduling, client briefing, account setup, service delivery (for example, training, consulting, primary care delivery, application engineering, and so on), service verification and/or inspection, project wrap-up, and reporting.

Audit Strategy

The typical audit strategy is to use trace forward or trace back, as described in Chapter 6, to evaluate each step in the product or service delivery process. The auditor will normally first look to see what parts are currently being run and will then select a part or assembly as a test object. The auditor then travels up or down the manufacturing and assembly process, stopping at each workstation along the way to verify conformance and effectiveness and to identify any opportunities for improvement or best practices. Everything associated with the process under review is fair game, including, but not limited to, the control of documents used at the workstation, operator training and awareness, material identification, the calibration of measurement devices, and control of nonconforming product. Operator instructions and local procedures at the workstation are used to verify conformance and competency. The checklists provided on the CD can be used to ensure that common inputs, outputs, and resources are considered.

Because the evaluation at each workstation is somewhat repetitive, planning the overall strategy is less complex than it is in other audits or in audits of a full value stream. Because there is so much that can be examined at each workstation, however, auditors can become easily overwhelmed. Carefully reviewing current issues, problems, and metrics for the production process during the audit planning phase as described in Chapter 5 will help focus the auditor on the critical items or inputs that need to be evaluated, along with those that do not. Space has been provided on the audit checklists to record measurement device serial numbers, document numbers, and operator names so that the evidence of control of these activities can be assessed after the auditor leaves the production floor.

For service activities the audit is a bit more complicated, since the activities performed at each step of the service delivery process will be more unique and less repetitive than those evaluated during a manufacturing audit. The auditor will probably need to spend more time planning, carefully reviewing the documentation and procedures for each activity to be evaluated.

If the audit program manager has scheduled a full value stream audit, then the order generation and quality planning and product or service realization audits are combined, possibly with day one examining the order generation and quality planning process, and day two evaluating the product and/or service realization process. The complicating factor in this audit is that the part/contract selected for the audit must be running in production long enough for the auditors to evaluate the production process. This may be difficult in companies that have transitioned to small-lot manufacturing or that produce small runs of a variety of products. In these audits a trace back strategy should be considered, starting at the back end with a product that is currently being manufactured and following the trail back to the order generation process.

Key Inputs and Resources

This section lists some of the key inputs and resources that support the product or service realization process. Auditors should consider these inputs and resources when planning their audit and include those that are most important for ensuring high-quality outputs and/or process effectiveness and efficiency. *Items marked with an asterisk should always be considered for inclusion.*

Information

Communication of the results of quality planning to the production floor is critical. The auditor should verify the accuracy, revision status, and adequacy of the following information.

• *Process flowchart.* The process flowchart, if used, should reflect the actual process and should be consistent with other process documentation (traveler, control plan, FMEA). The process flowchart can be a valuable process analysis tool, but only if it is current and contains essential information about the process. An accurate process flowchart is required for automotive suppliers.

• *Control plan or inspection plan.** The control plan or inspection plan should be current and should reflect the inspections, tests, or verifications that are routinely conducted to ensure the quality of product. The auditor should obtain the current control plan or inspection plan from QA prior to the audit and should verify that the verifications are being conducted at the proper frequency, using the proper sample size and measurement device, and are being evaluated to the correct acceptance criteria specified on the plan. Deficiencies here can have serious product consequences. Pay particular attention to any incoming inspection requirements—verify that receiving has current information about what inspections are required and acceptance criteria to apply to incoming materials.

• *Failure mode and effects analysis.** Although the FMEA is primarily seen as an automotive and aerospace tool, other industries such as healthcare are using the methodology to prevent and/or minimize the risks associated with process failures. Chapter 12 discusses the use and auditing of this tool in more detail. If FMEAs are used by the organization, then the auditor should obtain the current FMEA and evaluate its adequacy during the audit. It is not uncommon to find that real failure modes being experienced on the production floor were not recognized in the FMEA or that the occurrence and detection rankings were artificially low. This can be a major problem since most organizations use the current FMEA as a starting point for future process design. Failure to identify the real failure modes of a process or underestimating their risk can result in the carryover of current problems into future processes.

• *Operator instructions.** The auditor should always evaluate the adequacy of operator instructions. Revision status, legibility (especially important for organizations that have a high percentage of workers whose primary language is not English), and availability are always fair game. So too is their adequacy and completeness. Do they contain the information needed to properly perform the actions demanded at the workstation? The auditor should compare the actions performed by the operator to the instructions and note any significant deviations. Not every action needs to be detailed, but if it looks important and is not reflected in the instruction, then the auditor may want to question the operator about its importance. If it is important, then the auditor should verify that other operators also perform the step. The auditor may also want to question operators on the adequacy of the instructions. Very often they have the best suggestions about how an activity could be improved.

• *Setup instructions.* A specialized form of operator instruction, setup instructions are extremely important in processes such as injection molding and heat treat. The auditor may want to compare actual process settings with those called out in the setup instructions or technical data sheet. It is not uncommon to find the process being operated to parameters outside the range of those allowed in the setup instructions.

• *Product identification and traceability.* The auditor can ask the operator how products are identified and how they know they are good (inspection status). The auditor should also examine material identification to verify that it is being properly identified. If traceability is a requirement, then the auditor can also verify that traceability controls are properly implemented. Note that the auditor must be familiar with local requirements in order to be able to evaluate the response.

• *Packaging and labeling specifications.* Labeling errors are common and are often a major source of rejected product. Auditors should verify the availability and understanding of current packaging/labeling specifications for the product being evaluated.

• *Computer systems.* The inventory control system is often a source of inefficiencies and errors. Auditors should evaluate whether the inventory control system supports first in–first out (FIFO) product handling, along with its ability to properly located materials in storage. Is bar coding used? The auditor may also want to inquire about whether the system allows location updates if material is moved after its initial placement.

Human Resources

Human resources include the availability of adequate personnel as well as their training, competency, and understanding of their roles, responsibilities, and authorities. Most of these items were discussed in the previous section on auditing the order generation and quality planning processes.

• *The training and competency of personnel.**

• *Individual roles, responsibilities, and authorities.** Pay particular attention to responsibilities and authorities associated with verifications and disposition of nonconforming product.

• *General quality management system awareness.**

• *General awareness of process performance.* Operators should be aware of how well their process is performing, as determined by existing measures of performance. ISO/TS 16949, in particular, requires that process performance information be communicated to operators. Normally this information is posted on bulletin boards, zone control boards, or other visual displays. The auditor may want to question process operators to see if they are generally aware of overall process performance and any posted quality problems or concerns. Awareness is a necessary first step toward correction or improvement.

Infrastructure

Infrastructure requirements include production equipment, tooling, facilities, and measurement devices. Each will now be examined in more detail.

• *Equipment maintenance.* Auditors may want to inquire about equipment uptime, downtime, or overall equipment effectiveness prior to the audit. If equipment availability is poor or is trending in the wrong direction then the auditor may want to dive more deeply into how the equipment is being maintained (or not being maintained). The auditor should verify that maintenance requirements have been established and are being performed and may want to question the maintenance supervisor about the cause of the poor performance and if there is any action being taken.

• *Tooling.* The auditor may want to verify that production tooling is being properly maintained, refurbished, or replaced, and is properly identified (if customer owned).

• *Facilities.* Facilities include the production areas along with tooling used in the production process. The auditor should verify that customer-owned tooling used in the processes under review is properly maintained and identified. For the warehouse, this may include an adequate number of lift trucks and adequate space for material storage. It can also include warehouse setup—are fast-moving products optimally located to support efficient order picking and shipment?

• *Measurement devices.* All measurement devices used to accept product or to monitor the process should be reviewed to ensure they are calibrated and controlled in accordance with local procedures. Proper handling of inspection devices can also be important. The auditor may want to verify that any measurement studies required by local procedures or customer requirements have been performed and the results meet agreed-upon acceptance criteria. Space has been provided on the checklists to record document number and revision date so that the auditor can confirm calibration and gage study status after he or she leaves the production area. Measurement system studies will be examined more fully in Chapter 12.

Controls

The following controls are always potential areas for evaluation and should be included on the auditor's checklist.

• *Document control.** The auditor should always verify that the documents in use are available as needed and of the current revision level. Space has been provided on the checklists to record document number and revision date so that the auditor can confirm proper revision status after he or she leaves the production or service delivery area.

• *Record control.** The auditor should verify that the records required for the process are properly completed and maintained. The auditor should evaluate legibility and traceability to the activity or account that generated them.

- *Mistake-proofing controls.* The auditor should confirm that any mistake-proofing or poka-yoke controls developed for the process are in use and are being properly maintained. Many of these will be listed on the control plan, if the organization uses that method for controlling the process.

- *Statistical process control.* The auditor should review any control charts in use for process control. Verify that the data are being recorded as stated in the control plan or inspection plan and that any special causes are identified and actions taken as prescribed in local procedures or the control plan. Evaluating control charts will be examined more fully in Chapter 12.

- *Nonconforming product controls.* The auditor should examine any nonconforming or suspect product noted during the audit to verify proper labeling and control. If there is none, the auditor should ask the operators how they would handle it if it were identified. This is especially important at workstations where inspections and verifications are performed. Note that the auditor must be familiar with local requirements for the control of nonconforming product to be in a position to evaluate the response.

Primary Outputs

The primary outputs from the product or service realization process are identified in this section. Auditors should evaluate the quality and timeliness of these outputs at each workstation since they are necessary inputs into other production or service delivery activities and will affect the quality of the final product or service if they are incorrect or provided at the wrong time. Evaluation of the inspection or verification records against the control or inspection plan will provide evidence that the products or services are being verified as required and are acceptable. Auditors should observe the verifications being performed, if possible.

Production Planning

- *Production schedule or plan.* The auditor may want to verify that production schedules are generated with adequate lead time to allow setup for manufacturing. The production supervisor can normally provide this information.

- *Kanban cards, other lean documents.* The auditor may want to evaluate this area if audit planning indicated weaknesses in this area.

Production or Service Delivery

- *Product or service.** Products and services that meet customer requirements are the ultimate output of this phase. Verification that these meet customer requirements will be evaluated at each step of the production or service delivery process as noted in the opening paragraph of this section. For services, the auditor should observe the service as it is being delivered to the customer, if possible, to determine if the service meets local requirements for quality, friendliness, timeliness, or other defined service criteria.

Warehouse and Distribution

• *Final packaged product.** The auditor should verify the packaging and labeling of final product against the product specifications. Improper labeling is a common deficiency and should be closely examined, especially if the auditor noted weaknesses with labeling during audit planning and review of customer feedback (including product returns).

Process Performance Indicators and Metrics

The following list of performance indicators includes those commonly used to monitor and measure the product realization processes. Because of the wide variance in service operations, no attempt is made to present service delivery metrics. The auditor should never expect to see all of them in use. Most organizations use only a few measures for each production process. The auditor should be aware of those that are used and should evaluate them to determine if the process is achieving its desired results. The auditor may want to recommend consideration of others as an opportunity for improvement, *if it can be demonstrated that current metrics do not evaluate an important process or that current metrics are inconsistent with current strategic goals and priorities*. The auditor must keep in mind that it is the responsibility of the process owner and senior management to determine how the process should be monitored, not the auditor. Auditors can evaluate the effectiveness of processes, even in the absence of metrics, by using the techniques presented in Chapter 5:

• Output/employee

• Percent scrap

• Percent rework

• Percent first-pass yield

• Customer return rate

• Final ppm quality

• Overall equipment effectiveness

• Equipment uptime or availability

• Percent incomplete delivery

• Cycle time, production start to truck or stock

• Actual manufacturing cost to target manufacturing cost

• Process capability (individual process characteristics)

KEY AUDIT POINT: PRODUCTION SUPPORT

Production support includes maintenance, tooling management, and the calibration and/or test laboratory. These activities are essential to the production process and have been grouped together to facilitate an efficient audit. These processes could easily be evaluated on their own, if desired, although maintenance and tooling management go hand in hand in some companies.

Rather than separately break out the inputs, outputs, and performance indicators for each of these activities, I will instead present audit strategies along with key audit points and measurements the auditor may find or can use to determine process effectiveness. Auditors must remain aware, however, that these activities are, in fact, processes—the process of maintaining equipment, tooling, and facilities; the process of calibrating and maintaining measurement devices; and the process of conducting product testing. They each have their own key inputs and resource requirements and auditors should evaluate them as they would any product realization process.

Maintenance

The maintenance process is shown generically in Figure 8.5. There may be other activities accomplished as part of maintenance, such as equipment setup, maintenance improvement, and early equipment management, that are not shown but are discussed in the key audit points. The figure assumes the company is using some type of maintenance management software program. If not, replace the database symbol with your maintenance management program. (I used to use 5×8 file cards and hand-generated schedules).

The darker shaded items in Figure 8.5 represent components of the maintenance process that should be evaluated during audits of the production process as described earlier in this chapter. The auditor does not need to spend time evaluating these areas. Instead, the auditor should focus on the centralized functions of maintenance program management. In addition, the process of providing emergency or repair maintenance has been shown, since this process may not be included in routine audits of the production process.

Audit Strategy and Key Audit Points

The auditor will probably want to start the evaluation by reviewing maintenance performance information with the maintenance manager or supervisor. The auditor should inquire about any adverse trends or areas where maintenance performance is not meeting stated objectives. Note that ISO/TS 16949 requires that maintenance objectives be established. The auditor should verify that performance toward achieving these objectives is being tracked and actions taken where progress is lacking in meeting these goals.

The auditor should continue by asking to see the listing of key production equipment. This list may be contained in the maintenance database or it may be reflected on the master maintenance schedule. Wherever, the auditor should use his or her knowledge of the facility to quickly verify that all important production-related equipment is

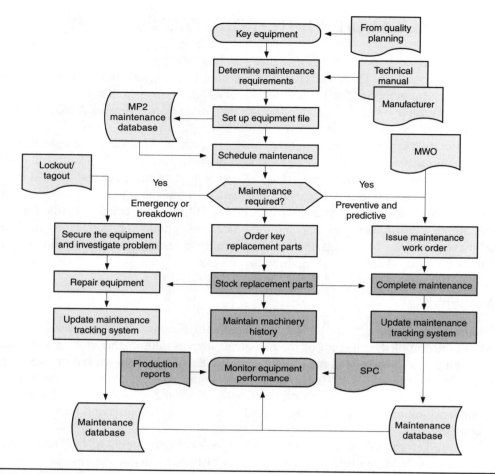

Figure 8.5 Maintenance process.

included. The auditor should also verify that key auxiliary equipment, such as air compressors, pumps, and ventilation systems are included on the list, especially if these components are required for production operation. Using any information gained about problem areas from the review of performance, the auditor should then select several pieces of equipment to use as objects for the remainder of the review.

The auditor should ask how maintenance requirements were determined for the selected objects. It is not uncommon to find that maintenance requirements were pulled out of thin air with no basis for assignment. This is particularly true with older equipment or equipment scavenged from other facilities. While there may not be a technical manual still available for older or custom-built equipment, there are many sources of information on maintenance of major subcomponents such as hydraulics, air systems, valves, electrical equipment, and power transmission components. The auditor should verify that these sources of information were reviewed. If no basis for the assignment of maintenance requirements exists, then the auditor should consider issuance of an opportunity for improvement, unless the facility has an extremely experienced maintenance staff. If the equipment technical manual does exist, then the auditor should ask to see the manual and should verify that the maintenance requirements recommended by the manufacturer are being performed. The auditor can ask questions about any that are recommended but not performed by the maintenance group. Failure to perform recommended maintenance could be a reason for poor equipment availability or performance. If the equipment is standard and relatively new, the auditor can also check to see if the manual is being controlled and updated.

The auditor can then ask to see the machinery history file, or equivalent, for the equipment selected as objects. This question will most likely lead the auditor to the maintenance database, which is where most companies centralize their information on key equipment. While in the database, the auditor can verify that information on key replacement parts, repair history, and equipment maintenance or repair instructions is maintained. The auditor can ask questions about features that are available but are not currently being used. Modern maintenance management systems are very powerful. While the auditor should not expect all of the capabilities and features to be used, he or she should question those that look like they would be helpful. Often these additional capabilities are not used because of lack of training or time to set them up. An opportunity for improvement would be warranted in these instances, if the maintenance representative agrees that the feature would add value. The auditor should ask about the process used to determine spare part allocations. Most maintenance management systems have built-in capabilities for monitoring repair part usage, and the auditor should ensure that these features in particular are being used. The auditor may want to review the file of deferred maintenance to see if there are many instances where maintenance is not being performed due to a lack of parts.

After reviewing the database, the auditor might then shift attention to evaluating the process for issuing maintenance work orders (MWO) and updating the database when maintenance is completed. If the organization has an instruction for planning, scheduling, and conducting maintenance, the auditor should ask the auditee to walk through the process using the procedure. During this walk-through, the auditor can verify that the information required on the MWOs is being filled in by the maintenance personnel and entered into the database by asking to see records for the equipment objects selected earlier. It is not uncommon to find that information relating to the time required to complete the task, the materials used, or problems encountered is not filled in by mechanics performing the maintenance. This information is especially important for nonroutine or emergency maintenance and can yield great benefits during maintenance planning. Failure to properly complete or enter this information could be an NC or OFI, depending on whether local procedures and policies require it to be obtained.

The auditor might then want to evaluate the process used to perform emergency or breakdown maintenance. If covered by local instructions, the auditor should ask the auditee to walk through the process. During the walk-through the auditor would ask questions similar to those noted in the previous paragraph.

There can be, and probably are, additional activities performed as part of the maintenance process that are not reflected in Figure 8.5. Examples may include equipment overhaul planning, outage planning, equipment setup, and machinery decommissioning and salvage. Maintenance improvement and early equipment management (equipment design and installation/verification planning) are features of a total productive maintenance program that could also be evaluated, as is the implementation of autonomous maintenance. The auditor can select some of these activities to evaluate during audit planning. Subsequent audits can examine others such that all maintenance activities are evaluated over a series of audits.

The audit of the maintenance process should be performed as is any other process-based audit. The following common inputs, resources, and/or controls should be evaluated during the course of the review:

- Document control of any local procedures, instructions (including lockout-tagout, permit-required confined space entry, and other safety instructions), or key external documents like equipment technical manuals.

- The control of maintenance records, including their completion, retention, and protection (backup for computer-based records).

- The availability of adequate numbers and the right mix of maintenance personnel. A long backlog of overdue maintenance may signal resource problems.

- The training, awareness, and competency of maintenance personnel.

- Understanding of the roles, responsibilities, and authorities of maintenance personnel. Pay particular note of personnel understanding of who is responsible for issuing MWOs, for ordering spare parts, for entering information into the maintenance database, and for release of equipment after maintenance.

- Maintenance infrastructure and work environment. Does the maintenance department have the tools and facilities it needs?

Performance Indicators

Maintenance is a critical process in any manufacturing organization. If there are no metrics for the maintenance process, the auditor should consider issuing an NC. The auditor may encounter the following performance indicators for the maintenance process. The more common metrics are listed first.

- Percent equipment availability

- Percent equipment uptime

- Overall equipment effectiveness (a composite metric that accounts for machine speed, availability, and quality yield)

- Percent maintenance tasks completed per schedule

- Maintenance backlog (percent or number of maintenance tasks)

- Percent maintenance tasks completed by production operators (autonomous maintenance)

- Number or percent of unplanned maintenance tasks or emergency repairs

- Percent maintenance tasks completed within standard time

- Number of tasks deferred due to lack of spare parts

- Average dollar value, spare parts inventory

Tooling Management

The core activities relating to tooling management are shown in Figure 8.6. Items shown in the shaded box labeled advanced quality planning should be evaluated during audits of the quality planning process. The auditor should, therefore, focus on activities associated with the stocking, maintenance, repair, and issuance of tooling.

Audit Strategy and Key Audit Points

The auditor should begin the audit of tooling management as any other audit, by first interviewing the tooling manager or supervisor. Any metrics used to measure tooling management performance should be reviewed. Note that metrics of overall performance

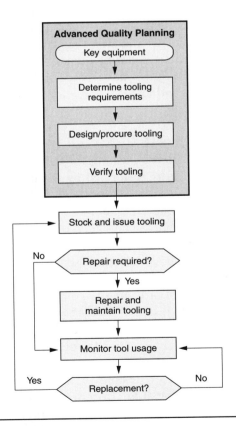

Figure 8.6 Tooling management.

may not exist for this process, but information relating to inventory levels, items on backorder, and tooling costs may be available and could be reviewed.

The auditor should thoroughly evaluate the process used to maintain tooling inventory. Usage tracking, order points, and the process used to requisition tooling can be reviewed. If there is a local instruction, then the auditor should ask the auditee to walk through the process. If this is subcontracted, then monitoring of tooling subcontractor performance should be performed and can be evaluated by the auditor.

The auditor should also review tooling maintenance: tooling, dies, and molds in storage. Is it properly identified and preserved? Any deficiencies in this area should be thoroughly evaluated.

Finally, although not shown in Figure 8.6, proper identification and maintenance of any customer-owned tooling should also be evaluated. ISO/TS 16949 requires identification of any customer-owned tooling such that ownership is visible. Common inputs and resources, such as document control, training, and roles and responsibilities should also be reviewed.

Calibration and Testing

The calibration of measurement devices in use on the plant floor should be checked during each audit of the production process, as should the measurement system uncertainties. The planning and results of product testing required for verification and validation of product likewise is evaluated during other ongoing audits, in this case during evaluations of the advanced quality planning process. The review here is of the centralized activities of calibration and testing. These are shown below the shaded box in Figure 8.7.

Audit Strategy and Key Audit Points

The auditor can start the evaluation by asking for the laboratory scope, if it has one, or for a list of calibrations and tests performed by the laboratory. ISO/TS 16949 and ISO/IEC 17025 both require laboratory scopes and the auditor should confirm their availability and accuracy if the company and/or laboratory is certified to either of these standards. The laboratory scope will contain a list of the calibrations and tests the laboratory is capable of performing, along with the ranges, test methods, and (for 17025) the best expected measurement uncertainties associated with the test or calibration. From this list the auditor should select a number of calibrations and/or tests to serve as objects for the audit. If calibration or testing is going on during the time frame of the audit, then these activities should become objects to use to verify the process.

The auditor should then ask to see the test methods or calibration methods and standards used to conduct calibration or testing on the objects selected. Methods used in the laboratory should be based on industry or nationally recognized methods, such as those issued by the American Society for Testing of Materials (ASTM) or the National Institute of Standards and Technology (NIST) or to a customer standard or drawing (for testing). Manufacturers' recommendations are also normally accepted for inspection

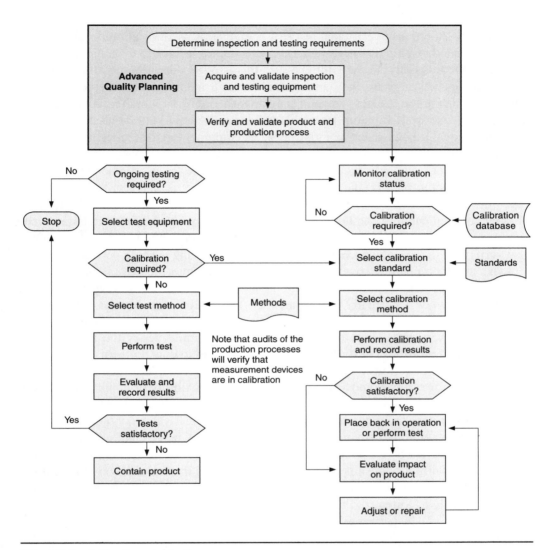

Figure 8.7 Calibration and testing.

devices. Assuming that they are traceable to a recognized method, the auditor may want to compare the local instruction to the recognized test or calibration method and ask about any differences. Pay particular attention to requirements relating to environmental conditions, equipment restrictions, and test sample setup. If there is no basis for the local instructions, then issue an NC for ISO/TS 16949 organizations or an OFI or NC for ISO 9001 organizations. The difference is that ISO/TS 16949 requires an organization to use traceable methods, ISO 9001 does not. Even so, if the calibration or test method doesn't exist, an NC would be appropriate even for an ISO 9001 company. If actual testing or calibration can be observed, then the auditor should evaluate performance against the instructions.

Auditors should also verify that test sets or standards used in calibrations are themselves calibrated to a higher-level standard that is traceable back to the national or international standards body. In the United States this is NIST. The storage of test sets can also be reviewed to ensure they are maintained in a manner that will preserve their integrity. When not in use, test sets and standards should be kept in their containers and in a secure location. Laboratory standards and test sets should not be used for production inspections. Likewise, the calibration of test equipment in the laboratory should be confirmed, as should the adequacy of any test equipment maintenance.

If the auditor's review of the methods indicate that there are environmental conditions that must be met to perform the test or calibrations, then verification of the laboratory's capability to monitor for these environmental conditions should be performed. Monitoring of laboratory temperature and humidity is a common requirement, and certain tests may require the ability to monitor ambient noise, vibration, and lighting. The auditor should also verify that there is evidence that any required monitoring is being performed.

The auditor should also examine calibration and test records, including those entered into the organization's calibration database, if it uses a software program. During this review I normally like to increase my sample size beyond the objects I selected at the start of the audit. I will normally evaluate 20 to 30 records or reports as each requires very little time to review. The auditor should verify the informational content on the report or record. Records and reports should contain the device or product being calibrated or tested, the date, the results obtained, the test method and/or test set used, and (for calibrations) a statement as to the acceptability or nonacceptability of the results. For calibrations, the record should also indicate the action that was taken on the device if it was found to be out of calibration or defective in any other way. I also pay particular attention to any results of tests or calibration results that were outside the acceptance criteria. For test results this should have resulted in the containment of product, while for calibration results this should have resulted in an evaluation of the impact of the deficiency on any product accepted with the device. This evaluation is required to be documented. I often find that this evaluation is either not performed or not documented, either of which represents a serious deficiency. The former is particularly significant as it could have serious product impact. Auditors should also verify that measurement devices are reevaluated after any repairs or modifications.

Estimations of measurement system or test method uncertainties should be determined by the laboratory for each calibration or test it conducts. These are often provided in the industry, national, or international test methods and can be used by the local laboratory if local procedures are based on these traceable methods. Verification of the calculations involved is beyond the capability of most internal auditors, and it should be sufficient to simply confirm that measurement uncertainty has been estimated. For organizations in the automotive industry, it is common to use the measurement system variation results obtained during measurement systems analysis (described in Chapter 12) as evidence that the overall measurement system uncertainty is known and accounted for.

For tests and calibrations performed by outside laboratories, the auditor should confirm that the outside laboratory has the capability to perform the calibration or test, normally through the receipt of the outside lab's certificate of accreditation by a national body such as the American Association for Laboratory Accreditation (A2LA) or the National Voluntary Laboratory Accreditation Program (NVLAP run by NIST) in the United States. Certification to ISO/IEC 17025 can be used by ISO 9001–certified companies. 17025 certification comes automatically with accreditation by A2LA or NVLAP. The certificate should list the calibrations and tests the laboratory is certified to run. The auditor should also verify that the results of outside calibrations are reviewed and any local databases updated to reflect the latest results.

Beyond these core activities, auditors should also review:

- Document control, including the control and update of any outside test methods used to perform calibration and testing

- The completeness, legibility, and retention of calibration and test records

- The training and competency of laboratory personnel

- Roles, responsibilities, and authorities, especially as they apply to the analysis and interpretation of results and review of final test reports

- Test sample identification, traceability, and retention

- The identification and control of any test specimens or measurement devices found to be nonconforming or defective

Auditors should note that internal laboratories certified to ISO/IEC 17025 or accredited by A2LA or NVLAP have special requirements that go well beyond those examined here. They also have specific requirements to perform internal audits of laboratory operations to the ISO/IEC 17025 standard. Internal management system auditors should receive special training before evaluating laboratory operations in these situations.

Performance Indicators

The auditor may encounter the following performance indicators for the calibration and testing processes. The auditor should review these with the laboratory management or supervision during the audit.

- Percent tests completed on time

- Test or calibration backlog

- Test report cycle time

- Test report accuracy

- Percent gages out of service

- Gage system stability, linearity, bias, and repeatability and reproducibility (for specific gage systems)

- Calibration cycle time

RESOURCE AND SUPPORT PROCESSES

These activities support all components of the management system, not just those involved in product or service realization. They have been grouped together for convenience and to allow for an efficient audit. Portions of these activities will be evaluated during other process-based audits. These audits will evaluate only the centralized elements of these processes.

Document Control

Every audit should evaluate how well documents associated with the process are controlled. Their revision status, availability, legibility, and adequacy should be verified by the auditor as they review these essential inputs. If you've made it this far in this handbook, then you know that all of the checklists I've provided have questions relating to document control along with areas where the auditor can note the document number and revision date for later verification. These ongoing reviews provide a clear indication of how effective the document management system is at accomplishing its core purpose: to provide accurate, understandable, and current documents where they are needed. This audit evaluates the infrastructure that provides that performance. It includes the process used to review, approve, prepare, and issue documents; the control of the master list or other coordination tool; and the process used to reclaim and, where appropriate, maintain obsolete documents. These actions are shown in Figure 8.8.

Auditors should note that audits of the centralized elements of document control may not be needed as frequently as other components of the quality management system if auditors are diligent at reviewing the control of documents during other audits and these evaluations show that the system is performing well. Some might argue that they are not needed at all. I disagree, since there are some components, such as the retention and control of obsolete, historical documents, that will not be evaluated during other process-based audits. Even so, the frequency between reviews of centralized document control can be extended if other audits show that documents are being adequately controlled.

Audit Strategy

The auditor should ask to see the document control procedure. This is one of the control elements of both ISO 9001 and ISO/TS 16949 that requires a written procedure. The auditor should ask the auditee to walk through the procedure.

Ask the auditee to show components of the system, such as the master list, files of archived documents, and so on, as they come to them in the procedure. During the reviews of these elements, the auditor should verify that they are being maintained. The auditor may want to sample a few documents to verify that only authorized personnel reviewed and/or approved documents. If this is checked during other process-based audits, then this may not be necessary.

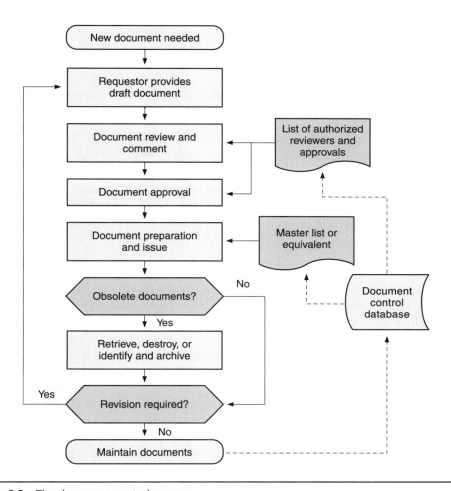

Figure 8.8 The document control process.

For the most part the auditor is verifying that there is a system to locate and distribute documents, there is a system that establishes the appropriate revision status, and that there is a system to properly archive and safeguard obsolete documents. The auditor may also want to evaluate the backlog of document change requests to determine if resources supplied are sufficient to allow timely document preparation and issue.

Performance Indicators

Auditors should not expect to find much in the way of performance indicators for the document control system. An indirect method for determining the overall effectiveness of this process is to evaluate the last four to six months of corrective action requests. The auditor should look for documented problems that cite document control (or lack thereof) as the root cause or major contributor. Examples might include:

- Incorrect version of procedure in use

- Incomplete or confusing procedure

- Error in the procedure

- No procedure in place

Each of these problems indicates a failure to properly review, approve, locate, or correctly decide if a documented procedure is needed. If the auditor finds several corrective actions with causes such as those just listed, then the evaluation of document control should be more penetrating. If there are numerous instances of document control errors, then the auditor may want to issue an NC if the problem is not recognized or if there is no long-term action being taken to permanently correct the situation.

Record Control

Like document control, every audit should evaluate how well records associated with the process are controlled. Their legibility, completeness, and storage should be verified by the auditor during the review of these essential inputs. Retrievability of records is constantly being evaluated by auditors as they ask to see objective evidence for those things that we say we do. Use of records for continual improvement is evaluated during audits of the continual improvement process.

This audit focuses on record retention, storage, and security. These actions are shown in Figure 8.9. Audits of the centralized elements of record control may not be needed as frequently as other components of the quality management system if auditors are

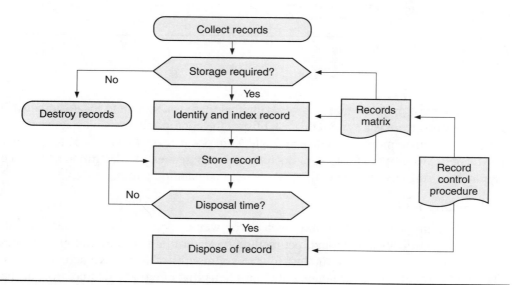

Figure 8.9 The record control process.

diligent at reviewing the control of records during other audits and these evaluations show that the system is performing well.

Audit Strategy

The auditor should ask to see the record control procedure and the records matrix. The auditor can select several records from the matrix and verify that these records are stored and retained as indicated in the matrix. Records in long-term storage should be properly indexed and protected against deterioration and loss. If the records matrix identified a retention time of a year, then the auditor could ask for a record generated six months ago to see if the records management system can retrieve the record. If record retention is decentralized, this may not be practical. If records are stored electronically, the auditor should verify that records are properly backed up and password protected. Finally, if the organization has a record disposal policy, then the auditor may want to verify that records are being disposed of as required by local procedures.

Performance Indicators

Similar to document control, auditors should not expect to find much in the way of performance indicators for the record control system. An indirect method for determining the overall effectiveness of this process is to quickly scan previous audit reports. A series of "no evidence of" findings may indicate deficiencies in record generation or retention. Auditors can use these findings, if there is a recognizable pattern, to help focus their evaluation of the record management system.

Because most organizations centralize document and record control, and because other audits evaluate how well these processes have been implemented, it makes sense to evaluate both of these processes together. This evaluation should take no more than an hour or so to complete, leaving more than enough time to evaluate other important support processes like purchasing and training.

Training

Trained, competent personnel are a critical resource for any process. Ensuring that competency is a primary goal of the training process. Like many other activities discussed in this section, training and competency should be evaluated during each and every process-based audit. The focus of this evaluation is on the centralized training functions.

Especially important is the process for identifying competency requirements. Auditors may find that personnel have met all of the defined competencies and have training records to prove it. If the critical competencies are not correctly defined in the first place, though, then the result will be poor-quality products and services, inefficient operations, and lower productivity. It should also be noted that competency identification is not a one-time event. Competency requirements change over time as new methods and technologies are adopted by the organization. I often find that organizations do a good job of identifying procedures personnel must be trained on, but a much poorer job of identifying competencies relating to software programs, maintenance and

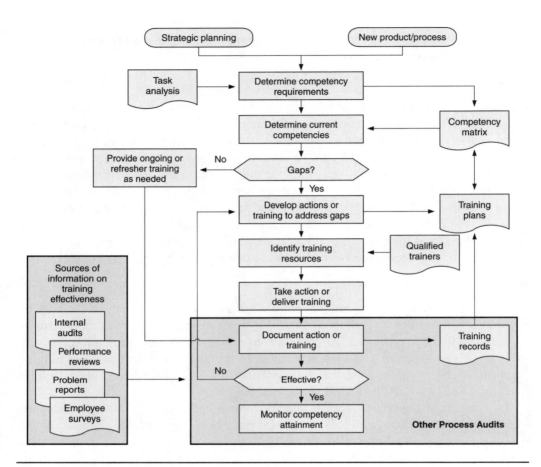

Figure 8.10 The training process.

use of key databases, and proper application of special methods such as failure mode and effects analysis and measurement systems analysis. For this reason, the audit of the centralized training activities focuses on the identification and communication of required competencies.

Another area in which training programs are often deficient is in the verification of training effectiveness. Although tests, pre- and post-training quizzes, and student feedback forms provide some information on the effectiveness of training delivery, the real test is whether personnel can properly do their job. This requires actual observation and ongoing monitoring. Training departments can and should use the results of internal audits, internal and external problem reports, and post-training feedback to evaluate how effective the training program is. A generic training process is shown in Figure 8.10.

Audit Strategy

The auditor can begin the evaluation by asking to see a copy of the training procedure, if one has been developed. Note that ISO/TS 16949 requires a documented procedure for training. Most procedures are laid out along the natural flow of the process, which in this case would be identification of competency requirements, delivery of training, and verification of training effectiveness. Ask the auditee to walk you through the process, paying particular attention to the following items.

• *Competency requirements.* The auditor should ask to see the competency matrix or its equivalent that identifies the competencies that must be achieved. Some organizations use job descriptions to identify competency requirements. While I don't necessarily like this method, if they adequately define the required competencies and are maintained, then I accept them.

The auditor should use his or her knowledge of the tasks performed within the organization to evaluate several functions for review. It helps if the audit program manager selects more experienced auditors to do this evaluation since they will have a better idea of the types of competencies required to perform functional tasks as a result of their previous audits. As an alternative, this review could be added to other process audit checklists. Although it would add to the length of time required to perform the audit, it would result in a more thorough and penetrating evaluation since the auditor would be very familiar with the types of competencies required, having just evaluated the process. It would also result in better coverage than could be attained from a sampling of functional duties performed. Be aware, however, that to do a credible job, auditors must be trained to ask probing questions. Just verifying that training records exist for operators will not adequately evaluate this process.

As the auditor reviews the competency requirements, he or she should pay particular attention to the scope of knowledge requirements and skills listed. Only listing procedures that personnel must be trained on fails to acknowledge the importance of competency in the use of software packages, databases, and tools such as FMEA, design for manufacturability and assembly, value stream analysis, finite element analysis, target costing, autonomous maintenance, lean and the use of the kanban system, materials requirements planning, or any number of other methods that are commonly used in today's organization. Some of these skills may have been obtained through previous education and experience—even so, they should be listed. Evaluation of current skills and training needs is the second part of the process. For production operators these skills are often incorporated into on-the-job training (OJT). If so, the auditor should ask to see the training plan or records for OJT to verify that necessary skills are identified and are being consistently provided to operators. Lack of a defined plan for OJT could be the basis for an NC. Without a plan, it is doubtful that OJT will be provided at a consistently high level.

During this review, the auditor should use knowledge of current problems and issues obtained during the planning phase to focus on areas of training weakness. If the company has had numerous complaints about the responsiveness of customer service representatives, the auditor should question what competencies are required to properly respond to customer inquiries and issues, and should verify that these skills or competencies are identified on the matrix. Later the auditor can probe more deeply into how these skills are taught and whether customer service personnel have obtained the required competencies. During this evaluation the auditor is testing the awareness and responsiveness of the training function as much as the customer service function.

The auditor should also question which competencies and skills are mandatory (required) and which are focused on growth and development (optional). New employees and employees rotating into new positions never come in fully trained. It takes some amount of time before they can be relied upon to perform as required without extra supervision and monitoring. I like to ask, "What skills are required before you would trust someone to perform their primary job with only minimal or normal supervision?" These skills and knowledge are the mandatory, or required, skills. Other skills, such as team problem solving, FMEA, and production forecasting may be advanced skills that should be mastered over a longer period of time. Some companies use functional skill levels to help make this distinction—skill level 1 for new operators (basic mandatory skills), skill level 2 (mastery of all basic skills and some additional higher-level skills), and skill level 3 (expert able to train others in use of the applicable skills). Whatever the system used, it is important to put some kind of priority on those skills essential to the basic job and needed to ensure the quality of the product or service provided to the customer. These skills should be provided quickly and to a consistent high quality. Deficiencies in this area should result in an opportunity for improvement or an NC if they can be directly linked to ongoing problems.

The auditor should also ask how competency requirements are updated and maintained. In the dynamic business environment of today, new technologies, methods, and processes are constantly being introduced. Some method of reevaluation and adjustment of competencies should be in place to respond to these dynamics. Some companies place training needs on the strategic planning agenda. Others rely on process owners to update the required skills. The training matrices or job descriptions should be controlled documents and the auditor should be able to identify updates and modifications. If the training matrices have been in use for some time and have never been updated, then the auditor should probe this area. The auditor should verify that some method is in use, otherwise issue an opportunity for improvement.

Finally, note that identification of required competencies requires the support of the various department and process owners who know the tasks best. Human resources really can't do a credible job without their input. Some type of formal or informal task analysis is required. Since so many different owners are involved in determining competency requirements, there is often a wide variance in the level of detail and quality of the output (the competency requirements). Auditors should be sensitive to this variation and should note functions where it doesn't look like much effort was put into defining the required competencies.

• *Competency attainment.* The next task is to verify that adequate progress is being made to attain the mandatory competencies. The auditor can ask how competency attainment is monitored. Competency attainment may be indicated on the competency matrix or on an individual's training plans. If the organization has criteria for training, such as "basic required skills must be attained during the initial three-month probationary period," then the auditor can sample several recently hired personnel (between three and six months ago) to see if the policy is being followed. Normally the auditor will select records of personnel hired since the training procedure or program was established. Employees who were working at the organization prior to that time are often grandfathered in, based on their previous demonstrated skills or experience. I accept this as long as there is some evidence that some review of their current skills against the newly identified competencies was performed and they weren't just signed off en masse as being competent. The evidence, if not in writing, may be in the form of an interview with the functional head of the department responsible for identifying and verifying current competencies.

The auditor is now looking to see if competency gaps have been identified and if actions to close those gaps are being taken, normally through the scheduling of training on an individual's training plan. This also indirectly monitors the deployment of resources in support of training. In today's lean and cost conscious business environment, it is not uncommon to find that the first thing cut is the training budget. Failure to meet established training goals, or recurring delays in providing required training due to resource limitations, should be noted as findings. Delays in providing optional training can be justified, delays in providing mandatory training cannot. If the auditor finds that mandatory training is not being provided, then he or she should inquire as to what safeguards are being taken to protect the customer pending provision of the training.

The auditor is primarily looking for trends and broad issues with competency attainment, since the training and competency of operators should be reviewed during other process-based audits. Because the competency of personnel is so critical to customer satisfaction and because training is so often underfunded or understaffed, this broad review is appropriate.

• *Verification of training effectiveness.* Training verification should verify that employees can actually do their jobs as a result of the training. Most verification instead evaluates training delivery and is highly biased toward the presentation skills of the trainer, the quality of the visual aids, or the trainer's skill in prepping the trainees for the post-training quiz. Effective verification normally requires observation of the individual performing the task, evaluation of indicators that he or she can or can't perform the task correctly, or feedback from the individual *after* trying to apply the training on the job. Direct observation works well for tasks with little variety. Tasks that may be hard to completely define, such as most service activities, as well as engineering, sales, and planning, need additional means of verification. This can come from reviews of customer feedback (both praise and complaints), problem reports, and returned products. In addition, direct employee communication about how well they felt the training prepared them to perform the task should be solicited, normally during periodic performance reviews.

During this phase of the evaluation, the auditor should verify that methods are in place to determine training effectiveness. The indicators are there in the form of internal audit reports, problem reports, customer feedback, and performance review comments. The question now is, are they being used by the training department and/or process owners to systematically make improvements in the training provided to employees? A blank stare in response to this question, or a truthful, "We don't measure training effectiveness" should result in an NC. Use of simple pre- and post-tests and training feedback forms should result in an OFI that recommends consideration be given to including these other sources discussed here to measure training effectiveness. Because of the cost of training and the resource constraints discussed in the previous section, training that *is* given must be effective. If not, it must be modified to become effective.

• *Strategic training.* This last area is not required by the ISO 9001 standard or by ISO/TS 16949. I still recommend it for organizations that are determined to get the most from their quality management system. It is based on the theory that not all competencies are created equal. Some competencies may be critical to an organization's ability to achieve their strategic objectives. As an example, if an organization is competing on a low-cost provider strategy and has identified the implementation and rollout of a Six Sigma program as a strategic initiative designed to reinforce that strategy, then the training of Green Belts and Black Belts becomes a strategic training issue. Likewise, the attainment of a capability to deploy design for manufacturability and assembly techniques may be flagged as strategic in this company. A company that is trying to improve its product development capabilities (cycle time and competitiveness of products) may see quality function deployment as a critical skill. Companies that have adopted a balanced scorecard approach are particularly inclined to label some training as strategic in nature, owing to the learning and growth perspective that is a feature of most scorecards.

The auditor can evaluate the strategic deployment of training by asking the training manager which competencies or skills have been targeted as strategic. For these, the auditor can then verify that plans are in place to rapidly provide the training necessary to achieve the competency needed. Failure to schedule the training or to provide the training as scheduled should be noted as a finding, the nature of which takes on strategic importance.

The discussion in this section has assumed that the organization has a centralized training function. Some organizations decentralize their training, assigning responsibility for everything to process owners and department managers. In this case the auditor would conduct the evaluation as outlined, but would need to interview several different department owners rather than the human resources manager or training coordinator. An audit plan outlining the interview schedule would be appropriate here. While the audit will take significantly longer to perform, it is probably more important, since decentralization results in many more individuals becoming involved in the control of training. This often results in ineffective training and a loss of control of the training process in isolated departments. It also opens up the opportunities to identify and communicate best training practices that should be communicated to other departments, a topic that will be discussed in more detail in Chapter 13.

Performance Indicators

Auditors should expect to find some kind of performance indicators in use to monitor training performance. Some common measures include:

- Training hours per employee

- Percent of employees considered fully trained or qualified

- Percent required competencies achieved

- Percent strategic competencies achieved

- Number of corrective actions citing training as the root cause or corrective action

This last metric can be used to verify the effectiveness of the overall process and should always be reviewed or developed by the auditor during evaluations of the training process. If the auditor finds a repetitive pattern of corrective actions citing the root cause as operator error or operator mistake or corrective action as retrain the operator, then the auditor should question the effectiveness of the training process itself. Effective training should equip employees to do the job correctly and should not have to be constantly repeated. Often, citing operator error is a way to get around determining the real root cause. Nonetheless, the auditor must base findings on the facts encountered, and the facts documented and accepted by the organization would indicate problems with the training program. In other words, call their bluff. During the evaluation of the cause of ineffective training the auditee may discover that the root cause is not really the training program, but is instead a failure to take the time to do good root cause analysis. Permanent corrective action may include training on how to do effective root cause analysis and a more careful review of the root cause cited in future corrective action requests. In citing the training program for a lack of effectiveness, the auditor will have prompted important and needed changes to the way the organization fixes problems.

Purchasing

Procurement is a critical process that is not significantly evaluated during other process-based audits. This process can easily be evaluated separately and probably should be if performance information identifies issues with supplied parts or materials. In these situations a deeper dive in the procurement process is warranted and more time will be required. Careful planning and preparation is critical to focus the audit on weak areas.

Considering the increased use of outsourcing for activities ranging from manufacturing to design and call center management, the verification of supplier capabilities and ongoing monitoring of their performance is a strategic issue. If your organization relies extensively on suppliers to ensure the quality of your products and services, then auditors need to be prepared to go well beyond verifying that the minimum requirements of the ISO 9001 or ISO/TS 16949 requirements are met and should focus also on the effectiveness of the overall procurement process. The communication and relationship with key suppliers should be evaluated, along with efforts to develop these suppliers.

The general structure of a procurement process is illustrated in Figure 8.11. Note that some of the activities associated with this process may have already been evaluated

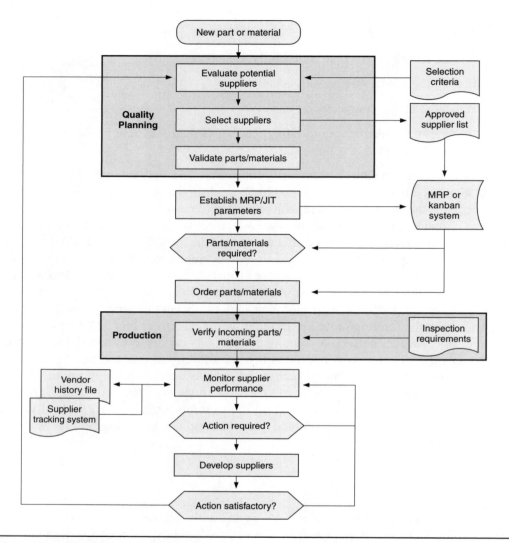

Figure 8.11   The procurement process.

during reviews of the quality planning process and during production or service delivery audits. The discussion that follows will focus on the overall procurement process, as opposed to the procurement planning that goes on during product design or verification of incoming materials.

Audit Strategy

As mentioned earlier, audit planning is especially important when evaluating the purchasing process. Prior to the audit, the auditor should review performance information relating to the quality and timeliness of incoming parts, materials, and/or services. The auditor may also want to stop by shipping and receiving or quality assurance to identify recent receipts of nonconforming product. These will be used later to select samples for evaluation. Finally, the auditor may also want to obtain the bill of material for several of the company's products, again to help select samples to evaluate during the audit. Armed with this information, the auditor is ready to proceed to the purchasing department.

As usual, the audit starts by asking the auditee if there is a procedure that describes the purchasing process. After noting the revision date for later comparison against the master list, the auditor should ask the auditee to walk through the process, stopping to ask questions relating to the topics below as they are encountered during the review. Since this is an area where ISO 9001 has removed the requirement for a written procedure, it is possible, although not likely, that the auditor will find there is no procedure. In this case it is important that the process owner be interviewed first, since he or she establishes the policies. Later interviews with buyers can then determine whether the policies are being followed. The remaining questions may be posed to the purchasing manager or to individual buyers. The initial interview with the process owner will also review process performance metrics and any actions being taken to improve process performance.

I normally start by asking if the company has a listing of approved suppliers. Although no longer required, almost all companies have them since they facilitate efficient purchasing. My first goal is to verify that criteria for selection of suppliers have been established and are being followed. Criteria for evaluation, reevaluation must be defined and should be documented in the organization's policies or procedures. I will normally select several parts or materials off the bill of material (BOM) obtained prior to the audit and ask the auditee who supplied the part or material for this product. I will then verify their inclusion on the approved supplier list (ASL) and will ask about the basis for selecting this supplier. Most companies use survey forms, sample evaluations, recommendations, and/or supplier audits to determine the capabilities of key suppliers. These methods should be documented in the company procedures. If not, I have the purchasing manager describe these methods and note them on my audit checklist.

If most of the current suppliers were grandfathered into the system, then I'll compare the current ASL to an old list if one is available to identify new suppliers who have been added since the requirements for systematic evaluation of new suppliers were issued. If the old ASLs are not retained, or if the list is on a database in real time, then I'll ask the purchasing agent to query the system for suppliers with no records of accounts payable prior to the issue date of the purchasing procedure. This should give me a listing of suppliers who have been added to the ASL since the issuance of the requirements to systematically evaluate new suppliers that I can pick from. Once I have my list of new suppliers, I will select several and will ask to see the results of the evaluations. ISO 9001 requires that the results of these evaluations be documented. At this point the auditor wants to verify that the capabilities of suppliers are evaluated as the basis for their inclusion on the ASL. If the auditor's planning identified difficulties with materials or parts supplied for a new product, then I include the supplier of the material or part in my sample.

It should be noted that ISO/TS 16949 requires that suppliers of production materials, parts, and services be certified as a minimum to ISO 9001:2000. This requirement cannot be grandfathered, so I also ask to see the evidence of certification for a number of suppliers using my bill of materials to help select the samples.

Once the auditor is satisfied with the process used to select capable suppliers, attention is then focused on how these suppliers are monitored and what might trigger a reevaluation of their capabilities and performance. The auditor should verify that required quality and delivery monitoring is being performed for individual suppliers. Performance information may have already been reviewed with the process owner, but I like to have buyers pull up information related to their assigned suppliers to make sure that they are aware of how their suppliers are performing and actions being taken to improve their performance. It also provides the lead-in to my next question: what action is being taken with suppliers associated with known problems? I can get this information from the performance information or from the list of deficient incoming shipments I obtained from receiving or QA prior to the audit. The focus here is to ensure that follow-up on supplier problems is being pursued in accordance with company policy and common sense. Findings are often generated due to a failure to take required action or failure to receive a satisfactory response or action plan from the supplier.

Many companies establish criteria for initial supplier evaluation, but not for reevaluation. I normally ask, "What would it take to get a supplier kicked off the approved supplier list?" Using the performance information reviewed, I then verify that actions are being taken in accordance with this policy, while considering the need to locate and qualify another source of supply before the supplier is removed. If no attempts have been made to locate or qualify an alternate source of supply for a vendor who should be removed, then I issue an NC. If no policy has been established for reevaluation or removal, I issue an OFI or NC, depending on the circumstances and how the company's policies are worded.

Supplier development would come next. As a minimum, ISO/TS 16949 requires that suppliers be encouraged to meet the requirements of the 16949 specification. Additional development activities might include the use of supplier audits (remember, done correctly audits are a *good* thing and can spur improvement), training, and going on-site to help a supplier prepare for a product launch or to improve its processes. This is where supplier partnerships leave the realm of words and become actions that build the long-term relationship. The auditor should not expect to find active supplier development activities going on for every supplier, but he or she should expect to find actions being taken for key suppliers. It is especially important for sole-source providers of key materials, parts, and services and these should be given special scrutiny by the auditor. Failure to find any examples of supplier development, beyond a letter encouraging suppliers to certify to a standard, should result in an OFI. Partnering with suppliers during product, process, and equipment design is also a form of supplier development that should be encouraged.

The auditor should also evaluate the process used to issue purchase orders to suppliers. The auditor should verify that mandatory reviews and approvals are obtained and that information essential to the product or service is provided to the supplier. In addition to having the auditee walk though the procedure, the auditor should observe the auditee preparing and issuing a purchase order if possible.

Other activities that go beyond the minimum requirements of ISO 9001 or ISO/TS 16949 but which may be evaluated include the procurement system itself. The optimization of order points, development of optimum modes of transportation, and control of inventory may be important, especially if the company has experienced stock-outs of required materials, high delivery costs, or high levels of material inventory. In effect, the auditor becomes a troubleshooter, using the identified problems to evaluate the controls in place or being enacted to prevent recurrence of the problems. It is not unusual to find the source of such problems lies with inadequate training, failure to use the system as designed, or a general lack of resources to perform the actions that would prevent the problem. The basic system design may also be a source of the problem, and those involved in the process can usually pinpoint inadequacies of the current system or how it can be improved. The key to evaluating these additional activities is to tie them directly to a current problem or lack of performance. As in any process-based audit, the auditor can also evaluate personnel training, knowledge of roles, responsibilities and authorities, resources, and the control of documents and records.

Performance Indicators

The auditor can expect to find a number of measures of purchasing process performance since supplier monitoring is required by the quality management system standards. Additional metrics may be available to measure productivity or efficiency. These metrics should be used by the auditor to evaluate overall system performance and to focus the audit. Common metrics include:

- Supplier quality performance
- Supplier delivery performance
- Premium freight
- Number of suppliers
- Requisition to order cycle time
- Requisition backlog
- Items on back-order
- Stock-outs, production material, and parts
- Order to delivery cycle time
- Percent of suppliers just-in-time

MONITORING, MEASUREMENT, AND IMPROVEMENT

These activities measure the performance of the management system and its related processes and initiates actions to it where needed. These processes are directly related, with one process providing essential inputs into the next. I recommend starting with a review of customer satisfaction indicators, including the methods used to generate and validate this information. The information gained from this review can help the auditor focus the review of the remaining processes in this group. The auditor can next evaluate the internal audit process and then move into the corrective and preventive action process using the corrective actions resulting from the internal audits as samples. Next, the auditor can examine the analysis of data, having just reviewed many of the sources of information that should be included in the analysis. Finally, the results of the data analysis should result in targets for improvement.

Customer Satisfaction Monitoring

Monitoring of customer satisfaction is required. Methods used to measure customer satisfaction may include the following:

- Surveys

- Quality and delivery indices

- Customer feedback, including complaints

- Customer rating systems

Auditors should verify that methods are in place to measure customer satisfaction and that these sources are used to identify areas requiring improvement. The auditor should question indicators that show poor or declining performance to identify whether actions have been initiated to turn the performance around.

Internal Audits

Auditors should be familiar with the internal audit process. The focus of this evaluation will be on audit scheduling, reporting of the results of the audit, and follow-up on audit findings. In addition, the auditor should evaluate the performance of the overall audit process.

The auditor can also evaluate audit planning and the thoroughness and completeness of the audits themselves if checklists similar to those included on the CD are used and are completed by internal auditors. Keep in mind that the auditor cannot audit his or her own audits. It may be advisable to use auditors who do not report directly to the audit program manager to minimize auditor bias. A general audit process is shown in Figure 8.12.

The auditor should commence the audit by interviewing the audit program manager. Ask to see the audit procedure and the audit schedule. Walk through the process with the audit program manager. Inquire about the rationale for the scheduling of the audits. Review the discussion on audit schedules in Chapter 4. Verify that status and importance of processes are considerations during audit scheduling. The auditor should also use the knowledge gained during the review of customer satisfaction to help evaluate status. It would be reasonable to expect additional audits of areas associated with

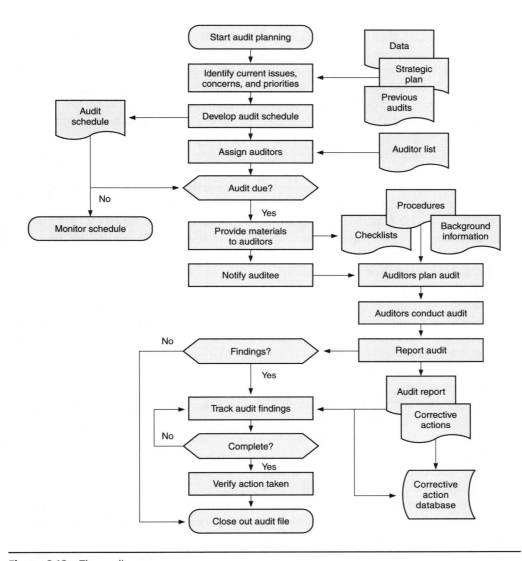

Figure 8.12 The audit process.

product or service problems. If the auditor notes that all areas are scheduled once per year, then consider issuing an opportunity for improvement or NC if significant problem areas exist.

The auditor can then examine audit performance. Are audits being completed per the schedule? Probe into the reasons for significant slippages to the schedule. Insufficient numbers of trained auditors or difficulty getting part-time auditors released to perform audits may explain the inability to get the audits done. Note that some rearrangement of the audit schedule should be expected if the audit program manager is responsive to the status and importance when scheduling audits.

The auditor can then pick several audit reports and any checklists retained from those audits to determine if the audits are focusing on known problems. As noted in earlier chapters, it is not reasonable to expect each audit to verify all possible inputs, resources, and controls, but if the auditor noted that none of the audits evaluated operator competency or document control or other common inputs, then this should be noted since the audits of the centralized activities these processes support assumes that these inputs will be evaluated routinely during process-based audits.

The auditor should compare the systemic weaknesses noted in these audit reports to external audits of the same areas or processes. If external audits found systemic weaknesses in areas where internal audits did not, then this may indicate a lack of effectiveness of the internal audit process. The internal audit must have been performed prior to and around the same period of time for this comparison to be valid.

The auditor can also evaluate the completeness of the audit reports and timeliness of their issuance against local requirements. The auditor may also want to verify auditor training and independence, if not known.

Audit findings should be reviewed. Auditors should evaluate whether the audit findings contain sufficient detail to fully understand the deficiency, opportunity, or best practice. Any nonconformance reports or corrective action requests should get special attention. If the auditor cannot understand the issue from reading the finding, then there is a high likelihood the auditee may not either. If the auditor finds numerous poorly worded or incomplete write-ups, then a finding should be generated.

The auditor should now ask to see the tracking system used to monitor the status of actions associated with audit nonconformances. The audit program manager may have a separate tracking system or may use the corrective action system. The auditor should check on the status of any audit nonconformances, evaluating whether action to correct the finding is proceeding. Any instances of overdue, outstanding corrective action should be investigated. Unless there is additional evidence of actions being taken to resolve the problem, issue an NC. Audits provide no value if action is not taken to resolve the deficiencies they find. Also confirm that verification of action taken is being performed and that audits are being used to verify the long-term effectiveness of actions taken to address nonconformities identified during previous audits.

Finally, the auditor should also confirm that the final audit file contains the information required by the local procedure. Typically this include the audit report and any checklists used. Maintaining the checklists is not mandatory unless required by local procedures, although I strongly recommend it.

Corrective and Preventive Action

If the internal audit program uses the corrective action system to administer and track audit nonconformities, then the last interview should easily flow into an evaluation of the corrective and preventive action systems. Before we discuss audit strategy, let me give you my operational definitions of corrective action, preventive action, and continual improvement.

- *Corrective action:* action taken to identify and eliminate the causes of an actual nonconformity.

- *Preventive action:* action taken to identify and eliminate the causes of a potential nonconformity.

- *Continual improvement:* action taken to improve a product, process, or system that is not associated with a nonconformity.

Although most readers of this book are already familiar with the definitions of corrective and preventive action, I often find confusion among auditees as to what constitutes preventive action, what constitutes corrective action, and what constitutes continual improvement. This confusion becomes evident when I ask for examples of preventive action and continual improvement. Corrective and preventive action only applies to nonconformities—there must be a violation or potential violation of requirements. Continual improvement applies, at least in a specific sense, to items not connected to any requirement. Implementing lean manufacturing concepts, when there is no requirement to do so, is an improvement. Note that from a systems perspective, continual improvement is built into an ISO 9001 quality management system. Clause 8.5.1 clearly indicates that complying with the other requirements in the standard, including those discussed in this section and those discussed in the next, taken together satisfies the requirements for continual improvement. ISO/TS 16949, however, goes further. It requires a defined process for continual improvement and reduction in manufacturing variation. Defined processes may include:

- Kaizen

- Lean manufacturing principles, including 5S, just-in-time, and total productive maintenance

- Value stream mapping and management

- Six Sigma

- Quality circles

- Design of experiments

- Statistical process control

Some of the projects undertaken may be corrective or preventive, if they are focused on meeting requirements. Others may be improvements, if they are not focused on requirements.

Now let's turn our attention to the corrective and preventive action process. Refer to Figure 8.13 for a generic process flow. Note that preventive action opportunities may be identified through the use of preventive tools like FMEA or through analysis of previous problem indicators and trends that may not have been evident during the correction of the specific problem.

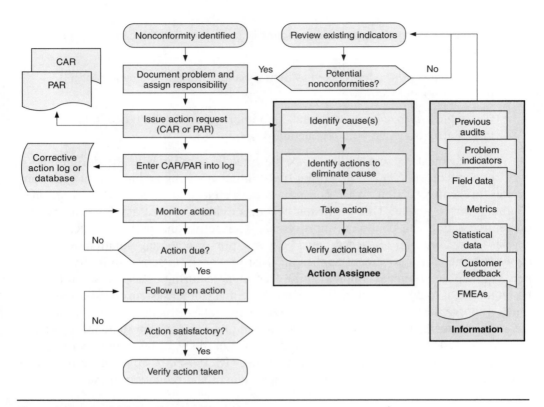

Figure 8.13   Corrective and preventive action.

Audit Strategy

The auditor should begin by asking to see the procedure(s) for corrective and preventive action. Ask the program coordinator to walk you through the process, stopping to ask questions and to view evidence for the upcoming key points. During the review, verify through an evaluation of the log, database, and corrective and preventive actions that information and timing requirements mandated by local procedures are being met. The reader may want to review the section on audit tracking systems in Chapter 7 before proceeding.

• *Corrective action use.* I often find that the only time a corrective action is issued is after an audit nonconformity is received. This indicates a lack of understanding of the corrective action process or a lack of commitment to invest the time required to identify true root cause and actions to prevent recurrence. The corrective action program should be used anytime a problem associated with a customer or local requirement requires root cause determination and action to prevent recurrence.

While some isolated problems may not require corrective action, repetitive or significant problems do. Problems involving product or service design, rejected and returned product, and repeated labeling problems are a few examples where corrective action is warranted. Taking care of these problems informally forgoes the benefits that a disciplined problem-solving methodology enacted through the corrective action process provides. Problems are likely to recur, but failure to identify them using the corrective action process makes them hard to monitor. Auditors should issue an OFI if they find that all or a majority of the corrective action requests were generated through the audit process. In addition, the audit program manager should add questions to other audit checklists to evaluate employee awareness and understanding of the corrective action process in this case.

• *Corrective and preventive action tracking.* Verify that the program coordinator is actively monitoring the status of outstanding corrective and preventive actions. Outstanding, overdue corrective actions should be followed up on, and bumped up to more senior management if follow-up is not successful in getting action to occur.

• *Quality of the action taken.* By this I mean, did the action taken to address the problem address immediate and containment actions, any short-term or temporary actions, long-term action to eliminate the cause and prevent recurrence, and any remedial action that may have been necessary? The reader should review the section in Chapter 7 on verifying audit corrective action for examples of each. These same action categories apply to nonaudit corrective and preventive actions. In addition, the auditor should ask questions to see if consideration was given to applying the results of the investigation and actions to other similar processes, products, and/or services. ISO/TS 16949 requires this consideration.

• *Rejected product test/analysis.* Automotive companies subscribing to ISO/TS 16949 must have a dedicated process to analyze product rejected by its customers. The auditor should review this process, ensuring that analysis is done in a timely manner, is documented, and that actions are taken to address the problems the analysis uncovers.

• *Problem-solving process.* ISO/TS 16949 requires a dedicated problem-solving process. For customer-initiated corrective action, the specification requires use of the customer-prescribed format, if one exists. Auditors in automotive companies should ensure that any customer-mandated formats are used when addressing corrective action for customer-initiated problems.

• *Action verification.* The auditor should confirm that the planned action was performed. In addition, long-term verification of the effectiveness of the action taken (Did it eliminate the cause?) may be appropriate for significant problems.

• *Preventive action opportunities.* The auditor should ask the program coordinator how preventive action opportunities are identified. Methods may include the use of the FMEA process or the analysis of multiple sources of information. Note that some tools like FMEA may have their own action tracking systems that would preclude issuance of a preventive action request (PAR). Even so, these actions still represent preventive action. The auditor should also ask for examples of preventive action taken since the last audit. If no examples can be provided, the auditor may want to initiate an opportunity for improvement since the capabilities of the preventive action methodology are not being used.

• *Process effectiveness.* The purpose of the corrective action process is to prevent recurrence of problems. The auditor should examine the extent to which this goal is being achieved by examining corrective actions issued since the last audit. The auditor is looking for repeat occurrences of the same problem description or the same root cause. A few repeat occurrences should be expected—we don't always nail the root cause correctly on the first attempt. Numerous recurrences indicate that the process for identifying root cause or for taking action to eliminate it is not effective. If the review shows numerous repeat occurrences of the same problem or same root cause, then issue an NC against the effectiveness of the corrective action process, citing the occurrences as the basis for the finding.

Analysis of Data

Data analysis is an often ill-defined process that takes all of the information generated from monitoring and measurement along with process and product performance information and through careful analysis generates outputs in the form of targeted areas for improvement. The key attributes of this process that should be verified include:

• What information is collected and reviewed?

• How is the information collected?

• Who performs the analysis?

• How are the results of the analysis recorded and reported?

• What outcomes arise out of the review (that is, results)?

Few companies have documented procedures for this process, and those that do normally use the procedure to identify what information is collected, by whom, when, and how is it reported. Where a documented procedure exists, it should be used to guide the auditor. Where it doesn't, the auditor should evaluate the process using the five basic attributes just identified.

Note that analysis of data should be an ongoing activity at all levels of the organization. In effect, auditing for effectiveness as has been presented throughout this handbook evaluates how well process owners use the performance information they obtain to correct and improve their processes. The focus of this audit will be to evaluate periodic, global reviews of data, normally undertaken prior to the management review or setting of quality objectives. While it's possible that an organization may not perform this kind of a focused analysis outside of the management review, it is unlikely. It is doubtful that senior management would want to sit through an exhaustive review of all of the items that must be discussed per clause 5.6. Such an evaluation could take a day or longer if the management review is held annually. Instead, this review can be done prior to the review and the results summarized to management. Auditors should therefore verify that this analysis is performed prior to the review, not during it. If it is not done prior to the review, then auditors should more thoroughly investigate the content of the management review itself to ensure adequate time is spent reviewing the details of the information required to be discussed.

As a minimum, the auditor should verify that customer satisfaction information, data relating to product conformity, process metrics and trends, information used to identify preventive action opportunities, and information on supplier quality and delivery performance is collected. These are required by ISO 9001. Additional information that should be analyzed includes internal and external audit results, corrective actions, and customer feedback that doesn't directly relate to satisfaction. Note that this analysis may be used to identify preventive action opportunities as shown in Figure 8.13. The auditor should ask to see the results of the last review to verify that sources required by the standard and by local procedures were included in this review. Note that the records of this review may be embedded in the management review records as discussed in the preceding paragraph.

Auditors should verify that the methods used to collect the information gather all relevant data that should be considered in the analysis. Since the information can come from many different sources, it is important to ensure that all of the important information finds its way into the review. Only looking at some of the supplier information or a few process metrics may result in an incomplete or even misleading analysis result.

Although portions of the analysis may be decentralized, someone has to be responsible for the overall process and needs to summarize the results for presentation to management. Are responsibilities assigned for data collection, analysis, and summarization?

Results may be presented in the form of tables, graphs, or trends. Recommendations for action may also be reported as a result of the analysis. Look for evidence that the results of the review find their way to those responsible for actions and decisions.

Look for evidence of actions or decisions based on the results of the analysis. If the review is conducted to support the management review, then this may be deferred until the audit of management review is conducted. If global data analysis is performed outside of the management review process, look for evidence of action in the form of corrective actions, preventive actions, objectives, and improvement projects initiated as a result of the analysis.

Continual Improvement

Finally, the auditor should verify that improvement of products and to the management system processes and systems is occurring. As noted previously, continual improvement is built into the ISO 9001 standard and meeting the requirements for corrective and preventive action; establishing a quality policy and setting objectives to meet the commitments embedded in the policy; performing effective internal audits; and analyzing and acting on data and information all provide evidence of improvement. By this stage of the audit the auditor should know whether the organization is meeting the requirements of ISO 9001 for continual improvement.

If the organization has other defined improvement processes, then this audit may be used to evaluate these processes. Note that ISO/TS 16949 requires defined processes for continual improvement. Methods may include Six Sigma, value stream mapping and management, value analysis, kaizen events, or lean. If defined procedures exist for these improvement processes, then the auditor can evaluate conformance to the established processes and the results from their use. If the organization has not formally defined these processes, which is often the case, then consideration should be given to using auditors who have been trained in the application of these tools for this evaluation. As long as they do not audit their own work this is acceptable. Generically, the key evaluation points for the auditor would be the following:

• *How are improvement projects identified?* Are there mechanisms to involve employees and to bubble and capture their ideas and proposals?

• *How are projects selected?* Are there criteria for acceptance or rejection of project proposals? This is especially important for programs like Six Sigma where significant dedication of resources and time is required.

• *Is the process being followed?* For programs like Six Sigma or lean, there are definite stages to the deployment of the tool. If the process is not followed, the results may suffer.

• *How are projects monitored?* The auditor can verify that the project is being monitored. For major projects like Six Sigma and lean, this can be important given the resources applied to the project. For more evolutionary improvement programs like quality circles and kaizen, it may not be so critical until the project comes to the action stage.

• *How are recommendations for action reported, and how are they approved?* The methods used to review and approve project proposals for action can be important to employee attitudes toward the program, as well as results.

• *Are the approved actions implemented?* Once approved, the actions need to be implemented. Auditors can evaluate the timeliness of action implementation and resources provided for deployment.

• *Were the actions effective?* The auditor should note if post-implementation monitoring is conducted to document performance gains from the improvement project. This is important to maintain ongoing support and commitment to the improvement program, and to make adjustments to the project selection and approval process. It also provides the evidence needed to establish best practices that should be given wider dissemination throughout the company.

I have evaluated numerous continual improvement programs where I have seen a high level of enthusiasm replaced with a general disregard for the methodology after the low-hanging fruit has been picked. The key to maintaining a healthy program is to continually evaluate the process and to make improvements to the improvement program itself. Unfortunately, continual improvement programs are rarely evaluated for improvement. Auditors should evaluate such programs for opportunities to make the process more productive and efficient in accordance with the organization's evolving needs.

KEY AUDIT POINT: MANAGEMENT RESPONSIBILITY

The final phase of our management system audit examines some of the key requirements that require active management involvement and support. By now auditors should be aware that many of the requirements contained in clause 5.0, Management responsibility, of ISO 9001 will be continually reviewed during other process-based audits. Examples include roles, responsibilities, and authorities and the provision of resources. This audit therefore focuses on two specific responsibilities that have not been fully evaluated, but which are vital to the quality program. They are the conduct of management reviews and the setting and achievement of quality objectives.

The introduction to this chapter noted that different groupings of audit topics beyond the ones that I have presented here are possible and may even be desirable to allow for a more efficient and effective audit. These last two audit topics are a case in point. They have been grouped together because many organizations use the management review to review current performance toward achieving defined objectives and to set new objectives. Therefore, it makes sense to evaluate them together. Likewise, in organizations where the analysis of data (including customer satisfaction metrics) and evaluation of continual improvement projects is an integral part of the management review, then it would make more sense to combine these activities with the management review and quality objectives audits discussed below.

Management Review

The purpose of the management review is to drive action. The auditor must always keep this in mind, since many organizations have evolved their management review to little more than a short status review. The management review is the key forum for management to get active and engaged in improving the quality systems performance and for driving action that leads to improvement. While management should demonstrate their overall commitment and support on a routine, day-in and day-out basis, the management review is somewhat like a strategic planning session, where high-level decisions and actions on what the organization needs to do are generated and then deployed. Management reviews should be major events in the lifecycle of the quality management system. Unfortunately the opposite is often true—the management review is a short, one- or two-hour report-out once a year that must be endured, versus anticipated.

Unfortunately, there may be little that the audit program can do in this situation, other than to verify that the minimum requirements of the standard are being met. This section will discuss how to verify that the management review meets these minimum requirements. Beyond that, the audit program manager may want to have senior management review chapters 1 and 2 and the section on the role of senior management in Chapter 4 to help foster a more positive attitude toward the quality management system in general and the management review as a tool to drive improvements in the QMS.

I normally like to interview the senior manager or executive during the evaluation of the management review process. If a procedure is available, I use it to follow along as the manager describes the process used to conduct the review. I also ask for the records from the last two management reviews conducted. The following requirements should be verified by the auditor while evaluating the management review process:

• *Who attends?* The management review is a top-level review. Most auditors consider top management to consist of the senior person at a facility and his or her direct staff. While not everyone has to be there, a majority should attend. If the organization has a procedure that provides guidance on who should attend, then the auditor should audit to that guidance.

• *How often are management reviews held?* The management review must be held at planned intervals. How long should that interval be? That really depends on the maturity and status of the quality management system. Most auditors consider annual reviews to be the minimum frequency. If the management system is relatively new, or if performance indicators show major problems with the organization's processes, then more frequent reviews are probably appropriate. Put it this way—if audits and performance trends indicate that the management system is in shambles, and if the frequency of the management review has been left unchanged at annually, then a finding is warranted.

• *How long does the review take?* While there is no required duration for the management review, the auditor should use what has been learned from the evaluations of the other improvement processes to evaluate whether sufficient time is being provided to conduct a thorough review. If a global review and analysis of data was performed prior to the review, then performance information could be summarized, shortening the time for the review. If the analysis of data will be performed as part of the review, then more time will be required. I find it hard to believe that an annual management review could be conducted in under two or three hours under any circumstances. I could see an hour-long review if it were held monthly, as is the case in some companies, where a portion of the system is evaluated at each review. Since there is no stated duration for the review, and since it is hard to tie duration directly to effectiveness, I do not issue findings relating to duration. I do use the auditee's answer to evaluate how deeply I research into other aspects of the review, however.

• *What sources of information are included in the review?* The auditor should look for evidence that the required inputs into the review are evaluated. These include:

– The results of audits.

– Customer feedback.

– Process performance indicators.

– Product conformance indicators.

– Status of corrective and preventive actions.

– Follow-up actions from previous reviews. (This is why I ask to see records of the last two reviews.)

 – Changes that could affect the quality management system (for example, new technologies, new processes, new customers, new facilities).

 – Recommendations for improvement.

ISO/TS 16949 adds to this list an analysis of actual and potential field failures and their impact on quality, safety, and the environment. It also requires management review of performance toward the achievement of quality objectives, review of customer satisfaction, and evaluation of the cost of poor quality.

There must be solid evidence that these items were included in the review, preferably as discussion points in the records or meeting minutes from the review. If the only evidence is that they showed up on the agenda, then look for evidence of their review in the actions arising from the review or ask the auditee to summarize the results presented for these items. If all show up on the agenda, but some have no discussion in the records, then I generally accept the evidence on the agenda. If there is no evidence for these items, or if the only evidence is the agenda (that is, there are no actions or discussion of the items in the records or meeting minutes, the auditee can't remember specifics of what was discussed), then I issue an NC. The standard requires that records of the management review, and any actions arising from it, be maintained.

 • *What actions resulted from the review?* Clause 5.6.3 of the ISO 9001 standard requires that the output from the management review include any decisions or actions relating to improvement of products, processes, or systems and resource needs. Clearly the intent of such a high-level review is to drive action. The auditor should review the records of the review to determine if actions are an output from the review. If my review of the last two management reviews fails to identify any actions or decisions arising from the review, then I issue an NC or an OFI, depending on what my knowledge of the quality management system status is. If the quality management system is falling down around our ears based on audit reports, customer feedback, and process performance data, then I issue an NC. If the quality management system is in reasonably good shape based on these indicators, then I issue an OFI. If the system is in great shape, then I may not issue a finding. The key to being able to generate a finding is to tie it into system status.

 • *How are the actions tracked?* If there were actions arising from the review, then ask how these actions are tracked. Use the records from the last management review to determine if the actions arising from the review were completed and/or discussed during the most current review. I normally issue an OFI if I find that there is no formal system for tracking actions arising from the review other than going back and looking at the review records from a year ago.

The auditor must use ample tact and perspective when evaluating the management review process. Senior managers may support findings in other areas of the company, but now you are hitting closer to home. Don't push too hard, but rather point out the benefits that a robust management review should provide. Tie findings into other problems noted during earlier audits. Reinforce the consequences of system failures, where known. You have to make them want to spend the time to do a thorough review.

Quality Objectives

The final item to evaluate is the setting and tracking of quality objectives. Many companies review and set quality system objectives during the management review process. In this case, this topic should be discussed during the evaluation of the management review. ISO/TS 16949 in particular requires evaluation of performance in achieving quality objectives as part of the management review.

Note that quality objectives are required to be set at relevant levels and functions throughout the organization and include objectives for product or service quality. Product- and process-level objectives will normally be deployed through design goals, product, service, and process criteria, and through goals and targets for process performance. This level of objective setting and attainment should be evaluated continuously during other audits as has been discussed throughout this handbook. Auditing for effectiveness specifically evaluates the achievement of these objectives. The discussion that follows applies to major organizational quality goals focused on major elements of the quality management processes or support functions. They focus primarily on improvement versus conformance to customer requirements. If the reader is familiar with the ISO 14001 environmental management system, then you could correlate these quality objectives with the goal of moving beyond compliance toward a more productive, efficient management system.

The auditor should start by asking to see a list of current quality objectives for the organization. Many organizations set annual quality objectives, in which case the auditor should ask to see the current and maybe the previous year's objectives. Note that in Chapter 4, I recommend scheduling the analysis and improvement and executive support audits (that is, this one) at the end of the year, which allows the auditor to gauge how well the organization did in achieving its quality objectives. If the organization has a documented procedure for setting objectives, then this should also be reviewed and the auditee asked to walk through the process.

How many objectives does an organization need to set? The standard doesn't say. As a minimum, you need to have at least one. If you only have one, however, then it should be a big one. Implementation of lean manufacturing in a major production process or making significant measurable improvement in your customer satisfaction ratings would qualify as major organizational quality objectives. The auditor should verify that the objectives, whatever they might be, are measurable and include time frames for accomplishment. The auditor should also verify deployment of the objectives to relevant functions and levels of the organization. This normally means the setting of more focused targets for improvement at lower levels and departments. Objectives should also have champions and action assignments.

After reviewing the objectives themselves, the auditor should review how the objectives are tracked along with performance toward achieving them. Setting intermediate milestones and actions that allow assessment of performance toward the objective is important. If the auditors find that the only monitoring of achievement is at the end of the year, then they should issue a finding.

If the auditor determines that performance toward achieving the stated objectives is lagging, then he or she should ask what actions are being taken to improve performance. If reasonable actions are being taken to restore performance, then the auditor should accept it, unless it's a clear case of too little, too late. In this case, an OFI should be issued, unless there is a systematic and sustained pattern of inadequate action and poor performance in achieving objectives, in which case the auditor could issue an NC.

Finally, note that ISO/TS 16949 requires that quality objectives be reflected in the business plan. In other words, the organization's quality objectives should be viewed as a strategic issue. Alignment of the organization's quality management system with its strategic goals through the proper deployment of a balanced scorecard helps to ensure this alignment.

Monitoring, Measurement, and Improvement Performance Indicators

The auditor may find any of the following performance indicators in use to monitor these activities:

- Customer satisfaction ratings or survey results
- Percent internal audits performed on schedule
- Number of qualified internal auditors
- Percent corrective actions recurred
- Dollars saved through corrective action
- Ratio corrective to preventive actions
- Number or percent of corrective actions overdue
- Cycle time, returned product analysis
- Number of improvement suggestions per employee
- Dollars saved, continual improvement projects
- Number of continual improvement projects completed
- Number or percent of quality objectives achieved or on track

SUMMARY

This chapter discussed a general strategy for conducting an audit of a quality management system. Both the macrostrategy and strategies for each major process were presented, along with tips for verifying the effectiveness of the activities. This chapter can serve as a reference to the auditor to assist in the planning of his or her audit.

The auditor will need to customize the strategy to suit the nature and importance of the individual organization's products and processes. The checklists on the CD that accompanies this handbook support the strategies provided and should be modified as needed to provide a complete audit strategy for the evaluation of the company's unique processes and local requirements.

9

Conducting Environmental Management System Audits

This chapter will build on parts I and II, applying these concepts to the performance of audits of environmental management systems based on the ISO 14001:2004 standard.[1]

ISO 14001 REVISITED

As noted in Chapter 1, the ISO 14001:2004 standard is based on five primary clauses (4.2–4.6), as shown in Figure 9.1. These five clauses can be grouped into five operational components as follows:

• *A planning component.* In ISO 14001, planning is represented by the initial and ongoing identification of significant environmental aspects and legal requirements associated with the organization's products, services, and activities, and the identification of appropriate methods to control them. Planning for unexpected events is captured by the emergency preparedness and control requirements. Planning is centered around the establishment of an organizational policy that declares the company's commitments for environmental performance.

• *An operational component.* In ISO 14001, requirements focused on operation and maintenance of the system are specified in the requirements for operational control.

• *A monitoring and corrective action component.* In ISO 14001, these activities are defined in monitoring and measurement, evaluation of compliance, nonconformance and corrective and preventive action, and the EMS audit clauses.

• *An improvement process.* Improvement is embedded in requirements for the setting of environmental objectives and in the conduct of management reviews.

• *Key support processes.* These activities support the overall environmental management system and include document and record control, structure and responsibility, communication, and training, awareness, and competence.

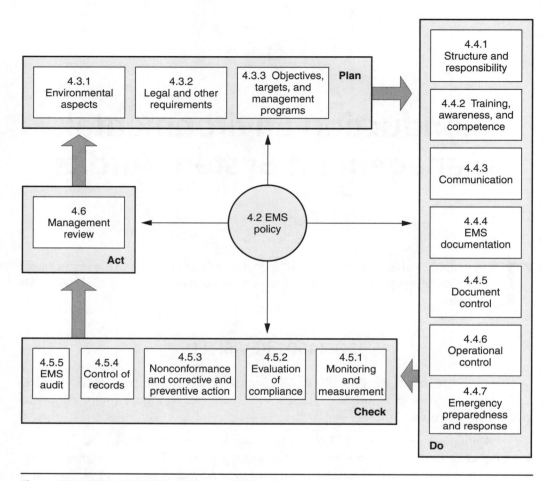

Figure 9.1 ISO 14001:2004 environmental management system.

In Figure 9.2 the organization's core business activities are represented by the darker shaded boxes and dashed lines. They represent the things that we do (activities) and things that we make (products) or provide (services). The ISO 14001:2004 components that monitor and control the environmental impact of these activities are then shown interacting with these core business activities.

AUDIT SCOPE

I like to group related ISO 14001 components together for my audits. I do this for two reasons. First, it provides for a more efficient and effective audit. The grouped elements are closely related, and it can be hard to evaluate one without evaluating the others in the group. Second, and just as important, I apply the process approach popularized by ISO 9001 to my environmental management system audits. By grouping these elements

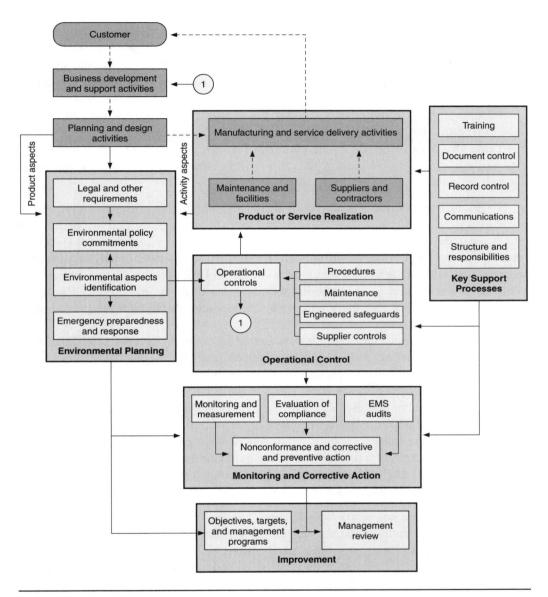

Figure 9.2 ISO 14001:2004 process flow.

together I form natural processes where the output from one process becomes the input into a related process. My audit groupings are a little different from the operational groupings shown in Figure 9.2, as will be discussed.

• *Environmental planning components.* These are normally evaluated first since the proper identification of significant environmental aspects and legal requirements that apply to the organization is central to all other components within the EMS. In Figure 9.2, inputs into the environmental planning process include the organization's planning and design activities (environmental aspects of products), product realization (environmental aspects of activities), and/or service realization (environmental aspects of services and activities that provide them). Also key to planning is the identification of legal and other requirements and planning for emergencies. All of these activities are folded around the environmental policy statement.

I depart slightly from Figure 9.2 in that I also normally audit evaluation of compliance during my audit of the planning components. I do this because there is a natural audit flow that arises from doing the identification of legal and other requirements and evaluation of compliance together. This flow will be presented when we discuss evaluation of the environmental planning components.

- *Operational control.* The operational control component verifies that the controls associated with the organization's significant aspects are in place and are being used and maintained. It is similar to the production audit of a quality management system. It answers the question, "Are we doing what we said we would do?" In any organization there will be multiple activities that need to be controlled, and there could be multiple controls for each activity. These audits will evaluate these controls. Note, I used the plural case, *audits,* because there may be multiple audits throughout the year focused around operational control.

I again depart from Figure 9.2 slightly in that I also evaluate a portion of the monitoring and measurement component during operational control evaluations and I may also spot-check compliance to regulatory requirements. If the organization has trained internal auditors who are also knowledgeable of environmental regulatory requirements, then the environmental compliance reviews could be folded into these operational control audits *almost* entirely.

Note that during these reviews I will also be checking on the control of documents and records associated with the activities I am evaluating, the training and competency of personnel performing these activities, and their knowledge of their roles and responsibilities for properly conducting the activities without harm to the environment.

- *Monitoring and corrective action.* This audit evaluates the overall monitoring and performance of the environmental management system. It includes an analysis of overall trends in environmental performance and actions being taken to correct any adverse trends. It also evaluates the internal audit program and the follow-up on any weaknesses noted during these audits. Both of these components feed into the nonconformance corrective and preventive action system, which will also be reviewed during this evaluation.

- *Improvement.* The evaluation of improvement activities will focus on the setting of environmental objectives and the establishment of environmental management programs to achieve them. Performance toward meeting these objectives will be assessed along with any actions being taken to ensure they are met if performance is lacking. The management review process will also be examined.

- *Key support processes.* The centralized activities for key support processes such as document and record control will be evaluated in this audit. I say *centralized,* since many of the outputs from these activities (accurate documents located where needed, legible and complete records, and so on.) will be evaluated during the other audits. Other items included in this review will be roles and responsibilities of key functions, communications, and training.

The remainder of this chapter will focus on strategies for conducting audits of these groupings. Readers will be referred to Chapter 8 for some of the items where the strategy is the same as it is for evaluating its equivalent component in the quality management system. For the most part, these include some of the components of the key support processes. The audit checklists provided on the CD accompanying this handbook have been structured along these groupings. Review these checklists as you read the discussions that follow.

KEY AUDIT POINT: ENVIRONMENTAL PLANNING

The environmental planning process forms the heart of the environmental management system. The activities that form this process are shown in Figure 9.3. This figure also outlines the key audit points that will be examined during the evaluation.

It is important that the auditor keep in mind the purpose of the environmental planning process, which is to identify those activities that must be controlled to maintain and improve the organization's environmental performance. The goal is to move beyond regulatory compliance. Many organizations focus almost exclusively on compliance to environmental regulations when they design their system. While important, compliance to environmental laws and statutes will not achieve the goal of ISO 14001 of achieving a level of sustainable development. America's contributions to the growing problems of global warming, depletion of natural resources, ozone depletion, and loss of biodiversity, despite the most stringent environmental regulations in the world, give testament to this. The auditor should verify that nonregulatory-based environmental aspects were considered during the initial and ongoing environmental reviews.

Note also the parallel path through the environmental planning process. The ISO 14001 standard, although focused on moving beyond compliance, does require an organization to meet its regulatory obligations. In the course of implementing ISO 14001, the company will have to demonstrate that it understands what environmental regulations it must meet, has access to what those regulations require, and is performing reviews to ensure it is meeting those requirements. For many small to medium-sized companies without environmental specialists on staff, this may be the first time that they have systematically evaluated their environmental compliance posture. What they learn must be incorporated into the planning for the environmental management system. This environmental compliance review may be done prior to the identification of significant aspects or it may be performed as part of the initial environmental review. The key audit point is that it must be done as part of the planning of the EMS and any deficiencies corrected or prevented through the application of corrective action and operational controls.

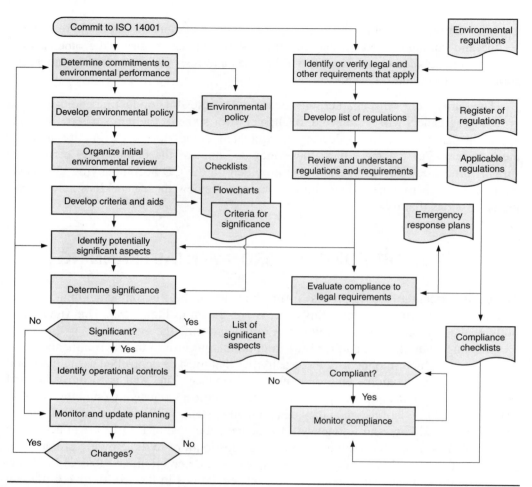

Figure 9.3   Environmental planning activities.

Audit Strategy and Key Audit Points

This section will define a general audit flow and strategy that can be used to evaluate the environmental planning process. The components of this process will be presented in the order in which the auditor would normally evaluate them.

Environmental Policy

The auditor should begin the audit by examining the environmental policy statement. The policy statement, or more importantly the commitments within the policy, form the heart of the planning process, which in turn forms the heart of the environmental management system. Rather than evaluating simple compliance to the standard, the auditor should determine if the policy and its development meet the intent of the standard. Compliance to the intent of the ISO 14001:2004 standard can be evaluated by examining the following key audit points:

• *Who was involved in the development of the policy statement?* The standard requires top management's involvement in the development of the environmental policy statement. There is no hard and fast definition of who makes up top management, but a general rule often used is that top management is comprised of the senior person present at a facility and his or her direct reports.

This involvement should be more than simply signing off on a policy developed by the environmental management representative or consultant. It should include active debate about what environmental stewardship means to the organization and what commitments it is willing to make. Later on, the company will be required to establish improvement objectives focused on meeting its commitments in the policy statement. Most improvement projects require some initial allocation of time, money, and other resources. Management should not make commitments that it is not willing to back up with sufficient resources. The auditor can assess the level of top management involvement by asking senior management how the policy was developed. If management's involvement was simply a signoff, and it admits to this, then the auditor should consider issuance of an opportunity for improvement. Engaging top management in the development of the environmental policy will help to ensure the alignment and support needed for real environmental performance improvement.

• *What is included in the scope of the EMS, and what is not?* The 2004 version of ISO 14001 added wording to indicate that the organization should define and document the scope of the EMS. The scope defines what is included and what is not. The auditor should ask to see the documented scope. It may be a separate document or it may be embedded in an environmental policy manual. The auditor should use the defined scope to help evaluate the response to the next question.

• *Is the policy statement appropriate, given the nature, scale, and environmental impacts of its activities, products, and services?* This is a difficult requirement to evaluate, because it is somewhat subjective. While the auditor should not try to second-guess the wording of a reasonable policy statement, he or she should challenge policy statements and related commitments that have absolutely nothing to do with the activities the organization performs. It makes no sense for a service organization that does not generate or handle hazardous materials or wastes to have a policy commitment to minimize or reduce the quantity of hazardous wastes it generates.

Instead of challenging what *is* in the policy statement, the auditor should focus on what's *not* reflected in the policy statement that should be or could be. As an example, a company that is heavily involved in the design, development, and launch of new products should somehow reflect its commitments into the design of environmentally-friendly products for the marketplace. The design of a product normally has a far greater overall impact on the environment than does its manufacturing. The auditor could issue an opportunity for improvement in this situation, assuming that the design of products is within the scope of the organization's EMS.

• *Environmental policy commitments.* These commitments form the core of the policy statement. They represent what the organization feels is important regarding its environmental performance and stewardship. They form the framework for environmental objectives and targets, and they can also provide the framework for developing the criteria to be used to determine the significance of the organization's environmental aspects.

Unfortunately, most organizations do little more than embed the three mandatory commitments from the ISO 14001 standard in their policy. While technically they meet the requirements of the standard, they fall far short of meeting its intent. The three mandatory commitments—continual improvement, prevention of pollution, and compliance to legal and other requirements—are too broad to provide any focus on what's really important to the organization. And they fail to provide a framework for the setting of environmental objectives and targets since *any* objective could be fit within one of the three mandatory commitments. What we want to do is use the policy commitments to help focus on what's most important to *this* organization.

The auditor should, of course, verify that the three mandatory commitments are found somewhere in the policy statement, in some form. Ideally, these mandatory commitments will not be stated verbatim as they appear in the ISO 14001 standard. Instead, the auditor should hope to find that they have been reworded to be more appropriate to the nature of the organization's environmental aspects and related impacts or that additional, more specific commitments have been added beyond the three mandatory ones to drive performance in areas that really matter. Some examples of specific commitments include:

– *We are committed to the ongoing reduction in our emissions of airborne pollutants and hazardous solid wastes.* This would be appropriate to an organization whose most significant aspects involve air emissions and hazardous waste generation.

– *We are committed to the protection of our lakes, streams, and the local ecosystem.* This commitment would be appropriate for an organization that operates near a local waterway or wetlands and has point source discharges to these waterways, or in a rural area surrounded by wildlife areas or forests.

– *We are committed to the use of environmentally friendly design principles in our products.* This commitment would be appropriate for an engineering design firm that has little in the way of air, water, or hazardous waste emissions.

– *We are committed to the involvement of our employees and the local community in the improvement of our environmental management system.* This commitment may be appropriate for an organization that operates in the midst of a local community where there are concerns about the company's operations. It can be especially important if the company is trying to improve its reputation in the community.

– *We are committed to the concept of natural resource conservation, including ongoing reduction in materials and resources consumed, including energy.* This commitment would be appropriate for almost any organization, since all companies use energy, but would be especially important to those that consume large amounts of paper, wood, water, minerals, oil, natural gas, or other natural resources such as steel manufacturers, the construction industry, and printers.

These are but a few of the specific commitments that might be offered up in the environmental policy statement. Their usefulness is in their ability to focus environmental objectives and targets toward specific improvements that have a large and real effect on the organization's environmental performance. They point to where an organization can really make a difference. Lacking this kind of specificity, companies often establish objectives to improve their recycling of aluminum cans, paper, and scrap wood pallets that, while helpful, do little to really make a significant improvement to the environment.

In Chapter 1 we discussed the evolution and maturing of an organization's management system. The evolution of a company's environmental policy often is one of the first areas where this maturing is seen. Many companies initially develop a policy around the three mandatory policy commitments. As the system matures, it should be expected that the policy will gradually evolve to include some of these more specific, focused commitments to drive improvements in areas of environmental importance. As an auditor I evaluate the policy statement in terms of this evolution. If the system is new, I may simply accept the environmental policy as is, at most adding an opportunity for improvement to consider commitments that more properly reflect the organization's activities, products, and services. If the system has been in place for a while, then I also look at the organization's performance in making improvements in areas relating to its significant environmental aspects. If I find improvement lacking, then I make the case more strongly, possibly tying the general nature of the policy statement into a finding relating to the lack of environmental performance improvement.

• *Documented, implemented, maintained, and communicated within the organization and to the general public.* All policy statements are documented, or at least I haven't found one yet that wasn't. Implementation and maintenance will be reflected in its maturing and/or modification as just stated, and in its success in driving environmental performance improvement, also discussed. Communication within the organization, including to persons working on behalf of the organization, will be evaluated during other audits. This leaves communication to the general public.

The auditor should ask how the policy is made available to the general public. Ask, "If my Aunt Betty, who drives by the plant every day and sees the ISO 14001 flag flying, calls and asks about the environmental policy, what would you tell her?" Answers may be that she would be directed to the company Web site where it is listed, she would be faxed a copy, or that the call would be directed to the environmental management representative who would send her a copy or read it over the phone. The key is, there has to be a process to make it available to the public. Almost every company has a Web site. Posting the policy on the Web site is one of the easiest and most effective ways of communicating it to the public. The auditor should issue an opportunity for improvement if the process for communicating the policy is cumbersome or inconvenient, for example, if the answer to my Aunt Betty question was, "Well, we would tell her to stop by and come into the lobby. It's posted there." This is neither practical or realistic.

Making the policy available to the public is important because it makes top management more accountable to follow through on the commitments they have made. If the general public is aware that we are committed to involving the local community in environmental performance improvement, you can bet they will want to know when, where, and how they can become involved. Likewise, if the organization has committed to reductions in its emissions of hazardous air pollutants, then it is reasonable to expect local citizens to review the publicly available toxic release inventories and to call management out if it doesn't follow through on its commitments.

You're probably thinking that I've killed quite a few trees expanding on the environmental policy statement, and you'd be right. I do so because the policy statement truly is a key to the entire environmental management system to much greater degree than in quality management systems or safety and health management systems. Unfortunately the practice of slapping together a nice, flowery policy statement that looks good on the wall but does little to drive improvement remains rampant, especially in companies that have had quality management system experience prior to implementing ISO 14001. Hopefully this discussion on the policy statement will give auditors insight on not only how to evaluate this critical document, but also why its important.

Environmental Aspects

If the policy is the heart of the EMS, then the identification of significant environmental aspects is the head. The goal of this process is to identify those activities that must be controlled to prevent harming the environment or to actually improve it. Even though we will consider the environmental aspects of our products, services, and activities, we can only control activities. This awareness is important because many organizations only identify and list the significant aspects they identify, neglecting the activities that produce them. Significant environmental aspects should be associated with the activities that relate to the aspects for control to have any practical meaning.

A second consideration is whether the audit is performed on a newly installed EMS or one that has been in place for some time. A review of the process used to identify and determine significance of a new environmental management system is more involved than one that is focused primarily on the updating of the significant environmental aspects for changes to the organization's products, activities, and services. Both will be discussed in the strategy that follows.

The auditor should start by asking to see the procedure for identifying significant environmental aspects. The standard requires that an organization have a procedure, but it doesn't necessarily have to be documented (although I certainly recommend it). If the process has been documented, then the auditor should ask the environmental management representative, or process owner, to walk through the procedure, stopping at key points as will be outlined. If it hasn't been documented, then the auditor should still ask the auditee to walk through the process, paying close attention to the key activities and making notes to follow up on when asking to see the objective evidence. The auditor will have to rely more on the standard and on the checklist in this situation.

During the walk-through, verify the following key elements of the process:

- *Was the evaluation of potential aspects comprehensive?* The auditor should verify that all areas, core activities, and products within the scope of the EMS were included in the evaluation. Many organizations conduct the review by portioning the plant into areas such as production areas, administrative areas, outside facilities and grounds, and auxiliary areas such as tank farms, pumps, and boilers. The auditor can look for evidence that each of these areas was included in the review. The auditor should inquire about any areas where there is no evidence, typically identified by their lack of inclusion on the list of potential or resulting significant aspects. If it becomes clear that major areas were not included in the review, generate an NC.

Another important item to consider relates to the review of the environmental aspects associated with the organization's products. This is especially important if the company designs the products that it sells. In this situation the organization has significant influence over the environmental impacts of its products and can control them through proper design. I have evaluated many companies where the organization designs its products but has never considered the environmental aspects of its products or how it might minimize their negative impact on the environment through design controls and practices. I even evaluated the research and development business unit of a major global corporation where product design was not considered, even though this was its primary activity! While properly controlling the acids, solvents, and wastes generated as a result of product testing is important, minimizing the hazardous materials used in the product design, optimizing the product's ability to be disassembled, reused, or recycled, and optimizing its energy efficiency is much more important.

The design of a product almost always has more overall impact on the environment than does its manufacture. The auditor should verify that product materials, weight, energy efficiency, and ability to be disassembled, recycled, reused, or otherwise properly disposed of are considered during the identification of significant environmental aspects. Issue an NC if there is no evidence of product review and the company is design responsible.

A final consideration is whether the evaluation included nonroutine as well as routine activities. Nonroutine activities could include bulk liquid loading and unloading, maintenance of equipment and facilities (whether performed by the organization or by contractors), and facility modification, expansion, or renovation. For facility modifications, the auditor may want to verify that the organization has a process to evaluate such modifications for their environmental impact before they are initiated, since each is unique and there may not have been any major facility projects under way when the initial environmental review was performed.

• *Were the reviews thorough?* Once the auditor is satisfied that the scope of the review was adequate, he or she may wish to verify that the team that performed the review knew what to look for. The auditor may ask what training the team received prior to conducting the review and ask to see any checklists used to guide the team in what to look for. Some companies like to use flowcharts of production activities to help identify potentially significant aspects. They document the inputs (materials and natural resources) and outputs (wastes and emissions) on the flowchart to help identify aspects. Ask to see the flowcharts.

Related to this topic is evaluation of who was involved in the review. Ideally, the review will be performed by a cross-functional team with representatives from each of the areas evaluated. This can be especially important to identifying the nonroutine activities that should be considered but which may not be going on when the walk-through is performed. If the auditor discovers that the review was performed by one person, then he or she should more aggressively evaluate the comprehensiveness and thorough-ness of the review by examining the evidence already cited. Nothing in the standard *requires* a cross-functional team be used to conduct the review, but it is highly unlikely that one person can do the job adequately. Since it is possible that one individual is the source of all knowledge, however, the auditor must focus on the results. If the auditor finds evidence that the review failed to consider important activities or that the review did not include obvious aspects like materials, wastes, emissions, resource usage, or products, then issue an NC.

• *How was the significance of the environmental aspects determined?* The auditor should examine the rationale used to determine significance of the aspects identified during the initial environmental review. Some organizations use a series of questions, such as, "Does this activity result in the generation of significant quantities of hazardous materials?" or "Is this aspect regulated?" or "Does the activity consume significant quantities of natural resources, including energy?" Other companies like to use a fail-ure mode and effects methodology, evaluating the severity of the impacts and their likelihood of occurrence. Most companies use some form of quantification or ranking to help distinguish those that are significant from those that are not. Ideally, the criteria used to determine significance will be related to the organization's policy commitments. As an example, consider several of the specific commitments presented in the discussion on the environmental policy and reproduced here.

Commitment: We are committed to the ongoing reduction in our emissions of airborne pollutants and hazardous solid wastes.
Criteria: "Does this activity result in the release of emissions to the air or the generation of hazardous wastes?"

Commitment: We are committed to the protection of our lakes, streams, and the local ecosystem.
Criteria: "Can this activity result in the release of wastes or pollutants to the local environment?"

Commitment: We are committed to the use of environmentally friendly design principles in our products.
Criteria: "Does this activity impact on the ability to design environmentally responsible principles into our products?"

Commitment: We are committed to the involvement of our employees and the local community in the improvement of our environmental management system.
Criteria: "Does the activity result in any significant odor, noise, dust, or other local concern to the community or our employees?"

Commitment: We are committed to the concepts of natural resource conservation, including ongoing reduction in materials and resources consumed.
Criteria: "Does this activity consume significant amounts of water, energy, or other natural resources?"

Since one of the mandatory commitments in the policy statement is a commitment to comply with regulatory requirements, it is common to include criteria relating to the regulated or nonregulated status of the aspect. By including specific commitments in the policy statement, and then using these commitments to determine the criteria used to identify significance, the organization creates an EMS that is aligned from top to bottom.

The key audit point is that the methods used to determine what is and what isn't significant should be reproducible. There should be a consistent process in place. A team evaluating the same environmental aspects next year should come to roughly the same conclusions as to what is significant and must be controlled. Consistency is important since the EMS functions within a dynamic system. Processes, products, and facilities change. Environmental concerns change. Perhaps even our criteria will change, but even so, such changes must be carefully reviewed and must have some basis. A consistent set of criteria helps to provide the basis for these changes.

The auditor should ask how the determination was made as to which aspects are significant. The auditor may ask why one aspect was deemed to be significant, while another was not. Verify that there is some method to the determination. If there was no rationale at all, generate an NC, citing the lack of a procedure (that is, process). If there was some reasonable rationale, but it was not formalized or applied consistently, consider generating an OFI.

Finally, the auditor should verify that the significant aspects are somehow linked to the activities that generate or control them. As noted in the introduction to this section, organizations control the activities in order to minimize the impacts of the aspects. Just citing "energy consumption" does not allow for control of this aspect. Citing energy consumption from lighting, energy consumption from heating, ventilation, and air conditioning, and energy consumption from production machinery operation allows for the application of real controls for these activities. Generate an OFI if the auditee cannot relate the significant aspects to the activities that produce or control them.

• *How is the information maintained up to date?* For audits that are performed well after the EMS has been in place and certified, this question becomes the focus of the evaluation. Up to this point the audit flow has focused on new management systems. For an existing system, the auditor should have confidence that the methods used to identify environmental aspects and their related significance have been verified to be adequate. The main question for an existing system, therefore, is whether these methods are being applied to product, process, and facility changes. The key questions are, How are those responsible for reviewing new products, services, and activities made aware of the need to perform an evaluation? and, Is the evaluation conducted prior to the implementation of the changes?

The auditor should begin by first identifying new or modified products, services, or activities, and facility modifications that have taken place since the last audit. If the auditor does not know what they were, then talk to the production manager, maintenance manager, or engineering manager to help generate a list of recent modifications or introductions. Try to select major modifications or new products that are significantly different from existing products. These items will become the auditor's samples for later verification during the interview.

The auditor should then interview the management representative about the methods used to keep the list of significant aspects current. Some organizations reperform the initial environmental review periodically to ensure that they identify any new significant aspects. While I generally accept such reviews, I don't necessarily like this strategy, primarily because it is reactionary versus proactive. An organization could operate for many months without proper controls under such a system pending completion of the annual or semiannual review. Instead, I prefer an approach that uses existing controls to manage change, modified to include the consideration of potential environmental aspects and/or impacts, to identify the need for a review. Many organizations use a management of change process to control and plan for new products, processes, and products. Others have an advanced product quality planning process. Some organizations use a management of change process and an annual review to ensure that new significant aspects are identified. The auditor should thoroughly understand the methods used by asking questions and by asking to see the documents, checklists, and other aids used to control changes. The absence of any consistent method to keep the significant aspects list updated should obviously result in an NC.

Once the auditor fully understands the methods used to stay up to date, then test the application of the methods by asking to see the results of the reviews for the items selected prior to the audit. If a management of change process was used, ask to see the checklist completed for the facility or process modification made two months ago. Assuming that new environmental aspects were identified for the change, then ask to see the results of their review for significance. If the auditor finds that the process was not followed or that the management representative was not even aware of significant changes to the company's products, services, activities, or facilities when he or she should have been, issue an NC.

Staying aware of changes to processes that could impact on the EMS is important from a regulatory standpoint as well as an environmental performance perspective.

Assume your company is a conditionally exempt, small-quantity generator of hazardous wastes. Due to new product or product modification, you now have to apply a glue and adhesive that is hazardous. As a result, your generation of hazardous waste triples to over 100 kilograms per month. While you were exempt from most of the regulations governing the control of hazardous wastes in the past, you now are required to implement additional requirements relating to employee training, manifesting, inspections, and reporting. Not doing so would be in violation of federal and state environmental regulations. Being made aware of this impending change would allow you to put the additional controls in place before you become a violator, or possibly even find a nonhazardous glue and adhesive that would avoid having to put in place new controls in the first place. Heaven forbid you fail to identify the change and it results in sufficient waste to put you over the threshold into a large-quantity generator. The bottom line is that the auditor should verify that methods are in place and are being used to maintain their listing of significant environmental aspects current.

• *Operational controls.* The auditor also needs to verify that the organization has taken its significant environmental aspects into account in the design, implementation, and operation of its EMS. This can be evidenced by the identification and implementation of appropriate controls to minimize negative environmental impacts or to maximize those activities that benefit the environment. The auditor can ask how the significant environmental aspects are controlled. At this stage, planning, the auditor is most concerned that appropriate controls have been identified. The operational control audits will confirm that they were properly implemented and are being maintained.

Evaluation of Compliance to Legal and Other Requirements

One of the first areas where organizations see a significant improvement after implementing ISO 14001 is in their environmental compliance posture. This is especially true in small to medium-sized firms that do not have environmental professionals on staff. In these organizations, the identification of the legal requirements that apply to their activities may require more effort than the implementation of the environmental management system itself. Even so, it is critically important that the organization not only identify the regulatory requirements it must meet, but also understand them and ensure that they meet them. This portion of the environmental planning audit focuses on verification that the organization is meeting its policy commitment to comply with legal and other requirements.

Other requirements in this sense mean requirements imposed by the management system design itself, by customers, and by voluntary adoption of environmental protocols such as the Business Charter for Sustainable Development and Responsible Care. Internal requirements will be called out in the organization's policies and procedures. Customer requirements will be called out in contracts and specifications. Voluntary protocols, like the Business Charter for Sustainable Development, should be listed along with the legal requirements that the organization must meet.

The auditor should begin by asking the management representative or individual responsible for environmental compliance for a listing of the regulations and other requirements that apply to the organization. While the standard does not require a listing, or register of regulations, as it is often called, typically there are far too many to commit to memory. As a result, a listing of some type is a practical necessity. Once the auditor has this list, verify conformance to the standard by evaluating the following:

• *Is the listing comprehensive and complete?* The auditor should verify that the listing includes federal, state, and local requirements. Most states have the authority to implement the federal requirements and do so by enacting state statutes that must be followed. If the state has the authority to implement the federal regulations, then listing the state statutes and public acts may be sufficient, since they must be at least as restrictive and are sometimes more stringent than the federal regulations. Local requirements may include local sewage and drinking water standards, laws, and permits. As noted, I also look to see if significant voluntary requirements like Responsible Care are listed, assuming they apply.

• *Is the listing sufficiently detailed?* Simply listing the Clean Air Act or the Resource Conservation and Recovery Act doesn't provide evidence that the organization understands the legal requirements it must meet. Ask the auditee, "Which titles of the Clean Air Act apply to us?" or "What parts of 40 CFR 260–279 must we comply with?" All too often organizations simply list the name of the law or Code of Federal Regulation (CFR) that contains the requirements. Some of the regulations are hundreds of pages long and contain only a few sections that are applicable to the organization.

The auditor can evaluate whether the auditee has sufficiently researched the regulations by asking the auditee to show the requirements that apply. I normally pick three or four regulations from the list to sample. This question evaluates two critical prerequisites of environmental compliance—does the organization have access to the regulations it must meet (also a standard requirement) and does the organization understand what they require? Often when I ask this question I get a blank stare or the auditee pulls up 40 CFR 260–279 and tries to get through the regulation for the first time. You don't stand much of a chance of meeting the requirements if you don't know what they say.

Many organizations now use hyperlinks to the federal or state Web site where the regulations are maintained. I strongly endorse this practice, since it is practical and greatly simplifies staying up to date with regulatory changes. Local regulations and laws normally have to be retained in hard copy format. If the organization meets the access requirements of ISO 14001 by keeping hard copies, then verify that these documents are controlled and maintained up to date. One of the challenges of using hard copies of the CFRs is keeping them current. They are revised on an annual basis and can be expensive.

• *Is there evidence that the organization considered its legal and other requirements during the design and implementation of its EMS?* The auditor has already reviewed the listing of significant environmental aspects so it should be clear if the company considered its regulatory obligations during the identification or ranking of its environmental aspects. If the auditor did not conduct a review of environmental aspects identification as part of the audit, then he or she should review the list to verify that significant regulatory obligations were embedded within the reviews and criteria for determining significance.

• *Is there evidence that the organization is evaluating its compliance to regulatory and other requirements?* Other requirements, such as Responsible Care, are normally evaluated during other evaluations. Compliance to regulatory requirements is typically verified through the use of environmental compliance reviews. Although it is possible to fold these reviews into other audits, they are typically performed by personnel with specialized knowledge of the environmental regulations. The auditor should ask the auditee about the processes used to conduct environmental compliance reviews and reviews of compliance to other, non–ISO 14001 requirements that the organization has adopted. If a documented procedure is available, have the auditee walk you through it. Pay attention to frequency of the audits, who performs them, how they are reported, and how any actions coming out of the review are tracked.

One of the reasons why I evaluate compliance to legal and other requirements now, instead of folding it into the monitoring and corrective action audit, is that it fits well with the audit strategy. At this point I have seen the listing of the requirements that apply to us and I have asked for and been presented with a copy of a number of the requirements themselves. It is now a simple matter to ask the auditee to provide me with evidence that we have evaluated our compliance to the requirements that I have in front of me. The auditee might provide me with a compliance report, completed checklists, or a consultant's evaluation. What I want to do now is evaluate the thoroughness of the review. Since I have the requirements in front of me, I can easily scan the records of the review to see if there is evidence that the requirements were evaluated. The evidence may be in the form of statements or conclusions in the compliance report or questions on the checklist, but what I want to know is, did we do a thorough job of evaluating our compliance to *all* of the requirements? This is where management system audits differ from regulatory compliance reviews. Whereas management system audits sample compliance to important requirements, compliance reviews should verify conformance to all requirements.

If the records of the compliance review are very general, stating, for example, "The review verified compliance to the Resource Conservation and Recovery Act, the Clean Air Act, and the Clean Water Act," then I generate a finding, typically in the form of an opportunity for improvement, that notes that the detail in the compliance records could be expanded to provide more assurance that the organization is meeting its regulatory requirements. If my other audits find regulatory violations, then I cite the issue as a nonconformance, using a lack of sufficient evidence and my own findings as the basis for the NC.

Some organizations rely on outside consultants or corporate staff to conduct their compliance reviews. I have no concern with this, as long as the records of the review provide sufficient evidence of compliance monitoring.

Now, you may be thinking that you are not an environmental specialist and therefore cannot evaluate the regulatory compliance sections of the standard. Take heart, you don't have to be an environmental expert to do a credible job. If you note the audit strategy presented, there is nothing that requires an extensive knowledge of environmental regulations on your part. All you have to do is ask the right questions and use the answers or evidence provided to guide you. The auditee will provide the list of regulations, which has already been evaluated, assuming you are certified, by the outside registrar auditor, who is knowledgeable in environmental regulations. From that list you pick several regulations and say, "Show me." The auditee then pulls down the regulations for you or prints off a copy. Next you ask the auditee to explain how compliance reviews are conducted and again say, "Show me" when you ask for records of reviews for the regulations just printed. You can easily scan the records to see if there are questions or statements relating to the requirements you have in your hands. If you can't find them, you say, of course, "Show me." Environmental expertise is required to do the compliance review, but not to verify that the review was done.

• *Were weaknesses identified in the compliance reviews acted on?* If violations or weaknesses were noted in the compliance reviews, then the auditor should verify that actions were taken or have been implemented to address the deficiencies. Check with corporate policy on how to cite the findings in this case.

Emergency Preparedness and Response

The last topic of the environmental planning audit is verification that the organization has the appropriate procedures and plans to respond to or to prevent environmental accidents and emergencies. I review this during the planning audit since, first, this should be a planning activity and not a routine occurrence, and, second, in the United States many of the plans and procedures are required by law and are therefore part of the regulatory framework.

The auditor can evaluate this area by asking for copies of the emergency response plans the organization maintains. Common plans include the following:

• Spill prevention, countermeasures, and control (SPCC) plan

• Storm water pollution and prevention plan (SWPPP)

• Pollution prevention plan (P3 plan)

• Fire and evacuation plan

Which plans are maintained by the organization is dependent on the nature of the organization's products, services, and activities. When the plans are presented, the auditor can ask the auditee to show the requirements that describe what must be in the plan, where the plan is required by law. With the regulatory requirements in hand, the auditor can spot-check the plans for their content and currentness. I commonly find deficiencies in these plans when compared to their regulatory requirements. In addition, some of these plans focus on specific types of accidents like spills of oil. The auditor should inquire about other types of accidents, like spills of solvents or ammonia if the auditor's review of the organization's significant aspects showed that these aspects are present. If there is no plan for responding to these other emergencies, generate an OFI. Note that many of these plans focus not just on response, but also on prevention. As such, the number of actual incidents or emergencies is an indirect measure of the quality of these plans.

The auditor should also verify that the plans are up to date. Some plans must be submitted to and approved by government agencies at specified periodicities. In addition, it is not at all uncommon to find that personnel named as emergency responders or coordinators no longer work at the facility. It doesn't do any good to call someone in the middle of the night during an emergency if he or she is no longer employed at the facility.

The auditor should ask for a list of incidents, accidents, and spills or other uncontrolled releases that occurred since the last audit. It helps if the auditor already knows about some of these events, which is likely if this is an internal audit. The auditor should verify that reviews were held after these occurrences and that the adequacy of the response, and the organization's response plans and procedures, were evaluated as part of these reviews. If no evidence of any review can be provided, generate an NC.

Finally, the auditor should verify that some form of drill, test, or walk-through was conducted to evaluate the adequacy of the procedures and plans and to familiarize those responsible for action. The organization is required to establish periodicity requirements for these tests, and the auditor should confirm they are being conducted as required. Failure to conduct the drills or tests should result in a nonconformance.

Performance Indicators

The auditor may expect to find the following indicators associated with the environmental planning components. The auditor should review these indicators where they exist to help evaluate overall performance and effectiveness and to help focus the audit. Areas of poor performance, as shown by the indicators, should be evaluated for actions to correct the performance. The lack of any action to address significant performance issues can serve as the basis for a nonconformance citing ineffective implementation. Note that the majority of the performance indicators will be associated with other components of the environmental management system:

- Percent of environmental compliance reviews completed to schedule

- Number of violations found during compliance reviews

- Number of violations found by outside agencies

- Percent or number of violations corrected

- Percent or number of emergency response tests/drills conducted

KEY AUDIT POINT: OPERATIONAL CONTROL

Operational control implements the actions and safeguards needed to minimize any adverse environmental impacts associated with the significant aspects identified during environmental planning. Operational controls can include procedures, practices, engineered safeguards, maintenance, and protective equipment and devices. They could also include requirements passed down to suppliers and contractors. The process organizations use to implement the operational controls normally looks something like that shown in Figure 9.4.

The controls themselves are normally defined as part of the environmental planning process. Most organizations find that many of the controls are already in place, although they may not have been formalized yet. Formalizing the controls in documented procedures and instructions is part of the process of developing operational controls. The mistake-proofing control shown in Figure 9.4 includes actions taken to ensure that the adverse impact cannot occur. An example would be to specify a nonhazardous substance for parts cleaning in place of the current hazardous substance. In many cases the

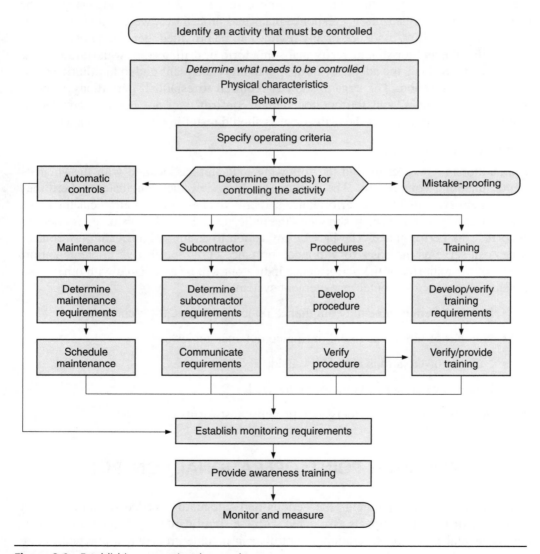

Figure 9.4 Establishing operational controls.

aspect (cleaning fluid for part washing) would cease to be significant after the mistake-proofing solution was implemented, therefore the stop symbol.

Although the process flow shown in Figure 9.4 is useful for understanding the process used to determine how to control significant aspects, I generally prefer to use the process flow shown in Figure 9.5 to illustrate the strategy used to evaluate operational control. The reader is reminded that this process would be repeated for each activity associated with a significant environmental aspect. Rather than conduct one audit of operational control, it is normally more efficient and effective to conduct multiple audits, with each series of audits focused on different processes, activities, or areas. This provides a more continuous evaluation of operational controls throughout the organization and allows easy integration with quality management and safety and health management system audits, if desired. The planning and conduct of combined audits is the subject of Chapter 11.

Note that the evaluation of operational control will also assess the outputs from some of the key support activities, including training and awareness of employees' roles, responsibilities, and authorities. The auditor should also examine the control of any environmental documents and records associated with the process, as well as the calibration of any environmental monitoring devices found to be in use. As noted in the

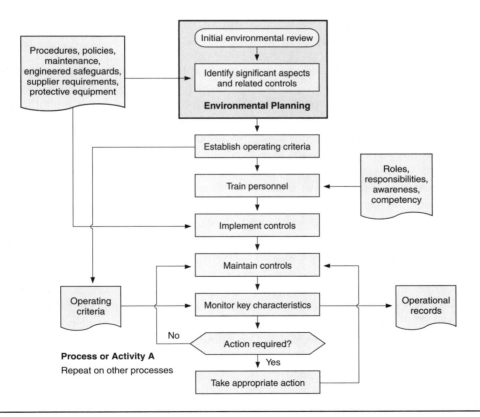

Figure 9.5 Operational control activities.

introduction to this chapter, the auditor should also verify that any monitoring of key characteristics and operating criteria is being performed as needed to maintain the environmental controls. When performed in this fashion, the operational control audit becomes a process-based audit similar to the process-based audits conducted of an organization's quality management system. The benefits of process-based versus element-based audits has been discussed in numerous sections of this handbook, but suffice it to say they allow for a more effective and efficient audit. The checklists on the CD have been structured around the evaluation of processes.

As an alternative to auditing by activities, the audit program manager could instead choose to audit by significant aspect category. Examples where this might be advantageous include aspects that involve numerous activities throughout the organization. An example might be an audit of the organization's recycling program or energy conservation program. Both of these aspects will reach into many different areas of the organization, some of which might not be examined during routine process-based audits. This approach also works well in organizations without quality management systems or where the environmental management system and quality management system are maintained as separate systems. Specific checklists for these audits would need to be developed based on the organization's procedures and policies for implementation of these programs.

Audit Strategy and Key Audit Points

The auditor should begin the audit by examining the list of significant aspects and their associated activities and controls. If the auditor has been assigned to evaluate a process, then identify all significant aspects associated with that process. For a manufacturing process there may be three or four. The auditor should note how these aspects are controlled. The aspects and their controls should be noted on the auditor's checklists.

If the auditor has been assigned to evaluate an aspect, then he or she should review the listing of significant aspects and identify the activities associated with the aspect. The auditor may note four or five areas where hazardous waste is handled, a dozen key points for nonhazardous industrial wastes, or the entire facility may need to be reviewed if assigned energy consumption and conservation.

Since many operational controls take the form of procedures, the auditor should obtain any procedures that relate to the control of the activities or significant aspects that are being audited. Examples include waste handling procedures, energy conservation guidelines, and material handling instructions. Operating permits also fall into the category of procedures since they contain the controls and monitoring that must be maintained. The auditor should prepare for the audit by reviewing these procedures and modifying and/or developing checklists of questions and key audit points. Audit planning was covered in detail in Chapter 5.

With a list of significant aspects for the process and an understanding of how they should be controlled, the auditor is now ready to conduct the review. You will be talking to the process operator. Introduce yourself, set the auditee at ease, and begin by asking, "Is there anything that we do here that could harm the environment if not done correctly?" The auditor is verifying operator awareness of the significant environmental aspects of the job. The standard requires that operators have such an awareness, along with the consequences to the environment if they do not follow procedures, for good reason. The procedures tell the operator *what* to do, awareness tells them *why* it's important. Win the heart, and you will eventually win the mind.

Note that I do not ask, "Are you aware of any significant environmental aspects associated with this process?" If you ask the question like that, you're just as likely to get a serious look of confusion from the auditee. Stay away from terms like *significant aspects,* most employees will not know what you mean. Unfortunately, I've also run into a few environmental management representatives who don't know what that means either, but that's another story.

Once the auditee replies, the auditor can ask about the effects to the environment if they are not done properly. Typical answers might be "It could pollute the air" or "It could put oil in the creek." The auditor is ensuring that the auditee understands why it is important to control the activity. The auditor can then ask how these activities are controlled. During the auditee's response, the auditor can verify that the activity is being properly controlled in accordance with company policies and procedures. The auditor should verify that controls are in place and operating (for example, filters installed, ventilation systems operating, advanced power management system features on computers enabled) and should ask to see any records required to be maintained by the operator.

The auditor is now verifying that monitoring of key attributes of the activity is being performed as required by local procedures and practices. For example, if the control of air emissions from a glue and adhesive operation is through use of filtered ventilation, and the procedure requires hourly monitoring of the differential pressure across the filter, then the auditor should verify that the hourly monitoring is being conducted. The differential pressure is in essence an operating criteria, and the hourly check is a monitoring requirement. Assume that the procedure for controlling this activity requires the operator to notify maintenance when the differential pressure reaches 2 psid so that the filter can be replaced. The auditor should ask the operator, "Are we required to do anything when the differential pressure increases? What do we do, and at what pressure?" Notice how the auditor is also verifying the operator's understanding of roles and responsibilities relating to control of the aspect, along with knowledge and understanding of what to do (that is, training and competency). For specific tasks, such as waste handling, the auditor may also want to jot down the auditee's name for later verification of training.

For activities such as hazardous waste handling, packaging, labeling, and bulk liquid unloading, it is desirable also to observe the activity being performed. This requires careful coordination with area management, normally through the audit program manager, since these activities may not be performed all that often. Their nonroutine nature makes it all that much more important to actually observe them, if possible. People are normally fairly competent in the performance of routine activities; it is usually the nonroutine activities that bite us. If the operators have specific responsibilities for emergency response relating to the activity or significant aspect, the auditor can also question them on these responsibilities.

Pay particular attention to operating criteria in procedures and operating permits. These criteria are normally specified to ensure that the operation has minimal impact on the environment. Examples include flow rates, temperatures, and pressures. Operating a plating bath at a higher temperature than required increases the air emissions and could lower the filtration effectiveness.

During the audit, the auditor should note the revision date of any EMS procedures or instructions found in the area for later comparison to the master list of documents. The auditor should also review any monitoring records for legibility and completeness. Any environmental monitoring equipment in use in the process should be checked for calibration. The auditor should also verify that proper maintenance is being performed on equipment and facilities used in the process when maintenance has been identified as a means of operational control.

If the organization has established any improvement objectives or targets relating to this activity or its significant aspects, then I also like to ask operators if they are aware of the objectives. Communication of improvement objectives should flow down to those most directly involved in meeting them, the employees most directly involved in the activity. I normally issue an OFI if I find that employees are not aware of improvement objectives and targets associated with their activities or areas.

Behavior controls are more difficult to assess. Behavior controls include things like properly disposing of batteries and fluorescent bulbs, turning off lights when not in the office, and recycling paper, cardboard, and aluminum cans. Awareness is the key. The auditor should interview numerous employees to verify that the level of awareness is as it should be. The auditor can spot-check waste storage areas, of course, but the chances of finding systemic deficiencies that way are slim, and I'm not going to go diving into the dumpster in the back of the plant. I prefer to use the monthly safety walk-throughs to spot-check compliance to behavior controls and review the results of those walk-throughs to assess how well personnel are complying with the policies. Awareness is still the key, however. Employees need to understand not only what they should do, but also why it's important.

If the auditor is evaluating an engineering process like design and development, then he or she should pick several of the company's products and ask how elements of design for the environment (DFE) were factored into the design of these products. The auditor should ask to see design review records and other documents that substantiate the auditee's responses. The auditor should absolutely note the names of those involved in the design to verify that they have received training in DFE.

Performance Indicators

The auditor should expect to find performance indicators for the operational controls being evaluated. The auditor should review these indicators to help evaluate overall performance and effectiveness and to help focus the audit. Areas of poor performance, as indicated by the indicators, should be evaluated for actions to correct the performance. The lack of any action to address significant performance issues can serve as the basis for a nonconformance citing ineffective implementation. The following are some examples of performance indicators used to measure how well we are controlling our significant environmental aspects:

- Amount disposed of or amount consumed (materials and wastes), normalized for production volume

- Amount in inventory (solvents and other hazardous materials, chemicals)

- Operating hours (reuse of chemical baths, cleaning agents)

- Energy usage, normalized to production volume

- Amount recycled

- Percent recyclable (product design)

- Energy efficiency ratings (product design) or survey results (facilities)

KEY AUDIT POINT: MONITORING AND CORRECTIVE ACTION

Monitoring and corrective action focuses on measuring the performance of the environmental management system and on the implementation of actions when it is not performing as it should. Note that some components of monitoring have been incorporated into other audits—monitoring of regulatory compliance is reviewed during the environmental planning audit and monitoring of operational control characteristics during the operational control audits. Likewise, corrective action for violations to regulatory requirements arising out of the environmental compliance reviews is evaluated during the environmental planning audit. The focus of this evaluation will be on the overall monitoring of environmental performance and on the corrective and preventive action program.

The general process of monitoring and corrective action looks something like that shown in Figure 9.6. Note that interrelationships among the environmental planning, operational control, and improvement processes have been shown in the shaded boxes. While there is a possibility of some overlap between the components, and therefore some redundancy between the audits, the audit does not take a large amount of time and the redundancy is minimal.

Some audit program managers may want to combine this evaluation with the evaluation of the improvement process. The improvement process includes a review of the setting of environmental objectives, management programs, and the conduct of the management review. There is a natural linkage between that audit and the evaluation of monitoring and corrective action. They were split into separate reviews because the interviewees will be different—the environmental management representative for the audit of monitoring and corrective action and executive management in the case of improvement. Even so, it may still make sense to combine the audits, realizing that an audit plan may be required to support the multiple interviews.

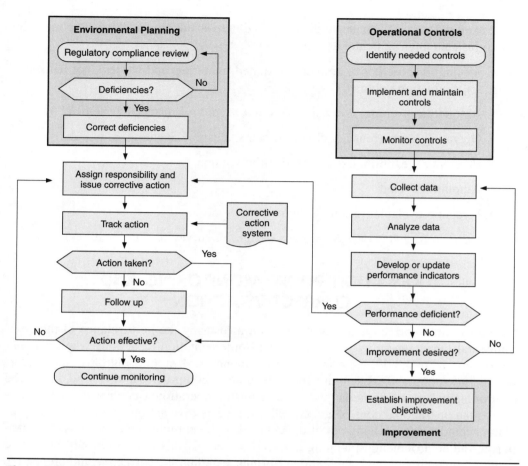

Figure 9.6 EMS monitoring and corrective action.

Audit Strategy and Key Audit Points

Monitoring

The auditor should begin by asking the auditee (typically the environmental management representative) how overall performance of the EMS is monitored. The auditor should ask to see the performance measures. During the review, the auditor should look for trends and performance to defined goals, where they have been established. The auditor should question any areas where performance is not meeting the goal or the trend is going in the wrong direction. For sustained negative trends or performance far below the goal, ask what actions are being taken to correct the performance. Failure to take action for significantly poor performance is the basis for a nonconformance. If the period-to-period performance cannot be assessed because of changes in operations (for example, large increases in production activity), then an opportunity for improvement should be issued stating that monitoring could be improved through normalization of the data.

Normalization means adjusting the indicator to account for volume fluctuations, usually due to production activity. Keep in mind the goal of this monitoring is to evaluate environmental performance improvement. If the indicators fail to provide useful data in this regard, they should be modified. For a more detailed discussion on how to evaluate the monitoring process, refer to the section on analysis of data in Chapter 8.

Areas where performance is satisfactory but where additional improvement is desired would normally become improvement objectives. If the audit program manager has combined this audit with the improvement audit, then the auditor could flow into an evaluation of the improvement objectives now. Otherwise, the auditor would move into an evaluation of the internal audit program.

EMS Audits

The auditor should ask to see the audit procedure, audit schedule, and copies of reports of all audits performed since the last evaluation of the program. Verify that audits are being scheduled, conducted, and reported per the local procedure. Note that areas of significantly poor performance, evaluated just prior to the start of this topic, should have received additional audits or should show up on the audit schedule as additional audits, to account for status of the activity. Refer to the discussion of how to evaluate internal audit programs in Chapter 8 for more information on what questions to ask and what points to verify.

Nonconformance, Corrective, and Preventive Action

Armed with information on overall EMS performance and the results of the internal EMS audits, the auditor can now evaluate the corrective and preventive action system. The auditor should ask for a copy of the corrective and preventive action procedure(s) and should verify that the system is being operated in accordance with the procedure. Refer to the audit strategy provided in the corrective and preventive action section of Chapter 8 for a more detailed discussion on how to evaluate this program.

Performance Indicators

This audit was focused on the evaluation of performance indicators, examples of which were provided at the end of the section that discussed how to evaluate operational control. In addition to these indicators, the auditor may find measurements relating to the performance of the corrective and preventive action and internal audit programs. A summary of some of these indicators follows:

- Percent internal audits performed on schedule

- Number of qualified internal auditors

- Percent corrective actions recurred

- Dollars saved through corrective action

- Ratio corrective to preventive actions

- Number or percent of corrective actions overdue

KEY AUDIT POINT: IMPROVEMENT

The improvement process includes the setting of environmental objectives and targets, the establishment of management programs to ensure achievement of these objectives, and the performance of periodic management reviews. The general flow of the improvement process is shown in Figure 9.7. Interrelationships with other core activities are shown in shaded boxes.

Environmental Objectives and Targets

Many companies review and set environmental objectives during the management review process. In this case, this topic should be discussed during the evaluation of the

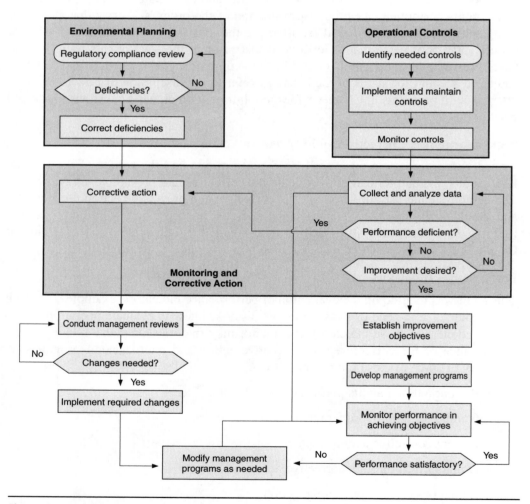

Figure 9.7 Improvement process.

management review. General comments on the evaluation of objectives can be found in the quality objectives section of Chapter 8. Additional specific audit points unique to the EMS follow.

The ISO 14001 standard requires the setting of environmental objectives and targets. There is a lot of confusion about what defines an objective and what defines a target. The ISO 14001 standard defines an environmental objective as: "An overall environmental goal, consistent with the environmental policy, that an organization sets itself to achieve." An environmental target is defined in the standard as: "A detailed performance requirement, applicable to the organization or parts thereof, that arises from the environmental objectives and that needs to be set and met in order to achieve those objectives." Clause 4.3.3 of the standards states that both objectives and targets should be measurable where practicable.

Many organizations define the objective in global terms such as "Reduce air emissions" and the target as by how much, for example "by 20 percent." I prefer to think of the target as the actions that must be accomplished to support the overall objective. For example, the objectives and targets to improve energy conservation might be as follows:

Environmental objective: Reduce energy usage by 25 percent from 2003 levels by the end of 2005. (Note that the objective is also measurable and has a time frame associated with it.)

To accomplish this objective, the organization may target the following activities:

Target 1. Relamp the production area with high efficiency lighting by June 2004. (Note this target also is measurable and has a time frame.)

Target 2. Install motion sensors in all conference rooms by March 2004.

Target 3. Conduct an energy survey of the facilities in the first quarter of 2004.

Target 4. Evaluate, select, and install an energy management system for the main building by June 2004.

Target 5. Evaluate the use of variable-speed motors for the oil transfer system during the first quarter of 2004.

Target 6. Provide refresher training on the energy conservation guidelines to all personnel in January 2004.

I prefer this method of defining objectives and targets since it provides more specific measurable goals that must be met by the various functions and levels of the organization. Each target would then have its own set of actions required to achieve it. Taken together, achieving the targets should allow the organization to meet its overall objective of a 25 percent reduction in energy usage. When defined as suggested here, the objective is derived from the policy commitments, and the targets focus on the activities related to the significant aspects that must be improved to meet the objective. This alignment of policy, objectives, targets, and aspects looks something like Figure 9.8.

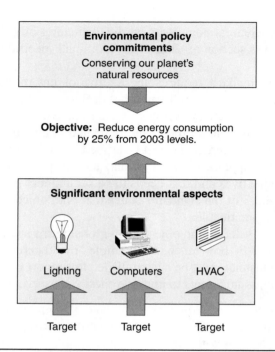

Figure 9.8 Objectives, targets, policy, and significant aspects alignment.

Audit Strategy and Key Audit Points

The auditor should ask to see the objectives and associated programs established for the current period. During this review, the auditor asks how these objectives were determined. If the auditor has recently completed the audit of the monitoring and corrective action process, then he or she should be familiar with the overall performance of the EMS and where improvement objectives may be warranted. In particular, the auditor should verify that the views of interested parties were considered during the setting of objectives (the ISO 14001 standard requires this). Interested parties include outside organizations like community residents, government agencies, and the organization's stockholders and employees. The auditor should ask to see the communication log to see if there were any concerns or opinions expressed by interested parties, and, if there were, that these were considered.

The auditor should compare the objectives to the management programs set up to help ensure their achievement. These management programs, or action plans, must contain details on what has to be done, who is responsible for doing it, and when it should be done. The auditor can use the actions and time frames to evaluate performance in achieving the objectives. Some form of tracking progress should be in place. If no tracking of performance in meeting objectives is evident, other than during an annual or semiannual management review, consider issuance of an OFI.

Such infrequent monitoring does not allow sufficient time to recovery actions if progress is deficient.

Communication of improvement objectives is also important. The auditor may ask the auditee about the methods used to communicate objectives throughout the organization. Note that the operational control audits evaluate the effectiveness of these methods by asking employees about any objectives established for their departments or activities. The auditor may want to issue an OFI if no formal means of communicating objectives have been established.

Of course, the most important item to verify is the organization's performance in meeting its objectives and targets. With the performance objectives and management programs in hand, the auditor should be able to establish whether the management programs have been effective in supporting achievement of the environmental objectives and related targets. The auditor should question any areas where performance is not meeting the defined targets. For sustained negative trends or performance far below the target milestone, ask what actions are being taken to correct the performance. Failure to take action for significantly poor performance is the basis for a nonconformance.

Management Review

The management review process has been revised in the 2004 version of ISO 14001 to more closely follow the process outlined in the ISO 9001:2000 standard. Refer to the management review section of Chapter 8 for a detailed discussion on how to evaluate this process. Although the inputs differ slightly, the process is the same.

Performance Indicators

The auditor may find some of the following metrics or indicators relating to the performance of the improvement process:

- Percent targets achieved

- Percent objectives met

- Number or percent of actions overdue

- Number of improvement projects undertaken

- Dollars saved from continual improvement activities

- Environmental performance gains from continual improvement activities

KEY AUDIT POINT: KEY SUPPORT PROCESSES

The final group of activities is the key support processes. These activities support all components of the management system. They have been grouped together for convenience and to allow for an efficient audit. Portions of these activities will be evaluated during other process-based audits. These audits will evaluate only the centralized elements of these processes.

Audit Strategy and Key Audit Points

Detailed discussions on how to evaluate most of the upcoming activities have been presented in Chapter 8 in the section titled resource and support processes. Review that section for audit strategies, process flows, and key audit points. Unique aspects of the environmental management system will be highlighted here.

Document Control

The evaluation of document control can follow the same flow and strategy as outlined in Chapter 8. The auditor should also verify proper control of environmental regulations and ensure that there is a method to stay aware of changes to them. Many companies rely on subscription services, links to government Web sites where changes are announced, and corporate staff to maintain this awareness. The auditor should verify that some method is in place and is being used. Note that this review may also be performed during the environmental planning audit when evaluating legal and other requirements.

Record Control

The evaluation of document control can follow the same flow and strategy as outlined in Chapter 8, with the additional consideration that many of the environmental records that must be maintained have legal retention requirements. Most, but not all, regulatory records must be retained for at least three years. The auditor may want to have the auditee show them the legal retention requirement for the records if doubt exists.

Training

The evaluation of training can follow the same flow and strategy as outlined in Chapter 8, with the additional consideration that some organizations have a legal obligation to provide certain types of training, such as hazardous waste training for employees who handle hazardous wastes and storm water operator training if the organization is operating under a storm water permit. The auditor may want to question the training coordinator or management representative how these mandatory training requirements are identified, in addition to verifying that the training was provided.

The auditor should also ensure that contract and agency personnel are made aware of the organization's environmental policies and practices, to the extent they apply to the work they are involved with.

Control of Purchased Products and Contractors (Purchasing)

The evaluation of purchased products and services is a little different for the EMS. In the environmental management system, we are most concerned with two things relating to our suppliers and contractors. First, we need to ensure that any relevant environmental policies and requirements are communicated to suppliers and contractors. This can be done through a pass-down of the requirements (for example, pass-down of any restricted or prohibited material lists) or by briefings before the contractor commences work on-site. Most organizations have a fairly robust process to do this. The auditor should verify that the process is being followed during the audit.

The second consideration, more often lacking, is obtaining information from suppliers or contractors regarding their activities and any significant environmental aspects arising from these activities. For suppliers of materials and products this is often accomplished through receipt of the Material Safety Data Sheet (MSDS) from the supplier. The auditor should ensure that the MSDSs for new products are reviewed for any environmental (or safety) concerns that may need to be addressed before using the new chemical or material. For contractors, an environmental survey is often used. The survey would ask questions regarding the types of materials and chemicals to be used, the types and amounts of wastes expected to be generated, and what is done with the wastes. The auditor should verify that methods are in place to address these two considerations and are being used.

Roles and Responsibilities

Roles and responsibilities connected with defined activities associated with significant environmental aspects will be evaluated during operational control audits. In this audit the auditor should focus on the definition, communication, and awareness of roles, responsibilities, and authorities of key individuals and functions needed to support the environmental management system. These include the management representative, internal EMS auditors, emergency response coordinators, and the cross-functional team assigned responsibilities for identifying environmental aspects and determining their significance. If these roles are examined during other audits, they do not need to be reviewed here.

Communications

The final evaluation examines the process used to communicate important environmental information within the organization and to outside interested parties. Communication of key information internally, like roles and responsibilities, awareness, and improvement objectives, will be continually evaluated during other audits. I usually like to ask how concerns, issues, and improvement suggestions are communicated up the ladder, however. I often find that no formal system exists for upward communication from employees. This will damage the support for the EMS and will result in losing ideas that could significantly improve environmental performance. The auditor should issue a finding if no formal system exists to support upward communication from the workforce. The auditor can test the effectiveness of the system, if it exists, by asking to see the log or file of concerns, issues, or suggestions provided by employees. A blank file or log tells you something isn't working.

The primary focus of this evaluation is on external communication. ISO 14001 requires that a system for receiving, documenting, and responding to inquiries or concerns relating to the environmental management system exists. This is almost universally met by the maintenance of some type of communication log. The auditor should ask about the methods used to respond to outside inquiries, including who receives them, how are they handled, and who responds. The auditor should also ask to see the log. In the case where there are no entries in the log, indicating no outside inquiries, the auditor should verify that a system is in place to handle them if any come in. An auditor wanting to be sly and devious could have Aunt Betty call in and request a copy of the environmental policy to see if the communication was logged. Just don't say I told you to.

Performance Indicators

Performance indicators for document control, record control, and training are provided in Chapter 8. Performance indicators for the communication process may include:

- Number of environmental improvement suggestions received from employees
- Number of improvement suggestions per employee
- Number of improvement suggestions implemented
- Dollars saved from employee improvement suggestions
- Environmental performance gains from employee improvement suggestions
- Average response cycle time for outside inquiries

SUMMARY

In this chapter we described the strategy for an audit of an environmental management system. The reader may have noted many similarities between audits of a quality management system and an audit of the EMS. Indeed, there are many similarities, to the point where it is not only possible but even desirable to jointly audit the QMS and EMS together. This topic will be discussed in Chapter 11, but first we will discuss how to audit a health and safety management system in Chapter 10. You may want to review the next chapter even if you do not currently have an OH&S management system in place, since it will give you some insight into the effort and actions that go into implementing this component of an overall management system, and the audit points will reinforce the discussion provided in this section.

10

Conducting Health and Safety Management System Audits

T his chapter will build on parts I and II, applying these concepts to the performance of audits of health and safety management systems based on the OHSAS 18001:1999 standard.[1] If you also have an environmental management system in place and reviewed Chapter 9, you will recognize many similarities between the strategies for performing environmental management system audits and audits of the OH&S management system.

OHSAS 18001 REVISITED

As noted in Chapter 1, the OHSAS 18001:2004 standard is based on five primary clauses (4.2–4.6) as shown in Figure 10.1. These five clauses can be grouped into operational components as follows:

• *A planning component.* In OHSAS 18001, planning is represented by the ongoing identification of job hazards, the assessment of the risks associated with these hazards, and the identification of appropriate methods to control them. Planning for unexpected events is captured by the emergency preparedness and response requirements. Planning is centered around the establishment of an organizational policy that declares the company's commitments for health and safety performance.

• *An operational component.* In OHSAS 18001, requirements focused on implementation and maintenance of the controls are specified in the requirements for implementation and operation.

• *A monitoring and corrective action component.* In OHSAS 18001, these activities are defined in performance monitoring and measurement, nonconformance, and corrective and preventive action, and the internal audit clauses.

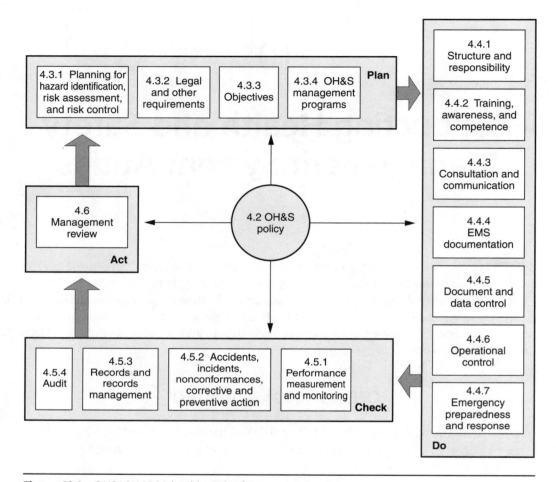

Figure 10.1 OHSAS 18001 health and safety management system.

• *An improvement process.* Improvement is embedded in requirements for the setting of health and safety objectives, management programs, and in the conduct of management reviews.

• *Key support processes.* These activities support the overall health and safety management system and includes document and record control, structure and responsibility, communication, and training, awareness, and competence. They are found in the implementation and operation and monitoring and measurement sections of the standard.

In Figure 10.2, the organization's core business activities are represented by the shaded boxes and dashed lines. They represent the on-the-job activities and facilities that can pose risks to your employees. The OHSAS 18001:1999 components that monitor and control the health and safety risks of these activities are then shown interacting with these core business activities.

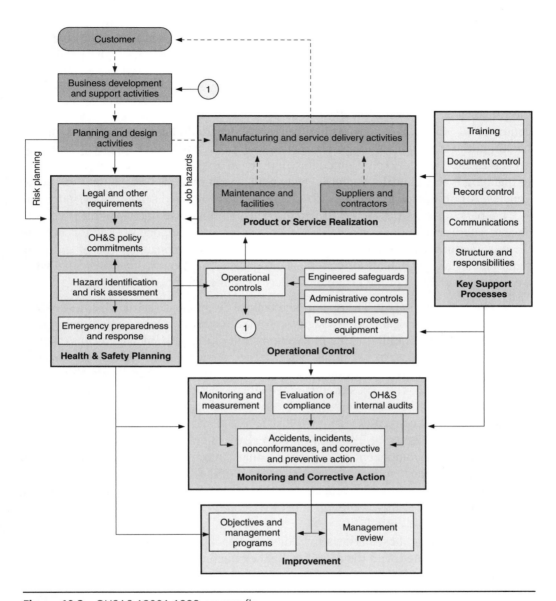

Figure 10.2   OHSAS 18001:1999 process flow.

AUDIT SCOPE

I like to group related OHSAS 18001 components together for my audits. I do this for two reasons. First, it provides for a more efficient and effective audit. The grouped elements are closely related, and it can be hard to evaluate one without evaluating the others in the group. Second, and just as important, I apply the process approach popularized by ISO 9001 to my health and safety management system audits. By grouping these elements together, I form natural processes where the output from one process becomes the input into a related process. My audit groupings are a little different from the operational groupings shown in Figure 10.2, as will be discussed.

• *Health and safety planning components.* These are normally evaluated first since the proper identification of health and safety hazards and assessment of their risks is central to all other components within the OH&S system. In Figure 10.2, inputs into the health and safety planning process include the organization's planning for safe processes and the safety of the processes, equipment, and facilities themselves. Also key to planning is the identification of legal and other requirements and planning for emergencies. All of these activities are folded around the health and safety policy statement.

I depart slightly from Figure 10.2 in that I also normally audit evaluation of compliance to safety regulations during my audit of the planning components. I do this because there is a natural audit flow that arises from doing the identification of legal and other requirements and evaluation of compliance together. This flow will be presented when we discuss evaluation of the health and safety planning components.

• *Operational control.* The operational control component verifies that the controls associated with the organization's significant hazards are in place and are being used and maintained. It is similar to the production audit of a quality management system. It answers the question, "Are we doing what we said we would do?" In any organization there will be multiple activities that need to be controlled, and there could be multiple controls for each activity. These audits will evaluate these controls. Note that I used the plural case, *audits,* because there may be multiple audits throughout the year focused around operational control.

I depart from Figure 10.2 slightly in that I also evaluate a portion of the monitoring and measurement component during operational control evaluations and I may also spot-check compliance to regulatory requirements. If the organization has trained internal auditors who are also knowledgeable of health and safety regulatory requirements, then the health and safety compliance reviews could be folded into these operational control audits *almost* entirely.

Note that during these reviews I will also be checking on the control of documents and records associated with the activities I am evaluating, the training and competency of personnel performing these activities, and their knowledge of their roles and responsibilities for properly conducting the activities in a safe manner.

• *Monitoring and corrective action.* This audit evaluates the overall monitoring and performance of the health and safety management system. It includes an analysis of overall trends in health and safety performance and actions being taken to correct any adverse trends. It also evaluates the internal audit program and the follow-up on any weaknesses noted during these audits. Both of these components feed into the accidents, incidents, nonconformances, and corrective and preventive action system, which will also be reviewed during this evaluation.

• *Improvement.* The evaluation of improvement activities will focus on the setting of health and safety objectives and the establishment of health and safety management programs to achieve them. Performance toward meeting these objectives will be assessed along with any actions being taken to ensure they are met if performance is lacking. The management review process will also be examined.

• *Key support processes.* The centralized activities for key support processes like document and record control will be evaluated in this audit. I say centralized, since many of the outputs from these activities (accurate documents located where needed, legible and complete records, and so on) will be evaluated during the other audits. Other items included in this review will be roles and responsibilities of key functions, communications, and training.

The remainder of this chapter will focus on strategies for conducting audits of these groupings. Readers will be referred to Chapter 8 for some of the items where the strategy is the same as it is for evaluating its equivalent component in the quality management system. For the most part, these include some of the components of the key support processes. The audit checklists provided on the accompanying CD have been structured along these groupings. Review these checklists as you read the discussions that follow.

KEY AUDIT POINT: HEALTH AND SAFETY PLANNING

The planning process forms the heart of the health and safety management system. The activities that form this process are shown in Figure 10.3. This figure also outlines the key audit points that will be examined during the evaluation.

The reader should note the parallel path through the health and safety planning process. The OHSAS 18001 standard requires an organization to meet its regulatory obligations. In the course of implementing OHSAS 18001, the company will have to demonstrate that it understands what health and safety regulations it must meet, has access to what those regulations require, and is performing reviews to ensure it is meeting those requirements. For many small to medium-sized companies without health and safety specialists on staff, this may be the first time that they have systematically evaluated their health and safety compliance posture. What they learn must be incorporated into the planning for the health and safety management system. This health and safety compliance review may be done prior to the identification of job hazards or it may be performed as part of the initial health and safety review. The key audit point is that it must be done as part of the planning of the OH&S system and any deficiencies corrected or prevented through the application of corrective action and operational controls.

One of the key differences between an OH&S management system and an environmental management system lies in the initial identification of risks. Whereas in an EMS the identification of all significant aspects (or risks) can be accomplished during the initial environmental review, in an occupational health and safety system this identification will be ongoing. The systematic review of all workplace hazards may takes months or even years. In essence, it is an ongoing activity due to the constantly changing nature

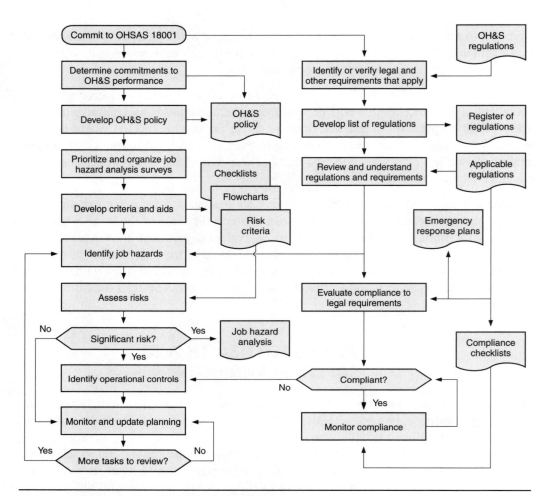

Figure 10.3   Health and safety planning activities.

of the workplace. The initial review should identify the jobs, tasks, and areas that must be evaluated and should prioritize them based on their perceived risk. The organization then conducts job hazard analysis on these tasks in a prioritized fashion. I do not recommend waiting until all of the JHAs have been completed before implementation of the rest of the management system. To do so would be to lose out on the significant benefits that an 18001-based system can provide during this lengthy time frame.

Audit Strategy and Key Audit Points

This section will define a general audit flow and strategy that can be used to evaluate the health and safety planning process. The components of this process will be presented in the order in which the auditor would normally evaluate them.

Health and Safety Policy

The auditor should begin the audit by examining the health and safety policy statement. The policy statement or, more importantly, the objectives and commitments within the policy, form the heart of the planning process, which, in turn, forms the heart of the health and safety management system. Rather than evaluating simple compliance to the standard, the auditor should determine if the policy and its development meets the intent of the standard. Compliance to the intent of the OHSAS 18001 standard can be evaluated by examining the following key audit points:

• *Who was involved in the development of the policy statement?* The standard requires top management's involvement in the development of the health and safety policy statement. There is no hard and fast definition of who makes up top management, but a general rule often used is that top management comprises the senior person present at a facility and his or her direct reports.

This involvement should be more than simply signing off on a policy developed by the health and safety management representative or a consultant. It should include active debate about what health and safety objectives the organization wants to achieve and what commitments it is willing to make. Later on, the company will be required to establish improvement objectives focused on meeting its commitments in the policy statement. Most improvement projects require some initial allocation of time, money, and other resources. Management should not make commitments that it is not willing to back up with sufficient resources. The auditor can assess the level of top management involvement by asking senior management how the policy was developed. If management's involvement was simply a sign-off, and it admits to this, then the auditor should consider issuance of an opportunity for improvement. Engaging top management in the development of the health and safety policy will help to ensure the alignment and support needed for real health and safety performance improvement.

• *Is the policy statement appropriate, given the nature and scale of its health and safety risks?* This is a difficult requirement to evaluate because it is somewhat subjective. Unless the policy statement makes no sense, I normally do not challenge it.

• *Health and safety policy objectives and commitments.* These form the core of the policy statement. They represent what the organization feels is important regarding its health and safety performance. They can also form the framework for health and safety objectives and related management programs.

Unfortunately, most organizations do little more than embed the two mandatory commitments from the OHSAS 18001 standard in their policy. The two commitments, continual improvement and compliance to legal and other requirements, are very broad, which makes it difficult to focus on what's most important to the organization. What we want to do is to use the policy commitments to help focus on what's most important to *this* organization.

The auditor should, of course, verify that the two mandatory commitments are found somewhere in the policy statement. Ideally, the auditor will also find a few more specific commitments have been added beyond the two mandatory ones to drive performance in certain key areas. Some examples of specific commitments include:

– *We are committed to the long-term safety and health of our employees.* This commitment goes beyond basic safety and health and could be used to drive smoking cessation programs, nutrition programs, and fitness programs.

– *We are committed to the development and maintenance of a culture of health and safety throughout the organization.* This commitment could be used to drive the implementation of a behavior-based health and safety system.

– *We are committed to the development of safe products that enhance the quality of life of our consumers.* This commitment would be appropriate for a firm that designs the products that it sells. It could be used to drive the design of products that go beyond meeting regulatory safety requirements.

These are but a few of the specific commitments that might be offered up in the health and safety policy statement. Their usefulness is in their ability to focus health and safety objectives toward specific improvements that have a large and real effect on the organization's health and safety performance. They point to where an organization can really make a difference beyond meeting minimum safety laws.

• *Documented, implemented, maintained, and communicated within the organization and to the general public.* All policy statements are documented, or at least I haven't found one yet that wasn't. Implementation, maintenance, and communication within the organization, including to persons working on behalf of the organization, will be evaluated during other audits. This leaves communication to the general public.

The auditor should ask how the policy is made available to the general public. Ask, "If my Aunt Betty, who drives by the plant every day and sees the OHSAS 18001 flag flying, calls and asks about the health and safety policy, what would you tell her?" Answers may be that she would be directed to the company Web site where it is listed, she would be faxed a copy, or that the call would be directed to the health and safety management representative who would send her a copy or read it over the phone. The key is, there has to be a process to make it available to the public. Almost every company has a Web site. Posting the policy on the Web site is one of the easiest and most effective ways of communicating to the public. The auditor should issue an opportunity for improvement if the process for communicating the policy is cumbersome or inconvenient; for example, if the answer to the Aunt Betty question is, "Well, we would tell her to stop by and come into the lobby. It's posted there." This is neither practical or realistic.

Health and Safety Hazards

If the policy is the heart of the OH&S system, then the identification of significant health and safety hazards is the head. The goal of this process is to identify those activities that must be controlled to prevent harm to the company's employees or the general public.

As noted in the introduction to this chapter, the identification of workplace hazards and determination of their related risks will be an ongoing activity. The auditor should verify that a systematic process is in place to identify and evaluate these hazards and that progress is being made to complete the JHAs throughout the workplace.

The auditor should start by asking to see the procedure for identifying significant health and safety hazards. The standard requires that an organization have a procedure, but it doesn't necessarily have to be documented (although I certainly recommend it). If the process has been documented, then the auditor should ask the health and safety management representative, management appointee, or process owner to walk through the procedure, stopping at key points as will be outlined. If it hasn't been documented, then the auditor should still ask the auditee to walk through the process, paying close attention to the key activities, and making notes to follow up on when asking to see the objective evidence. The auditor will have to rely more on the standard and on the checklist in this situation.

During the walk-through, verify the following key elements of the process:

• *Is the strategy for identifying workplace hazards comprehensive?* The auditor should verify that all areas, core activities, and processes are included in the evaluation. Many organizations conduct the review by portioning the plant into areas such as production areas, administrative areas, outside facilities and grounds, and auxiliary areas such as tank farms, pumps, and boilers. Others structure the review around job functions such as warehouse staff, production operators, maintenance and administrative, management, and clerical functions. The auditor can look for evidence that each of these areas or functions are included in the review or in plans for future reviews. The auditor should inquire about any areas where there is no evidence of inclusion, either in the JHAs already performed or in the plans for future reviews. If it becomes clear that major areas or functions are not included in the review, generate a finding. An example of a job listing that identifies the activities to be reviewed for an area, along with priorities for completing them, is provided in Table 10.1. In this system, the strategy would be to first evaluate and analyze all priority 1 tasks, followed by priority 2, and then priority 3. The red (R), yellow (Y), and green (G) column provides information on the status of completing the reviews. Criteria for assignment of red–yellow–green is contained in a comment on the spreadsheet. Using this and the spreadsheets for the other areas of the facility, the auditor could establish whether a comprehensive system was in place to evaluate workplace hazards.

Another consideration is whether the evaluation includes nonroutine as well as routine activities. Nonroutine activities could include bulk liquid loading and unloading, maintenance of equipment and facilities (whether performed by the organization or by contractors), and facility modification, expansion, or renovation. In the job list, the auditor can see that nonroutine activities have been considered when planning the JHAs.

• *Were the reviews thorough?* Once the auditor is satisfied that the scope of the review was adequate, he or she may wish to verify that the team that performed the review knew what to look for. The auditor may ask what training the team received prior to

Table 10.1 Example job hazard list.

Area: Warehouse

No.	Job or Activity	Equipment Used	Hazardous Materials Involved	Functions Involved	Job-Specific Safety Procedure or Program?	Pri. 1/2/3	Analyzed?	Status
	Routine							
	Loading/unloading trailers w/forklift	Forklift		Material handler	Yes	2	No	Y
	Manual loading/unloading trailers	Portable conveyer		Material handler		1	Yes	G
	Packing and labeling cartons for shipment	Tape dispenser, label gun		Warehouseman		3	No	Y
	Unpacking cartons	Box knife		Warehouseman		2	No	R
	Applying shrink-wrap to pallets	Shrink-wrap machine		Material handler		1	Yes	G
	Assembly of product racking	Pneumatic hand tools		Warehouseman		1	Yes	G
	Tear-down of fixed racking	Pneumatic hand tools		Warehouseman		1	Yes	G
	Safe operation of order picker	Order picker		Material handler	Yes	2	No	Y
	Safe operation of forklift	Forklift		Material handler	Yes	2	No	Y
	Floor cleaning with broom	Broom and mop		Warehouseman		3	No	Y
	Floor cleaning with power washer	Power washer	Floor cleaning agent	Warehouseman		2	Yes	G
	Manual picking of products	Pick cart, bar code reader		Warehouseman		2	Yes	G
	Use of computer terminal	Computer terminal		Warehouseman		3	No	Y

Continued

Continued

No.	Job or Activity	Equipment Used	Hazardous Materials Involved	Functions Involved	Job-Specific Safety Procedure or Program?	Pri. 1/2/3	Analyzed?	Status
	Stacking and disposal of wooden pallets	Forklift		Material handler		1	Yes	G
	Crating	Hand tools, table saw		Warehouseman		1	Yes	G
	Operation of the waste compactor	Waste compactor		Material handler, Warehouseman		1	Yes	G
	Safe operation of ladders	Ladders		Warehouseman		1	Yes	G
	Proper use of safety harness	Safety harness		Warehouseman	Yes	2	No	Y
	Proper use of table saw	Table saw		Warehouseman	Yes	2	Yes	G
	Nonroutine							
	Spill cleanup	Spill kit		Material handler, Warehouseman	Yes	2	No	Y
	Proper use of eye-wash station	Eye-wash station		Material handler, Warehouseman	Yes	2	No	Y
	Proper use of fire extinguisher	Fire extinguisher		Material handler, Warehouseman		1	Yes	G
	Emergency shutoff of storm drains	Storm drain cutoff valves		Material handler, Warehouseman		2	No	R
	Replacement of forklift propane tanks	Forklift, hand tools	Propane	Material handler		1	Yes	G
	Charging of order picker batteries	Order picker, hand tools	Electric batteries	Material handler		1	Yes	G

conducting the review. Personnel performing job hazard analysis should have training before conducting the evaluations. The auditor may also ask to see any checklists used to guide the auditors in what to look for. A portion of a checklist used to guide the conduct of JHAs is shown in Figure 10.4.

Related to this topic is evaluation of who was involved in the review. Ideally, the job hazard analysis will be performed by cross-functional teams with representatives from each of the areas evaluated. Many companies train and then use safety committee members to perform the JHAs. This can be especially important to identifying the non-routine activities that should be considered, but may not be going on when the analysis

---

Hazard Identification Checklist

Area: _____   Date: _____   Analyst: _____

Does the workplace or its surrounding environment present any of the following hazards?

❑ **Slips**/falls on level surfaces (protrusions, uneven surfaces, holes, wrinkled flooring material, wet or slippery surfaces, oil, cracked concrete or curbs, unguarded pits or shafts)

❑ **Falls** of persons from heights (lack of guardrails, improper usage of ladders, failure to use harnesses, etc.)

❑ **Falls of tools**, materials, etc., from heights (lack of kickplates, failure to use restraining devices)

❑ Inadequate **tool safeguards** (guarding, insulation)

❑ Inadequate **headroom**

❑ Hazards associated with **manual lifting/handling** of tools, materials, etc.

❑ Inadequate **machine safeguards**

❑ **Vehicle** hazards, e.g., plant vehicles and forklifts

    ❑ No designated walkways for personnel or unsafe layout of forklift travel path

    ❑ Inadequate room/congestion

    ❑ Loading/unloading routes for tractor-trailers

❑ **Plant layout** (e.g., change rooms in center of plant, congestion)

❑ **Fire and explosion** hazards (flammable or combustible materials, reactive chemicals, high-voltage electricity)

    ❑ Container safety devices installed (grounding and bonding devices, caps, flash arrestors, etc.)

    ❑ Incompatible materials separated and/or stored separately

    ❑ Fire suppression systems (e.g., sprinkler systems) installed, operational

    ❑ Combustible materials removed

❑ Substances that may be **inhaled** (chemical fumes and vapors—see MSDS, dust, etc.)

❑ Substances that may cause harm by coming into contact with or being **absorbed** through the skin (chemicals handled without adequate PPE—see MSDS)

❑ Substances that may cause harm by being **ingested** (i.e., entering the body via the mouth or injection

Figure 10.4 JHA checklist.

is performed. If the auditor discovers that the review was performed by one person, then he or she should more aggressively evaluate the comprehensiveness and thoroughness of the review by examining the evidence already cited. Nothing in the standard *requires* a cross-functional team be used to conduct the review, but it is highly unlikely that one person can do the job adequately. Since it is possible that one individual is the source of all knowledge, however, the auditor must focus on the results.

An example of a form used to record the results of a job hazard analysis is shown in Figure 10.5. Completed JHAs could be sampled and reviewed by the auditor for an indication of the thoroughness of the analysis. Other methodologies such as hazard and operability studies (HAZOP) or FMEA are also sometimes encountered as methods to determine hazards and their related risks.

If the auditor finds evidence that the JHAs failed to consider important hazards, or that the reviews did not include obvious hazards like chemicals, ergonomics, and fire and explosion hazards, then the auditor should consider issuance of a finding. Note also that the OHSAS 18001 standard requires employee involvement in the development and review of policies and procedures used to manage risk. Using employees representing all areas of the organization is another way to demonstrate involvement of employees in the design of the OH&S management system.

• *How were risks determined and classified?* The auditor should examine the rationale used to determine and classify the risks associated with the hazards identified during the job hazard analysis. The most common method for assessing risks combines the likelihood of occurrence of the hazard with its severity if it does occur. Note that results of this assessment are documented on the JHA form shown in Figure 10.5. The results of this analysis are then used to classify risks as negligible, tolerable, moderate, high, and

Basic Job Steps	Haz. Cat.	Hazards	Current Controls	S	L	RC	Recommendations/Actions
Hazard categories: SB—struck by, CW—contact with, Cby—contact by, CB—caught between, SA—struck against, CI—caught in, CO—caught on, O—overexertion or repetitive motion, FS—fall at same level, FB—fall to below, E—exposure to chemicals, vapors, noise, etc.							
S: Severity ranking L: Likelihood of occurrence RC: Risk category (S × L) Refer to procedure 2-20, Job Hazard Analysis and Risk Assessment							

Figure 10.5 Job hazard analysis form.

unacceptable. Actions and controls to minimize risks can then be focused on unacceptable, high, and then moderately risky activities, in that order. Tolerable risks can be lowered as time and resources permit. This is by no means the only way to assess risk, but the organization must have some systematic method that provides a reasonable and actionable assignment of risk categories in order to be in compliance with the standard and to determine where actions need to be taken.

An example of a portion of a spreadsheet used to analyze the risks of hazards determined through JHA is shown in Figure 10.6. The auditor could review this form to determine if a systematic approach exists and is being used to analyze risks. The severity and likelihood of occurrence rankings are shown on the spreadsheet, and, as in the job listing, the criteria for assignment of these rankings is embedded in comments in the spreadsheet itself. This format shows the tasks, the hazards associated with the tasks, current controls, risk rankings, actions taken, recalculated risk rankings after the action is taken, and a summary of the actions themselves. The auditor could quickly scan the worksheet to determine whether the process is systematic and has been properly applied.

The key audit point is that the methods used to determine what is and what isn't a significant risk should be reproducible. There should be a consistent process in place. A team evaluating the same health and safety hazards next year should come to roughly the same conclusions as to what is a significant risk and must be controlled. Consistency is important since the jobs change often within a dynamic system. Processes, products, and facilities change. Health and safety concerns change. A consistent set of criteria helps to provide the basis for these changes. Verify that there is some method to the assignment of risk. If there was no rationale at all, generate an NC, citing the lack of a procedure (that is, process). If there was some reasonable rationale, but it was not formalized or applied consistently, consider generation of an OFI.

• *How is the information maintained up to date?* For audits that are performed well after the OH&S system has been in place and certified, this question becomes a central focus of the evaluation. Up to this point, the audit flow has focused on initial job hazard analysis. For an existing system, the auditor should have confidence that the methods used to identify health and safety hazards and their related risks have been verified to be adequate. The main issue for an existing system, therefore, is whether these methods are being applied to product, process, and facility changes. The key question is how are those responsible for reviewing new products, services, and activities made aware of the need to re-perform a job hazard analysis?

The auditor should begin by first identifying new or modified products, services, or activities and facility modifications that have taken place since the last audit. If the auditor does not know what they were, then he or she should first talk to the production manager, maintenance manager, or engineering manager to help generate a list of recent modifications, job redesigns, or new product or process introductions. These items will become the auditor's samples for later verification during the interview.

The auditor should then interview the management representative or management appointee about the methods used to keep the job hazard analysis current. Many organization's use a management of change process to control and plan for new products and

Primary Activity or Source (Note—always leave one blank column at end of last step	Hand Grinding		
Functions involved	Machinist		
Steps with identifiable hazards	Pick up casting.	Grasp and hold casting while lifting.	Pick up castings.
Hazard associated with step SB—Struck by / SA—Struck against CW—Contact with / Cby—Contacted by CI—Caught in / CO—Caught on CB—Caught between / O—Overexertion rep. motion E—Exposure FS—Fall same level / FB—Fall to below	SB—Worker drops 15-lb. casting on foot.	CW—Worker contacts sharp burrs causing lacerations.	RM—Worker twists or strains while lifting 15-lb. castng.
Step specifically **regulated** (Y/N)?	N	Y	N
Engineered **safeguards** (Y/N)?	N	N	N
Procedure controls (Y/N)?	N	N	N
Trained for safe performance (Y/N)?	N	N	N
Personal protective equipment (Y/N)?	N	N	N
Severity of hazard (1/3/9)	3	3	3
Likelihood of **occurrence**, considering existing controls and history (1/3/9)	3	9	9
Total risk **ranking** (S × L)	9	27	27
Initial category based on ranking (I/H/M/T/N)	M	H	H
Action (I/M/E)—Reference job actions sheet	E	I	I
Engineered **safeguards** (Y/N)?	Y	N	Y
Procedure controls (Y/N)?	N	N	N
Trained for safe performance (Y/N)?	Y	Y	Y
Personal protective equipment (Y/N)?	Y	Y	N
Recalculated severity after action (1/3/9)	3	3	1
Recalculated occurence after action (1/3/9)	1	1	1
Recalculated total risk **ranking** (S × L)	3	3	1
Current category based on ranking (I/H/M/T/N)	T	T	N
Summary of resultant hazard controls—List specific procedures (by number), PPE, and safeguards in place to prevent worker injury or illness or workplace damage	Redesigned work table. Provided gloves with better grip.	Provided cut-resistant gloves.	Redesigned work table to require minimal lifting.

Figure 10.6   Risk determination and classification worksheet.

processes. This process could be modified to include consideration of job changes that could impact the health and safety of employees. Some organizations use a management of change process and an annual review to ensure new hazards are identified. Others have an advanced product quality planning process. The auditor should thoroughly understand the methods used by asking questions and by asking to see the documents, checklists, and other aids used to control changes. The absence of any consistent method to stay on top of new hazards should result in a finding.

Once the auditor fully understands the methods used to stay up to date, then test the application of the methods by asking to see the results of the reviews for the items selected prior to the audit. If a management of change process was used, ask to see the checklist completed for the facility or process modification made two months ago. Assuming that new health and safety hazards were identified for the change, then ask to see the results of their risk analysis. If the auditor finds that the process was not followed or that the management representative was not even aware of significant changes to the company's tasks, services, activities, or facilities when he or she should have been, issue an NC.

Staying aware of changes to processes that could impact the OH&S system is important from a regulatory standpoint as well as a health and safety performance perspective. The organization is required by law to maintain a healthy and safe workplace. Recognizing new hazards and putting in place controls to minimize their risks is a regulatory requirement.

The bottom line is that the auditor should verify that methods are in place and are being used to maintain the organization's JHAs current.

• *Operational controls.* The auditor also needs to verify that the organization has taken its significant health and safety risks into account in the design, implementation, and operation of its OH&S system. This can be evidenced by the identification and implementation of appropriate controls to minimize or lower the risk associated with its activities and facilities. The auditor can ask how significant health and safety hazards are controlled. At this stage, planning, the auditor is most concerned that appropriate controls have been identified. The operational control audits will confirm that they were properly implemented and are being maintained. The spreadsheet in Figure 10.6 indicates some of the controls used to minimize these risks. The job hazard analysis would typically provide more detail.

Evaluation of Compliance to Legal and Other Requirements

One of the first areas where organizations see a significant improvement after implementing OHSAS 18001 is in their health and safety compliance posture. This is especially true in small to medium-sized firms that do not have health and safety professionals on staff. In these organizations the identification of the legal requirements that apply to their activities may require more effort than the implementation of the health and safety management system itself. Even so, it is critically important that the organization not only identify the regulatory requirements it must meet, but also understand them and ensure that they meet them. This portion of the health and safety planning audit focuses on verification that the organization is meeting its policy commitment to comply with legal and other requirements.

Other requirements in this sense mean requirements imposed by the management system design itself, by customers, and by voluntary adoption of health and safety protocols, such as OHSA's Voluntary Protection Program (VPP). Internal requirements will be called out in the organization's policies and procedures. Customer requirements will be called out in contracts and specifications. Voluntary protocols, like the VPP, should be listed along with the legal requirements that the organization must meet.

The auditor should begin by asking the management representative, management appointee, or individual responsible for health and safety compliance for a listing of the regulations and other requirements that apply to the organization. While the standard does not require a listing, or register of regulations, as it is often called, typically there are far too many to commit to memory. As a result, a listing of some type is a practical necessity. Once the auditor has this list, verify conformance to the standard by evaluating the following:

- *Is the listing comprehensive and complete?* The auditor should verify that the listing includes federal, state, and local requirements. Most states have the authority to implement the federal requirements and do so by enacting state statutes that must be followed. If the state has the authority to implement the federal regulations, then listing the state statutes and public acts may be sufficient, since they must be at least as restrictive and are sometimes more stringent than the federal regulations. Local requirements may include local building codes and fire and evacuation regulations. As noted, I also look to see if significant voluntary requirements like the VPP are listed, assuming they apply.

- *Is the listing sufficiently detailed?* Simply listing the Occupational Safety and Health Act doesn't provide evidence that the organization understands the legal requirements it must meet. Ask the auditee, "Which parts of the act apply to us?" Some organizations simply list the name of the law or CFR that contains the requirements. The Occupational Safety and Health Act is hundreds of pages long and may contain only a few sections that are applicable to the organization. Some of the many provisions of the Occupational Safety and Health Act were listed at the end of Chapter 3. Not all of these will apply to every organization.

The auditor can evaluate whether the auditee has sufficiently researched the regulations by asking the auditee to show the requirements that apply. I normally pick three or four regulations from the list to sample. This question evaluates two critical prerequisites of health and safety compliance—does the organization have access to the regulations it must meet (also a standard requirement) and does the organization understand what they require? Often when I ask this question I get a blank stare, or the auditee pulls up 29 CFR 1900 through 1910 and tries to get through the regulations for the first time. You don't stand much of a chance of meeting the requirements if you don't know what they say!

Many organizations now use hyperlinks to the federal or state Web site where the regulations are maintained. I strongly endorse this practice, since it is practical and greatly simplifies staying up to date with regulatory changes. Local regulations and laws normally have to be retained in hard copy format. If the organization meets the access requirements of OHSAS 18001 by keeping hard copies of the CFRs, then verify that these documents are controlled and maintained up to date. One of the challenges of using hard copies of the CFRs is keeping them current. They are revised on an annual basis and can be expensive.

• *Is there evidence that the organization is evaluating its compliance to regulatory and other requirements?* Other requirements, such as VPP, are normally evaluated during other evaluations. Compliance to regulatory requirements is typically verified through the use of health and safety compliance reviews. Although it is possible to fold these reviews into other audits, they are typically performed by personnel with specialized knowledge of the health and safety regulations. The auditor should ask the auditee about the processes used to conduct health and safety compliance reviews and reviews of compliance to other, non–OHSAS 18001 requirements that the organization has adopted. If a documented procedure is available, have the auditee walk you through it. Pay attention to frequency of the audits, who performs them, how they are reported, and how any actions coming out of the review are tracked.

One of the reasons why I evaluate compliance to legal and other requirements now, instead of folding it into the monitoring and corrective action audit, is that it fits well with the audit strategy. At this point I have seen the listing of the requirements that apply to us and I have asked for and been presented with a copy of a number of the requirements themselves. It is now a simple matter to ask the auditee to provide me with evidence that we have evaluated our compliance to the requirements that I have in front of me. The auditee might provide me with a compliance report, completed checklists, or a consultant's evaluation. What I want to do now is evaluate the thoroughness of the review. Since I have the requirements in front of me, I can easily scan the records of the review to see if there is evidence that the requirements were evaluated. The evidence may be in the form of statements or conclusions in the compliance report or questions on the checklist, but what I want to know is, did we do a thorough job of evaluating our compliance to *all* of the requirements? This is where management system audits differ from regulatory compliance reviews. Whereas management system audits sample compliance to important requirements, compliance reviews should verify conformance to all requirements.

If the records of the compliance review are very general, stating for example, "The review verified compliance to the requirements of 19 CFR 1900–1910," then I generate a finding, typically in the form of an opportunity for improvement, that notes that the detail in the compliance records could be expanded to provide more assurance that the organization is meeting its regulatory requirements. If my other audits find regulatory violations, then I cite the issue as a nonconformance, using a lack of sufficient evidence and my own findings as the basis for the NC.

Some organizations rely on outside consultants or corporate staff to conduct their compliance reviews. I have no concern with this, as long as the records of the review provide sufficient evidence of compliance monitoring.

Now you may be thinking that you are not a health and safety specialist and therefore cannot evaluate the regulatory compliance sections of the standard. Take heart, you don't have to be a health and safety expert to do a credible job. If you note the audit strategy presented, there is nothing that requires an extensive knowledge of health and safety regulations on your part. All you have to do is ask the right questions and use the answers or evidence provided to guide you. The auditee will provide the list of regulations, which has already been evaluated, assuming you are certified, by the outside registrar auditor, who is knowledgeable in health and safety regulations. From that list you pick several regulations and say, "Show me." The auditee then pulls down the regulations for you or prints off a copy. Next you ask the auditee to explain how compliance reviews are conducted and again say, "Show me" when you ask for records of reviews for the printed regulations. When you get copies of the reviews, you can easily scan the records to see if there are questions or statements relating to the requirements you have in your hands. If you can't find them you say, of course, "Show me." Health and safety expertise is required to do the compliance review, but not to verify that the review was done.

• *Were weaknesses identified in the compliance reviews acted on?* If violations or weaknesses were noted in the compliance reviews, then the auditor should verify that actions were taken or have been implemented to address the deficiencies. Check with corporate policy on how to cite the findings in this case.

Emergency Preparedness and Response

The last topic of the health and safety planning audit is verification that the organization has the appropriate procedures and plans to respond to or to prevent health and safety accidents and emergencies. I review this during the planning audit since, first, this should be a planning activity and not an routine occurrence, and, second, in the United States many of the plans and procedures are required by law.

The auditor can evaluate this area by first asking for copies of the emergency response plans the organization maintains. Common plans include the following:

• Control of bloodborne pathogens

• Personal injury response plan

• Spill plans

• Fire and evacuation plan

Which plans are maintained by the organization is dependent on the nature of the organization's products, services, and activities. When the plans are presented, the auditor can ask the auditee to show the requirements that describe what must be in the plan, where the plan is required by law. With the regulatory requirements in hand, the auditor can spot-check the plans for their content and currentness. I commonly find deficiencies in these plans when compared to their regulatory requirements. Note that many of these plans focus not just on response, but also on prevention. As such, the number of actual incidents or emergencies is an indirect measure of the quality of these plans.

The auditor should also verify that the plans are up to date. It is not at all uncommon to find that personnel named as emergency responders or coordinators no longer work at the facility. It doesn't do any good to call someone in the middle of the night during an emergency if he or she is no longer employed at the facility.

The auditor should ask for a list of incidents, accidents, and injuries or other emergencies that occurred since the last audit. It helps if the auditor already knows about some of these events, which is likely since this is an internal audit. The auditor should verify that reviews were held after these occurrences and that the adequacy of the response, and the organization's response plans and procedures, were evaluated as part of these reviews. If no evidence of any review can be provided, generate an NC.

Finally, the auditor should verify that some form of drill, test, or walk-through was conducted to evaluate the adequacy of the procedures and plans and to familiarize those responsible for action. The organization is required to establish periodicity requirements for these tests, and the auditor should confirm they are being conducted as required. Failure to conduct the drills or tests should result in a nonconformance.

Performance Indicators

The auditor may expect to find the following indicators associated with the health and safety planning components. The auditor should review these indicators where they exist to help evaluate overall performance and effectiveness and to help focus the audit. Areas of poor performance, as indicated by the indicators, should be evaluated for actions to correct the performance. The lack of any action to address significant performance issues can serve as the basis for a nonconformance citing ineffective implementation. Note that the majority of the performance indicators will be associated with other components of the health and safety management system.

- Percent of job hazard analyses completed

- Accident or injury rate, lost workdays, and/or near misses per area, trended over time

- Number of violations found during compliance reviews

- Number of violations found by outside agencies

- Percent or number of violations corrected

- Percent or number of emergency response tests/drills conducted

KEY AUDIT POINT: OPERATIONAL CONTROL

Operational control implements the actions and safeguards needed to minimize any adverse health and safety risks associated with the hazards identified during health and safety planning. The major types of operational controls are engineered safeguards (guarding, interlocks, railings, and so on), administrative controls (procedures, policies, practices) and personal protective equipment, or PPE (gloves, aprons, faceshields). Good safety practice is to apply the controls in the order just presented, that is, first apply engineered safeguards, then consider administrative controls, and rely on PPE as a complementary or last resort. The process organizations use to implement the operational controls normally looks something like that shown Figure 10.7.

The controls themselves are normally defined as part of the health and safety planning process. Most organizations find that many of the controls are already in place, although they may not have been formalized yet. Formalizing the controls in documented procedures and instructions is part of the process of developing administrative operational controls. Again, remember that the preferred approach is to first apply engineered safeguards, then administrative controls, and lastly PPE.

Remember, this process would be repeated for each job or task associated with a significant health and safety risk (unacceptable, high, and moderate risk). Rather than conduct one audit of operational control, it is normally more efficient and effective to conduct multiple audits, with each series of audits focused on different processes, activities, or areas. This provides a more continuous evaluation of operational controls throughout the organization and allows easy integration with quality management and

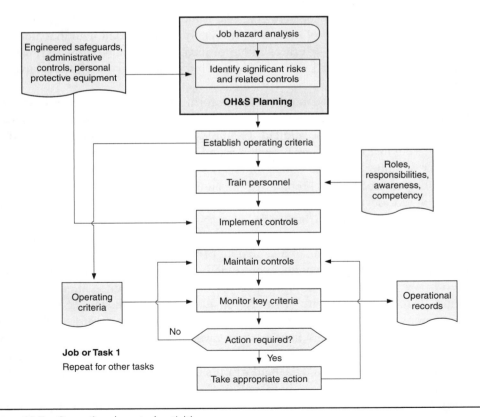

Figure 10.7 Operational control activities.

environmental management system audits, if desired. The planning and conduct of combined audits is the subject of Chapter 11.

Note that the evaluation of operational control will also assess the outputs from some of the key support activities, including training and awareness of employees roles, responsibilities, and authorities. The auditor should also examine the control of any health and safety documents and records associated with the process, as well as the calibration of any health and safety monitoring devices found to be in use. As noted in the introduction to this chapter, the auditor should also verify that any monitoring of key characteristics and operating criteria is being performed as needed to maintain the health and safety controls. When performed in this fashion, the operational control audit becomes a process-based audit similar to the process-based audits conducted of an organization's quality management system. The benefits of process-based versus element-based audits have been discussed in numerous sections of this handbook, but suffice it to say they allow for a more effective and efficient audit. The checklists on the CD have been structured around the evaluation of processes.

Audit Strategy and Key Audit Points

The auditor should begin the audit by examining the job hazard analysis for the task to be evaluated and the task's associated controls. If the auditor has been assigned to evaluate an area, then identify all of the job hazard analyses associated with that area. Keep in mind that some tasks or activities may not have been reviewed by JHA yet. The job listing shown in Figure 10.3 should provide information on which tasks have been evaluated and which have not.

Since many operational controls take the form of procedures, the auditor should obtain any procedures that relate to the control of the activities or significant hazards associated with the tasks to be audited. Examples include waste handling procedures, chemical mixing instructions, and procedures and instructions for operation of forklifts. The auditor should also make copies of the job hazard analysis for the tasks to be reviewed. The auditor should prepare for the audit by reviewing these procedures and modifying and/or developing checklists of questions and key audit points. Audit planning was covered in detail in Chapter 5.

With the job hazard analysis that defines the significant hazards and controls for each task to be reviewed and an understanding of how these tasks should be controlled, the auditor is now ready to conduct the review. You will be talking to the operator involved in performing the task. Introduce yourself, set the auditee at ease, and begin by asking, "Are there any health or safety considerations for this task?" The auditor is verifying operator awareness of the significant health and safety hazards of the job. The standard requires that operators have such an awareness, along with the consequences (that is, injuries or damage) if they do not follow procedures. The procedures tell the operator *what* to do, awareness tells them *why* it's important. Win the heart, and you will eventually win the mind.

Once the auditee replies, then the auditor can ask about the effects if they are not done properly. Typical answers might be, "It could pull me into the machine" or "It could cause an explosion." The auditor is ensuring that the auditee understands why it is important to control the activity. The auditor can then ask how these activities are controlled. During the auditee's response, the auditor can verify that the activity is being properly controlled in accordance with company policies, procedures, and the job hazard analysis. The auditor should verify that controls are in place and operating (for example, equipment guards installed; earplugs, eye protection, or other PPE worn; procedures and policies being followed) and should ask to see any records required to be maintained by the operator.

The auditor should verify that monitoring of key attributes of the activity is being performed as required by local procedures and practices. For example, assume a chemical mixing process specifies a maximum temperature to safely control the chemical reaction and that the operating instruction requires monitoring of the temperature every 15 minutes. The auditor should verify that temperature monitoring is being performed through examination of the mixing records. The chemical reaction temperature is an operating criteria, and the quarter-hour checks are monitoring requirements. If, instead, the reaction was instrumented with an alarm circuit if the maximum temperature was exceeded (an engineered safeguard), then the auditor would verify that the alarm circuit was operational.

The auditor should ask the operator, "Are we required to do anything if the maximum temperature is exceeded? What do we do, and at what temperature?" Now the auditor is also verifying the operator's understanding of roles and responsibilities relating to control of the risk, along with knowledge and understanding of what to do (that is, training and competency). For specific tasks such as lockout-tagout, confined space entry, and forklift operation, the auditor may also want to jot down the auditee's name for later verification of training.

For most activities it is desirable to also observe the activity being performed. This may require careful coordination with area management, normally through the audit program manager, since these activities may not be performed all that often. Their non-routine nature makes it all that much more important to actually observe them, if possible. Examples include lockout-tagout and permit-required confined space entry. People are normally fairly competent in the performance of routine activities, it's usually the nonroutine activities that bite us. If the operators have specific responsibilities for emergency response relating to the activity such as confined space rescue, the auditor can also question them on these responsibilities.

During the audit, the auditor should note the revision date of any OH&S system procedures or instructions found in the area for later comparison to the master list of documents. He or she should also review any monitoring records for legibility and completeness. Any health and safety monitoring equipment in use in the process should be checked for calibration. The auditor should also verify that proper maintenance is being performed on equipment and facilities used in the process when maintenance has been identified as a means of properly controlling the risk. This includes maintenance on any PPE such as respirators.

If the organization has established any improvement objectives or targets relating to this activity or its hazards, then I also like to ask operators if they are aware of the objectives. Communication of improvement objectives should flow down to those most directly involved in meeting them, the employees most directly involved in the activity. I normally issue an OFI if I find that employees are not aware of improvement objectives and targets associated with their activities or areas.

Performance Indicators

The auditor should expect to find performance indicators for the operational controls being evaluated. The auditor should review these indicators prior to the audit to help evaluate overall performance and effectiveness and to help focus the audit. During the audit, the auditor should discuss them with area management and operators to verify awareness of health and safety performance, and actions being taken to improve it. Areas of poor performance, as demonstrated by the indicators, should be evaluated for actions to correct the performance. The lack of any action to address significant performance issues can serve as the basis for a nonconformance citing ineffective implementation. The following are some examples of performance indicators used to measure how well we are controlling our significant health and safety risks:

- Accident or injury rates in the area under evaluation

- Near misses in the area under evaluation

- OHSA 300 log

- Lost workdays in the area under evaluation

- Accident or incident reports

KEY AUDIT POINT: MONITORING AND CORRECTIVE ACTION

Monitoring and corrective action focuses on measuring the performance of the health and safety management system and on the implementation of actions when it is not performing as it should. Note that some components of monitoring have been incorporated into other audits—monitoring of regulatory compliance is reviewed during the health and safety planning audit and monitoring of operational control criteria is evaluated during the operational control audits. Likewise, corrective action for violations to regulatory requirements arising out of the health and safety compliance reviews is evaluated during the health and safety planning audit. The focus of this evaluation will be on the overall monitoring of health and safety performance and on the corrective and preventive action program.

The general process of monitoring and corrective action looks something like that shown in Figure 10.8. Note that interrelationships among the health and safety planning, operational control, and improvement processes have been shown in the shaded boxes. While there is a possibility of some overlap between the components, and therefore some redundancy between the audits, the audit does not take a large amount of time and the redundancy is minimal.

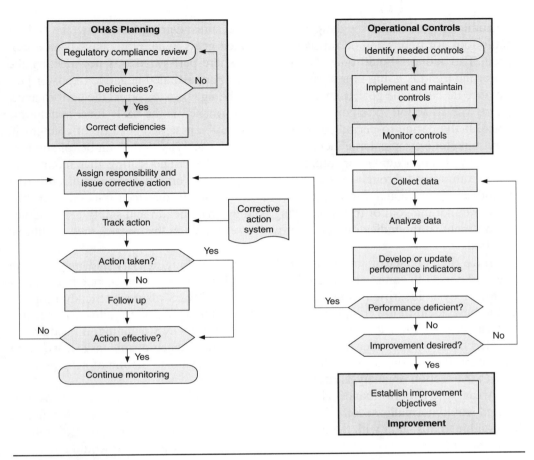

Figure 10.8   OH&S system monitoring and corrective action.

Some audit program managers may want to combine this evaluation with the evaluation of the improvement process. The improvement process includes a review of the setting of health and safety objectives, management programs, and the conduct of the management review. There is a natural linkage between that audit and the evaluation of monitoring and corrective action. They were split into separate reviews because the interviewees will be different—the health and safety management representative or appointee for the audit of monitoring and corrective action and executive management in the case of improvement. Even so, it may still make sense to combine the audits, realizing that an audit plan may be required to support the multiple interviews.

Audit Strategy and Key Audit Points

Monitoring

The auditor should begin by asking the auditee (typically the health and safety management representative) how overall performance of the OH&S system is monitored.

The auditor should ask to see the performance measures. During the review, the auditor should look for trends and performance to defined goals, where they have been established. The auditor should question any areas where performance is not meeting the goal or the trend is going in the wrong direction. For sustained negative trends or performance far below the goal, ask what actions are being taken to correct the performance. Failure to take action for significantly poor performance is the basis for a nonconformance. If the period-to-period performance cannot be assessed because of changes in operations (for example, large increases in production activity or the number of employees), then an opportunity for improvement should be issued stating that monitoring could be improved through normalization of the data. Normalization means adjusting the indicator to account for volume fluctuations, usually due to production activity. Keep in mind, the goal of this monitoring is to evaluate health and safety performance improvement. If the indicators fail to provide useful data in this regard, they should be modified.

Since the conduct of job safety analysis is an ongoing activity and may take an extended period to complete, the auditor should also evaluate performance in completing the analysis identified as being required during OH&S planning. Steady progress should be evident in the completion of JHA and in taking action to reduce risk. If this performance was already evaluated during the audit of OH&S planning, it need not be repeated here. On the other hand, considering the importance of this task, it wouldn't hurt either. For a more detailed discussion on how to evaluate the monitoring process, refer to the section on analysis of data in Chapter 8.

Areas where performance is satisfactory but where additional improvement is desired would normally become improvement objectives. If the audit program manager has combined this audit with the improvement audit, then the auditor could flow into an evaluation of the improvement objectives now. Otherwise, the auditor would move into an evaluation of the internal audit program.

OH&S System Audits

The auditor should ask to see the audit procedure, audit schedule, and copies of the internal audit reports generated since the last audit of the program. Verify that audits are being scheduled, conducted, and reported per the local procedure. Note that areas of significantly poor performance, evaluated just prior to the start of this topic, should have received additional audits or should show up on the audit schedule as additional audits to account for status of the area. Refer to the discussion of how to evaluate internal audit programs in Chapter 8 for more information on what questions to ask and what points to verify.

Nonconformance, Corrective and Preventive Action

Armed with information on overall OH&S system performance and the results of the internal OH&S system audits, the auditor can now evaluate the corrective and preventive action system. The auditor should ask for a copy of the corrective and preventive action procedure(s) and should verify that the system is being operated in accordance with the procedure. Refer to the audit strategy provided in the corrective and preventive action section of Chapter 8 for a more detailed discussion on how to evaluate this program.

Performance Indicators

This audit was focused on the evaluation of performance indicators, examples of which were provided at the end of the section that discussed how to evaluate operational control. In addition to these indicators, the auditor may find measurements relating to the performance of the corrective and preventive action and internal audit programs. A summary of some of these indicators follows:

- Percent internal audits performed on schedule.

- Number of qualified internal auditors.

- Percent corrective actions recurred.

- Percent job hazard analyses completed, period to period.

- Percent of tasks classified as negligible or tolerable. (This metric focuses on improvement in lowering overall risk through risk reduction activities.)

- Number or percent of corrective actions overdue.

KEY AUDIT POINT: IMPROVEMENT

The improvement process includes the setting of health and safety objectives and targets, the establishment of management programs to ensure achievement of these objectives, and the performance of periodic management reviews. The general flow of the improvement process is shown in Figure 10.9. Interrelationships with other core activities are shown in shaded boxes.

Health and Safety Objectives

Many companies review and set health and safety objectives during the management review process. In this case, this topic should be discussed during the evaluation of the management review. General comments on the evaluation of objectives can be found in the quality objectives section of Chapter 8. Additional specific audit points unique to the OH&S system follow.

Audit Strategy and Key Audit Points

The auditor should ask to see the objectives and associated programs established for the current period. During this review, the auditor asks how these objectives were determined. If the auditor has recently completed the audit of the monitoring and corrective

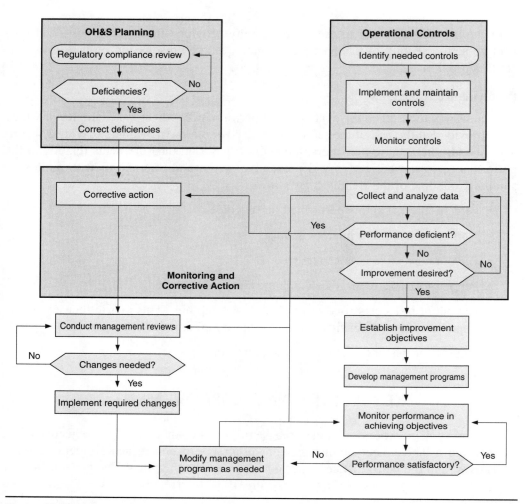

Figure 10.9 Improvement process.

action process, then he or she should be familiar with the overall performance of the OH&S system and where improvement objectives may be warranted. In particular, the auditor should verify that the views of interested parties were considered during the setting of objectives (the OHSAS 18001 standard requires this). Interested parties include outside organizations like community residents, government agencies, and the organization's stockholders and employees. The auditor should ask to see the communication log to see if there were any concerns or opinions expressed by interested parties, and, if there were, that these were considered.

The auditor should compare the objectives to the management programs set up to help ensure their achievement. These management programs, or action plans, must contain details on what has to be done, who is responsible for doing it, and when it should be done. The auditor can use the actions and time frames to evaluate performance in achieving the objectives. Some form of tracking progress should be in place. If no tracking of performance in meeting objectives is evident, other than during an annual or semi-annual management review, consider issuance of an OFI. Such infrequent monitoring does not allow sufficient time to recovery actions if progress is deficient.

Communication of improvement objectives is also important. The auditor may ask the auditee about the methods used to communicate objectives throughout the organization. Note that the operational control audits evaluate the effectiveness of these methods by asking employees about any objectives established for their departments or activities. The auditor may want to issue an OFI if no formal means of communicating objectives have been established.

Of course the most important item to verify is the organization's performance in meeting its objectives. With the performance objectives and management programs in hand, the auditor should be able to establish whether the management programs have been effective in supporting achievement of the health and safety objectives. The auditor should question any areas where performance is not meeting the defined goals. For sustained negative trends or performance far below the goal, ask what actions are being taken to correct the performance. Failure to take action for significantly poor performance is the basis for a nonconformance.

Management Review

Refer to the management review section of Chapter 8 for a detailed discussion on how to evaluate this process. Although the inputs differ slightly, the process is the same.

Performance Indicators

The auditor may find some of the following metrics or indicators relating to the performance of the improvement process:

- Percent targets achieved

- Percent objectives met

- Number or percent of actions overdue

- Number of improvement projects undertaken

- Health and safety performance gains from continual improvement activities

KEY AUDIT POINT: KEY SUPPORT PROCESSES

The final group of activities is the key support processes. These activities support all components of the management system. They have been grouped together for convenience and to allow for an efficient audit. Portions of these activities will be evaluated during other process-based audits. These audits will evaluate only the centralized elements of these processes.

Audit Strategy and Key Audit Points

Detailed discussions on how to evaluate most of these activities have been presented in Chapter 8 in the section titled Resource and Support Processes. Review that section for audit strategies, process flows, and key audit points. Unique characteristics of the health and safety management system will be highlighted here.

Document Control

The evaluation of document control can follow the same flow and strategy as outlined in Chapter 8. The auditor should also verify proper control of health and safety regulations, and assurance that there is a method to stay aware of changes to them. Many companies rely on subscription services, links to government Web sites where changes are announced, and corporate staff to maintain this awareness. The auditor should verify that some method is in place and is being used. Note that this review may also be performed during the health and safety planning audit when evaluating legal and other requirements.

Record Control

The evaluation of document control can follow the same flow and strategy as outlined in Chapter 8, with the additional consideration that many of the health and safety records that must be maintained have legal retention requirements. The auditor may want to have the auditee show the legal retention requirement for the records if doubt exists as to what the legal retention requirements are.

Training

The evaluation of training can follow the same flow and strategy as outlined in Chapter 8, with the additional consideration that some organizations have a legal obligation to provide certain types of training, such as permit-required confined tank entry training and forklift operator training. The auditor may want to question the training coordinator or management representative as to how these mandatory training requirements were identified, in addition to verifying that the training was provided.

The auditor should also ensure that contract and agency personnel are made aware of the organization's health and safety policies and practices, to the extent they apply to the work they are involved with.

Control of Purchased Products and Contractors (Purchasing)

The evaluation of purchased products and services is a little different for the OH&S system. In the health and safety management system, we are most concerned with two things relating to our suppliers and contractors. First, we need to ensure that any relevant health and safety policies and requirements are communicated to suppliers and contractors. This can be done through a pass-down of the requirements (for example, pass-down of any safety rules and requirements) or by briefings before the contractor commences work on-site. Most organizations have a fairly robust process to do this. The auditor should verify that the process is being followed during the audit.

The second consideration, more often lacking, is obtaining information from suppliers or contractors regarding any significant health and safety hazards arising from their activities and products. For suppliers of materials and products, this is often accomplished through receipt of the Material Safety Data Sheet (MSDS) from the supplier. The auditor should ensure that the MSDSs for new products are reviewed for any health and safety concerns that may need to be addressed before using the new chemical or material. Note that there are legal requirements for this hazard communication. For contractors, a health and safety survey is often used. The survey would ask questions regarding the types of materials and chemicals to be used, how these materials and chemicals will be controlled, and the types of safety zones or controls that will be required during the activity. The auditor should verify that methods are in place to address these two considerations and are being used.

Roles and Responsibilities

Roles and responsibilities connected with defined activities associated with significant health and safety hazards will be evaluated during operational control audits. In this audit, the auditor should focus on the definition, communication, and awareness of roles, responsibilities, and authorities of key individuals and functions needed to support the health and safety management system. These include the management representative and/or appointee, internal OH&S system auditors, emergency response coordinators, safety committee members, and the cross-functional team assigned responsibilities for job hazard analysis and determining their risks. If these roles are examined during other audits, they do not need to be reviewed here.

A unique element of the OHSAS 18001 standard is the requirement to designate a management appointee. Although the responsibilities of this position are similar to those of a management representative, as given in ISO 9001 and ISO 14001, there is a fundamental difference in who fills this role. Unlike the management representative role in a quality or environmental management system, which is normally filled by a mid-level manager, the management appointee role must be filled by a senior manager. By senior manager, I mean vice president, plant manager, or senior director. The 18001 standard makes this clear through its examples, which state, "e.g. in a large organization, a Board or executive committee member." This position is clearly designed to place accountability and authority for the OH&S system squarely in the lap of senior management and to engage their involvement along with their support. Many organizations also designate a local OH&S management representative to monitor the day-to-day operation and maintenance of the system, reporting to the management appointee. I have no problem with this as long as there is evidence that shows that the management appointee is clearly engaged and involved in the operation, maintenance, and improvement of the OH&S management system. Evidence of involvement can be demonstrated by attendance of various meetings and reviews, by review and/or approval of key safety policies, and by involvement in the development of health and safety objectives. The auditor should verify that a management appointee has been designated, that it is a senior executive, and that this executive is involved in the operation, maintenance, and improvement of the health and safety management system.

Communications

The final evaluation examines the process used to communicate important health and safety information within the organization and to outside interested parties. Communication of key information internally, like roles and responsibilities, awareness, and improvement objectives, will be continually evaluated during other audits. A unique element of OHSAS 18001, not found in ISO 14001 or ISO 9001, is the requirement for employee consultation. The standard requires that employees be involved in the development and review of policies and procedures used to manage risks, that they be consulted when there are changes that affect workplace health and safety, that they be represented on health and safety matters, and that they be informed of who their OH&S representatives are and who is the management appointee.

For an OHSAS 18001 system, therefore, it is critical that there be a process to communicate concerns, issues, and improvement suggestions up the ladder. I sometimes find that no formal system exists for upward communication from employees. This will damage the support for the OH&S system and will result in losing ideas that could significantly improve health and safety performance. Many organizations use their safety committees to meet the requirements for consultation. This works well, as long as the safety committee members adequately represent the workforce, are consulted as the standard requires, and understand their responsibilities to act as employee representatives. The auditor should issue a finding if no formal system exists to support upward communication or consultation from the workforce. The auditor can test the effectiveness of the system, if it exists, by asking to see the log or file of concerns, issues, or suggestions provided by employees. A blank file or log tells you something isn't working.

Another focus of this evaluation is on external communication. OHSAS 18001 requires that a system for communication with interested parties exist. Interested parties for a health and safety system might include state and local government officials, the local fire department, hospitals and other emergency planners, and insurance providers. This is almost universally met by the maintenance of some type of communication log. The auditor should ask about the methods used to respond to communications from outside parties, including who receives them, how are they handled, and who responds. The auditor should also ask to see the log. Although it may be that there are no entries in the log, indicating no outside inquiries, the auditor should verify that a system is in place to handle them if any come in.

Performance Indicators

Performance indicators for document control, record control, and training are provided in Chapter 8. Performance indicators for the communication process may include:

- Number of health and safety improvement suggestions received from employees

- Number of improvement suggestions per employee

- Number of improvement suggestions implemented

- Health and safety performance gains from employee improvement suggestions

- Average response cycle time for outside inquiries

SUMMARY

In this chapter we described the strategy for an audit of an occupational health and safety management system. If you also reviewed Chapter 9, then you undoubtedly recognized the similarities to the audit of an environmental management system. The next chapter will examine the conduct of joint quality, environmental, and health and safety management system audits.

11

Conducting Combined Management System Audits

Chapter 1 discussed the common components of the ISO 9001,[1] ISO 14001,[2] and OHSAS 18001[3] management system models. The existence of these components provides an opportunity to conduct integrated or combined audits of the management system. These common components include:

- *A planning component.* In ISO 9001 and its industry variants, planning is represented by management system planning and product realization planning. In ISO 14001 and OHSAS 18001, planning is represented by the identification of significant environmental aspects or hazards and risks associated with the organization's products, services, and activities, and the identification of appropriate methods to control them. Note that all of the standards require the establishment of an organizational policy that declares the company's commitments to quality, environmental performance, and/or health and safety performance.

- *An operational component.* In ISO 9001 this is represented by the management system, resources, and product realization processes. In ISO 14001 and OHSAS 18001, requirements focused on operation and maintenance of the system are specified in the implementation and operation clauses.

- *A monitoring and corrective action component.* In ISO 9001 these activities are defined in the monitoring and measurement, internal audit, control of nonconforming product, analysis of data, and corrective action processes. In ISO 14001 and OHSAS these activities are defined in checking and corrective action elements.

- *An improvement process.* In all of the standards, improvement is embedded in similar requirements for preventive action, for the setting of improvement objectives, and in the conduct of management reviews. In the ISO 9001 model, additional requirements are added to address process improvement as needed based on the results of process performance monitoring.

When combined with the common centralized activities of document and record control, training, purchasing, and communications, these components provide a realistic framework for conducting combined audits of the quality, environmental, and/or health and safety management systems. Performing combined audits can provide additional benefits to the audit program manager and to the management system itself. The focus of this chapter is to present these benefits along with some important considerations in the development of a combined audit strategy.

BENEFITS OF COMBINED AUDITS

Combined audits can provide several benefits. To begin, they reinforce the concept of an integrated management system. They can also reinforce the transition from managing functional elements to managing processes and systems of processes. Rather than auditing quality planning, environmental planning, or health and safety system planning, auditors would evaluate a holistic process of product and process planning.

Combined audits also provide for more efficient audits. Instead of separately analyzing quality system controls, environmental operational controls, and health and safety controls for a given process, auditors evaluate the process once, including all controls (quality, environmental, and health and safety) relating to that process. There is less duplication of effort, both during the audit planning phase and the audit execution phase.

The quality, environmental, and health and safety controls for a process are often interdependent, so evaluating one form of control provides important information on other controls. For example, quality system controls designed to minimize scrap and rework may directly impact on the organization's ability to reduce its volume of oily scrap steel and to conserve natural resources. Evaluating quality and environmental controls at the same time allows evaluation of these interdependencies and provides for a more effective audit. Thus, combined audits can lead to more effective audits.

Figure 11.1 illustrates some of the commonalities and interdependencies in an integrated quality, environmental, and health and safety management system. The reader may want to refer to this diagram during the sections that follow.

AREAS OF COMMONALITY

There are significant areas of commonality between the requirements in the various standards. These areas of commonality can be leveraged by conducting combined audits of these processes.

• *Planning.* There are many commonalities between planning for the environmental management system and planning for the health and safety management system. The processes for determining legal and other requirements are essentially the same for both systems and should result in the same output—a detailed listing of the requirements that the organization must meet. There are also similarities between the methods used to plan and organize the identification of the aspects or hazards that must be controlled. The main differences are in the methods used to identify significant aspects (the initial

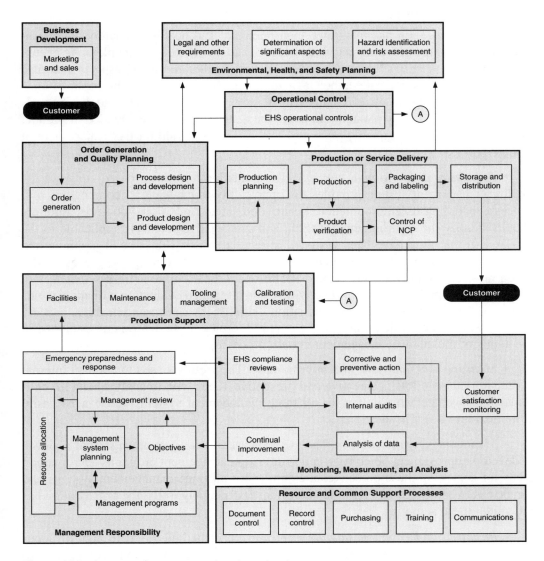

Figure 11.1 Integrated management system structure.

environmental review) and high-risk hazards (the job hazard analysis) that must be controlled. Once the systems are in place, however, the methods used to maintain an awareness of new significant aspects and job hazards are usually the same—the management of change program, advanced quality planning, periodic reevaluations, or some combination of these three. This simplifies the conduct of combined audits, especially after the initial assessments have been completed and the organization finds itself in a maintenance and improvement role.

If the organization has integrated environmental and health and safety considerations into its quality planning activities by, for example, modifying its planning checklists to include questions relating to environmental, health, and safety aspects that must be accommodated or controlled, then it should be possible to evaluate the organization's methods for staying aware of changes to its environmental aspects and job hazards during reviews of quality planning. In effect the audit becomes an evaluation of product or process planning, not quality planning. The same can be said for the management of change process.

• *Process and operational controls.* The transition to process-based audits of the quality management system provides the opportunity to evaluate all components of a process, including its environmental, health, and safety operational controls. Auditors should identify the environmental, health, and safety (EHS) controls applicable to the process(es) that they have been assigned to evaluate during their audit planning and should then verify proper implementation and maintenance during the process audit. Since most environmental, safety, and health operational controls are associated with production and production support activities, this integrated evaluation will allow continuous evaluation of most of the organization's significant aspects and health and safety hazards. Additional evaluations may be required to pick those controls not included in the audits of the quality management system processes.

• *Measurement, analysis, and improvement.* The methods used to conduct internal audits, to issue and track corrective and preventive action, and to analyze data for continual improvement are similar for all three management systems and can be easily combined into a single audit.

• *Management responsibility.* The methods used to conduct management reviews, to develop improvement objectives, and to develop management programs and/or action plans for achieving these objectives are similar for all three management systems and can be easily combined into a single audit. This is especially true if the organization has integrated these activities.

• *Resource and common support processes.* The methods used to control documents and records, to communicate with and to monitor suppliers and contractors, to plan and deliver training, and to communicate with the workforce are similar for all three management systems and can be easily combined into a single audit.

AREAS OF DIFFERENCE

Despite the many commonalities between the three management system standards, there are some areas that will require focused reviews because of methods or because the quality management system does not have a comparable counterpart for certain requirements in the ISO 14001 or OHSAS 18001 standards. The most notable of these include:

- *Emergency preparedness and response.* With the limited connection to contingency planning required by ISO/TS 16949, there is no equivalent requirement for emergency planning in the quality management system. This component of ISO 14001 and OHSAS 18001 should be reviewed as a separate audit or as part of an environmental, health, and safety planning audit.

- *Environmental, health, and safety planning.* Although the ongoing planning elements can be evaluated as part of product and process planning as discussed in the previous section, the framework for conducting the evaluations and assessments should be the focus of a separate audit, in particular during the initial audits of the EMS and/or OH&S system development and implementation.

- *Environmental, health, and safety compliance reviews.* The quality management system does not have equivalent requirements for regulatory compliance reviews as are found in the ISO 14001 and OHSAS 18001 standards. The adequacy and thoroughness of compliance reviews should be evaluated separately or during review of environmental, health, and safety planning, as described in chapters 9 and 10.

- *External communications.* Although the quality management system does contain requirements to establish communication channels with customers, it does not broaden the scope of this communication to other interested parties. A focused evaluation of the process used to communicate with outside interested parties will probably be necessary to ensure compliance with the ISO 14001 and OHSAS 18001 requirements.

- *Operational controls.* Although many, if not most, routine operational controls can be evaluated during process-based audits of the organization's product and/or service delivery processes, the broader coverage of the environmental and health and safety programs will undoubtedly require some additional reviews to ensure that all operational controls are evaluated at some routine periodicity. Another consideration will be the evaluation of non-routine, but potentially significant activities such as bulk liquid unloading, lockout-tagout, and confined space entry, which in all likelihood will not be assessed during routine process-based audits of the quality management system processes.

With this background on the commonalities and differences between the quality, environmental, and health and safety management systems, we can now develop strategies for conducting combined audits of the management system.

COMBINED ISO 9001/16949 AND ISO 14001 AUDITS

Because of the popularity of the ISO 9001 and ISO 14001 standards, many organizations have implemented both a quality and an environmental management system. This section will discuss how to capitalize on the synergies of an integrated management system during management system audits. The base audit strategy will focus on integrating the EMS audit areas into the QMS evaluation.

Quality Planning and Design

The evaluation of quality planning and design should be conducted as described in Chapter 8. The auditor should also, however, include DFE principles adopted by the organization on its checklists and reviews of any design activities. In addition, the auditor should also confirm that environmental considerations are reflected and are being addressed during production process planning. In organizations that use checklists to guide their quality planning, these considerations may show up as questions relating to process emissions, wastes, and usage of natural resources.

The quality planning audit should also evaluate how changes to products and processes are controlled. The auditor should ensure that these changes were also assessed for their potential to impact the environment or current environmental objectives. If there were potential impacts, then the auditor should verify that they were evaluated for significance and that any necessary actions needed to control the new or modified activities were implemented.

Process Control

Quality requirements should be evaluated as discussed in Chapter 8. Auditors should also review the list of significant environmental aspects to identify any that apply to processes that they have been assigned to evaluate. These aspects, and their related controls, should be noted on the auditor's checklist. During the evaluation, the auditor should verify that these controls are in place, are being maintained and monitored, and that process operators have an awareness of these significant aspects and their related controls. This same method can also be applied to maintenance and other production support activities.

As noted in previous chapters, process audits should also evaluate important inputs and resources in addition to the process steps. The auditor may evaluate the training and competency of operators, knowledge of their roles and responsibilities, document and record control, and the control of any monitoring and measurement equipment associated with the evaluated process. The auditor should draw both quality and environmental samples when performing these reviews during a combined audit.

Purchasing

The purchasing process is discussed in previous sections. Auditors should select a few environmental subcontractors as part of the sample set and should examine how the environmental aspects of their services were identified and the organization's environmental requirements communicated.

Laboratory Operations (Calibration and Testing)

The auditor can easily evaluate both quality and environmental control by considering quality-related and environmental-related testing and calibration as being the same. The same types of controls apply to both.

Document Control and Record Control

The control of documents and records are usually the first processes that are integrated. As such, auditing the centralized activities associated with these processes should, in fact, verify conformance to both environmental and quality system standards.

Monitoring, Analysis, and Improvement

The internal audit, corrective and preventive action, and analysis of data can easily be evaluated together. The auditor should draw samples from both the environmental and the quality management system when performing a combined audit.

Management Responsibility

The auditor can evaluate the setting of both quality and environmental goals and objectives, along with the management programs and/or action plans used to achieve them. Performance in achieving both can easily be reviewed during the same evaluation, especially if the setting of quality and environmental goals and objectives has been integrated.

Training

The process used to identify training needs, to schedule training, and to verify its effectiveness is normally the same for both the quality and environmental management system. The auditor may, however, want to spend a little more time focusing on how any regulatory-based environmental training requirements were determined.

As noted in the section entitled Areas of Difference, there will still be areas where focused quality and environmental audits will be required. The majority of the EMS can, however, be folded into the QMS audit program.

COMBINED ISO 14001 AND OHSAS 18001 AUDITS

Many companies that have implemented ISO 14001 eventually expand their management system to include control and improvement of their health and safety activities. Because of the many common processes shared between ISO 14001 and OHSAS 18001, integrating these management systems is natural. Management system audits of these combined activities is also natural.

Environmental and Health and Safety Planning

As explained earlier, the methods used to identify and assess an organization's significant environmental aspects and to identify and determine the health and safety risks in the workplace are typically different and should be evaluated separately. The processes used to maintain an ongoing awareness of new environmental aspects and health and safety risks, however, are typically the same, normally involving the management of change (or equivalent) process. Auditors can easily evaluate how well this process is working by selecting significant change initiatives (for example, new processes, new facilities, or significant modifications) and evaluating to what extent they were evaluated for the environmental, health, and safety risks they present. The auditor can then assess whether the organization's method of determining significance was followed for any potential environmental aspects or methods for assessing risk followed for any new job hazards.

This handbook has recommended including evaluation of legal and other requirements and emergency preparedness and response during the planning audit. It is highly likely that the same process will be used to stay aware of any new legal or other requirements for both the environmental and health and safety management systems. The auditor can evaluate the combined process, selecting samples from the environmental and safety and health areas. Most of an organization's emergency response procedures involve both environmental and health and safety considerations, so these too can be easily combined during an audit.

Operational Controls

The implementation, maintenance, and monitoring of operational controls used to reduce the risk associated with an organization's activities, materials, and/or wastes can often be combined into the same audit by focusing on processes and areas versus stand-alone programs. For example, an audit of a stamping operation could evaluate the maintenance of controls associated with significant environmental aspects such as waste handling as well as conformance to defined safety rules and practices.

Many common environmental and health and safety concerns apply to a large number of activities. Examples include waste handling, recycling, resource (and energy) conservation, the wearing of personal protective equipment like earplugs, and the use of guards and barriers where needed. Evaluating environmental, health, and safety practices and/or controls throughout the year as part of process-based audits will be much more effective than will conducting one large audit of each program (waste handling, energy conservation, hearing conservation, machine guarding) once each year. The former strategy helps to ensure that organizational awareness remains high throughout the year, while the latter is likely to result in gradual deterioration of awareness and compliance after the audit is completed.

Some environmental aspects and health and safety hazards are better associated with areas versus processes. Examples include storm water runoff (parking lot, loading areas) and flammable material storage. Another example is administrative and clerical areas, where the large variety of tasks performed are more conveniently evaluated as a group, since these tasks normally share common environmental, health, and safety concerns and controls. I recommend planning audits around major core activities and picking up any environmental, health, and safety controls not accounted for in the process audits in area evaluations.

Finally, there are also some activities that are required to be reviewed at some periodicity by law. Examples include lockout-tagout procedures and hazardous waste storage areas. The audit program manager must ensure that all regulatory-based inspections and reviews are conducted in a comprehensive fashion. Although portions of these activities may be evaluated during management system audits, focused reviews of the regulated activity are still necessary.

Purchasing

The purchasing process for both environmental and safety and health is focused on two essential areas of communication. The first is understanding what environmental or safety and health risks a contractor or supplier poses to the organization or to its policy commitments. The second is communicating the organization's environmental, health, and safety procedures, practices, and policies to the contractor or supplier. The methods used to ensure that this communication takes place is normally the same for both environmental and health and safety suppliers/contractors and can be evaluated together.

Document Control and Record Control

The control of documents and records are usually the first processes that are integrated. As such, auditing the centralized activities associated with these processes should, in fact, verify conformance to both environmental and health and safety system standards.

Monitoring, Analysis, and Improvement

The internal audit, corrective and preventive action, and analysis of data can easily be evaluated together. The auditor should draw samples from both the environmental and the OH&S management system when performing a combined audit.

Management Responsibility

The auditor can evaluate the setting of both OH&S and environmental goals and objectives, along with the management programs and/or action plans used to achieve them. Performance in achieving both can be easily reviewed during the same evaluation, especially if the setting of environmental, health, and safety objectives has been integrated. Likewise, the management review is normally integrated and should be evaluated for both the EMS and the OH&S management system.

The process used to identify training needs, to schedule training, and to verify its effectiveness is normally the same for both the environmental and OH&S management system. The auditor should pay particular attention to how legal, environmental, health, and safety training requirements were determined.

COMBINED QUALITY, ENVIRONMENTAL, AND SAFETY AND HEALTH AUDITS

For those organizations that have taken the leap and implemented integrated management programs based on ISO 9001 or ISO/TS 16949, ISO 14001, and OHSAS 18001, the possibility of performing combined management system audits of the entire management system is possible. I recommend that the organization first combine its environmental and health and safety system audits as explained in the previous section and then integrate the EHS audits into its quality management system audits as described in the combined ISO 9001/16949 and ISO 14001 audit section. Such an audit program will be focused on auditing processes versus programs or elements and will result in the most efficient, effective audits.

The main barrier to implementing this audit strategy will be in developing internal auditors who are knowledgeable of the requirements of each of the management system standards and the organization's policies that implement these requirements. It will probably require the use of audit teams composed of auditors competent in each of the three areas until the necessary cross-training and competencies have been developed. Well-designed checklists should be used to help guide the auditors pending development of these competencies. A transition toward the use of full-time auditors will help speed the development of these competencies. Once these actions are completed, however, the significant benefits associated with conducting combined audits will be realized.

SUMMARY

Combined audits are more efficient and more effective than are independent audits of the same activities for their quality, environmental, and health and safety aspects. Although additional planning and auditor training will be needed to successfully conduct combined audits, the long-term benefits far outweigh the short-term costs. In particular, organizations that have integrated their management systems should transition toward the use of combined audits. Not only will there be fewer audits to manage, but the audits will be more productive, take less overall effort to perform, and will reinforce the process and systems approach to management.

12

Auditing the Automotive Core Tools

T he core tools are a set of interrelated methodologies that are used to help ensure the quality of products and processes within the automotive industry. These tools are used to proactively identify and manage the risks associated with the production environment. Several of these tools, such as the use of failure mode and effects analysis (FMEA) and statistical process control (SPC), are common in industries other than automotive. Some, like advanced product quality planning (APQP) and measurement systems analysis (MSA) are not, but should be. Some, like the production part approval process (PPAP), are unique to the automotive industry.

These tools, or their equivalents, are required methodologies for suppliers to most automotive original equipment manufacturers (OEMs). Companies supplying these OEMs are normally required or encouraged to implement management systems based on ISO/TS 16949, which, in turn, references these core tools. The Ford Motor Company and General Motors, in particular, require that internal auditors be trained in the use and evaluation of the core tools. Historically, auditors have been weak in their knowledge of the use of these tools and in methods to evaluate their application. This chapter examines the basic application of these tools within an automotive manufacturing setting and provides tips and strategies to evaluate how effectively they are being used.

Although this chapter is most directly applicable to auditors of automotive quality management systems, auditors in other industries may want to review this chapter if their organization uses some of these methods (for example, SPC) or if they want to evaluate whether they should use the tool. The core tools and a summary of their purpose and focus follow:

• *Advanced product quality planning (APQP).*[1] This methodology provides common guidelines for a structured approach to define and establish the steps needed to ensure a quality product that will satisfy your automotive customer. It provides a framework to pull together the other requirements and tools presented in ISO/TS 16949 and associated reference manuals (PPAP, FMEA, MSA, SPC).

- *Failure mode and effects analysis (FMEA).*[2] This methodology provides general guidelines for preparing an FMEA of products and processes, including the application of techniques used to conduct the analysis. It provides guidance on how to use the FMEA to improve current and future product and process designs. The AIAG reference manual is divided into two parts—design FMEA for assessing and mitigating the design risk of new or modified products, and process FMEA for assessing and mitigating the risks associated with production processes.

- *Measurement systems analysis (MSA).*[3] This methodology provides an introduction to measurement system analysis, along with guidance on how to conduct measurement system studies to ensure the quality of data used for product and process evaluation.

- *Production part approval process (PPAP).*[4] This methodology defines generic requirements for production part approval. It is used to determine if all customer engineering design record and specification requirements are properly understood and whether the process has the potential to produce product consistently meeting these requirements during an actual production run at the quoted production rate.

- *Statistical process control (SPC).*[5] This methodology provides an introduction to statistical process control and presents general guidelines for the selection and application of statistical techniques to monitor, analyze, and improve production and supporting processes.

APQP—THE FRAMEWORK FOR THE CORE TOOLS AUDIT

APQP provides a unified structure and process for developing the systems and processes needed to meet the requirements of the ISO/TS 16949 specification.[6] These requirements are spread throughout TS 16949. APQP pulls together these requirements along with the methodologies of the other core tools into a unified, structured approach. Advanced quality planning uses a phased approach to plan and develop products and processes. The five phases of APQP are:

- Planning and definition

- Product design and development

- Process design and development

- Product and process validation

- Feedback, assessment, and corrective action

These phases are shown in Figure 12.1.

Note that these phases overlap—they are not performed in series. APQP is based on simultaneous product and process design and development and relies on effective communication between all of the various functions involved in new product launch.

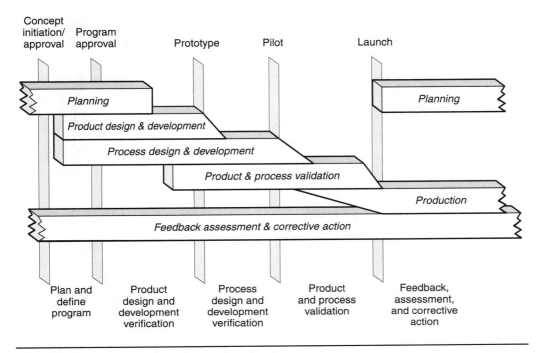

Figure 12.1 The advanced product quality planning process.

Reprinted from the *Advanced Product Quality Planning (APQP) Manual* with permission of DaimlerChrysler, Ford, and GM Supplier Quality Requirements Task Force.

Evaluating whether this communication is taking place is one of the most important tasks of the auditor.

A better understanding of the role of APQP is to consider the components, or activities, that make up APQP. Figure 12.2 shows these activities under the phases in which they would normally be developed.

Audit strategies for the shaded components will be described within this chapter. These are associated with the other core tools, including design and process FMEA, MSA, SPC (in the form of process capability studies and reduced variation), and PPAP. The APQP process provides the framework to properly apply these and the other methods during product and process design, development, and deployment.

With this introduction we can now introduce the strategy we will use to evaluate the advanced quality planning process and the core tools. The APQP process will be used as the basis for the audit. The auditor will follow the APQP process from the planning phase through product and process design and development, validation, and deployment of the planning outputs to the production floor. Each of the core tools will be evaluated as it is encountered during the audit.

I normally recommend that the auditor select at least two objects for the APQP audit. One object should be a product or part that has recently launched and is currently being run on the production floor. The auditor will be able to use this object to test

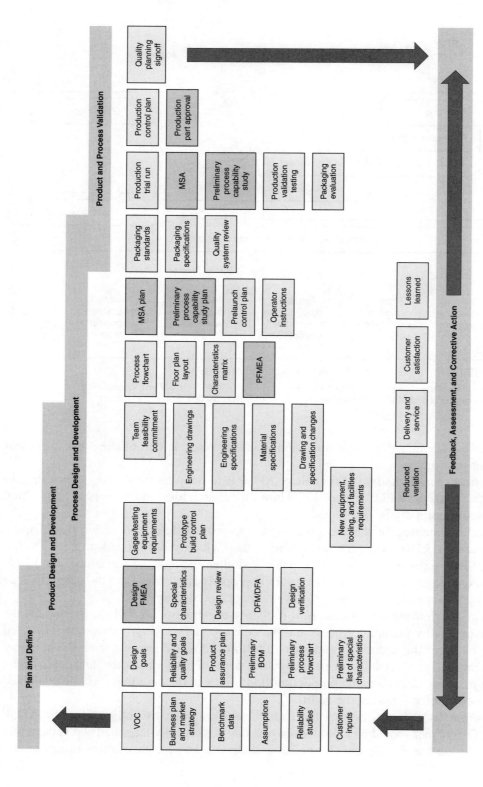

Figure 12.2 The components of advanced product quality planning.

whether the outputs from the quality planning process (control plans, work instructions, job setups, and FMEA) were properly deployed in production. The second object should be a part or product that is still under development, preferably at a late stage. Organizations are only required to maintain the records specified by the PPAP or equivalent approval package (for example, provisional approval package for Toyota). Some of the other records or aids, such as timing plans, may not be retained beyond project completion. By selecting one object that is still under development the auditor will be able to evaluate the proper use of these and similar tools.

The auditor will normally start the audit by interviewing the account managers responsible for the parts or products selected as objects. The focus of this interview will be to determine how the customer and product requirements were determined and whether they were communicated to the product and process design teams. The auditor will then use this information to interview the launch or APQP team leader. Using the information in the PPAP package, the FMEA, PPAP, MSA, and other components of the APQP process will be evaluated during these interviews. Finally, the auditor should move onto the production floor to verify deployment of critical outputs from the APQP process, including statistical process controls. The flow of the APQP audit is shown in Figures 12.3 and 12.4.

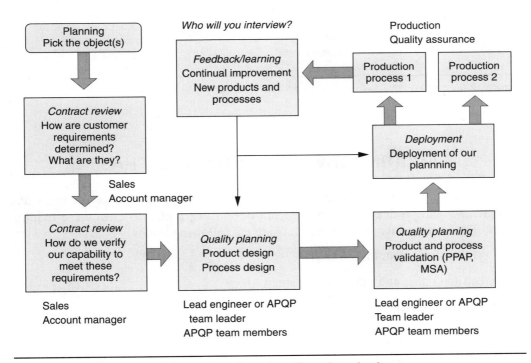

Figure 12.3   Process flow of the APQP audit—who will you interview?

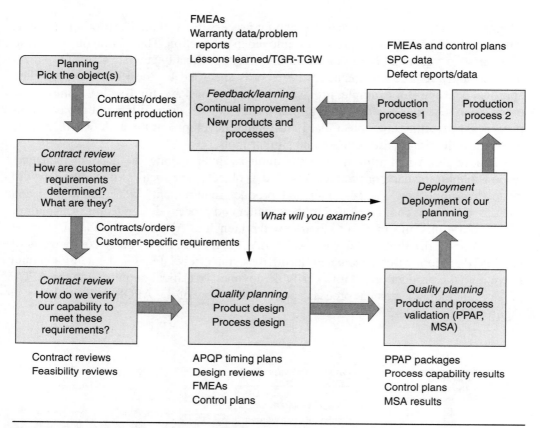

Figure 12.4   Process flow of the APQP audit—what will you look at?

AUDITING THE PLAN AND DEFINE PHASE

The plan and define phase of APQP focuses on defining customer requirements and expectations and product requirements, and developing a plan to meet these requirements. The components of this phase include the following inputs:

- Voice of the customer (VOC)
- Business plan and marketing strategy
- Benchmark data
- Assumptions
- Reliability studies
- Customer inputs

and outputs:

- Design goals

- Quality and reliability goals

- Preliminary bill of material (BOM)

- Preliminary listing of special characteristics

- Preliminary process flowchart

- Product assurance plan

The general flow of this evaluation was presented in the order generation and quality planning section of Chapter 8. In essence, the auditor should ask the account manager to see the contract and related documents that define customer requirements for the product. These documents represent the voice of the customer and customer inputs. The auditor should note some of the customer requirements for verification during the evaluation of product and process design, development, and validation. Note any required verifications, testing, reliability targets, or other technical requirements specified in the contract or related documents.

In addition to the contract documents, the auditor may want to ask the account manager what other sources of information provide insight into customer expectations. Some of these sources include:

- Market research, including the results of focus group studies

- Customer interviews and surveys

- Market testing

- Media analysis

To the extent that the organization collects this information, it should be used to help define the product. The auditor should ask to see any such information that has been recently gathered or that directly relates to the product being evaluated. Significant feedback relating to product attributes and features, likes and dislikes, and other insights that could impact the design of the product should be noted. Later the auditor will want to verify that this information was made available to and considered by the team involved in product design. Failure to communicate market-related information is a common weakness in many organizations. If the account manager participates as an active member of the APQP team, then the auditor can assume that this information was considered by the team. The auditor may want to question the account manager about how the information was used to help optimize the design of the products selected as the objects of the audit. The auditor should cite an opportunity for improvement if it's discovered that this information is collected but not communicated to or used by the APQP team. Finally, the auditor may also ask to see evidence of manufacturing feasibility review for the projects selected. This review will be examined in more detail in the next section.

Armed with information about the customer's requirements and expectations, the auditor will next interview the lead engineer or APQP team leader. The auditor will ask the auditee to walk through the product development process, using the organization's design procedure as a guide. The auditor should begin by asking about the customer requirements that must be met and customer expectations that should be satisfied. The auditor should review the design drawings for the products selected as objects. These drawings will contain dimensional requirements, reliability and functional testing requirements, and any special material considerations that must be met during the development process. The auditor will want to confirm that the testing, verification, and reliability requirements noted during the first interview and this review are reflected on the planning documents and/or goals for the product.

The auditor can also ask about *assumptions* required for product design. Assumptions may be required about consumer use patterns, environmental conditions, or material conditions such as stress and strains that the product will see. These assumptions should be defined and documented along with other design inputs. One of the keys for good product design is to challenge the basis for any design assumptions. The auditor should verify that all design assumptions were documented and have some basis for their selection.

ISO/TS 16949 requires *competitive analysis,* a form of benchmarking. The auditor should ask whether any reverse engineering studies or other competitive analysis has been performed. Although there is no guarantee that these studies will directly relate to the products selected as objects for this audit, the auditee should be aware of the studies that have been done. A lack of awareness of competitive analysis that has been performed by the organization may result in an opportunity for improvement. Failure to use or consider studies that directly apply to the products being reviewed should result in a nonconformance.

ISO/TS 16949 also requires the organization to set *quality and reliability targets* for products. Reliability goals are often based on *reliability studies.* The auditor should inquire into the reliability and quality goals that were established for the parts and/or products selected as objects. The auditor can ask how these goals were established. Were they based on reliability studies, customer requirements, or historical warranty data?

The *preliminary process flowchart, preliminary bill of material,* and *preliminary listing of special characteristics* are not required by ISO/TS 16949, but are often developed to facilitate cost estimating and quotations. These initial outputs normally evolve into the final process flowchart, final bill of material, and (possibly) final listing of special characteristics. Because they are not required and because they usually evolve into final documents, the auditor may not desire or be able to audit these components. What the auditor may want to do is question how the cost estimates and pricing models for the product were determined. This type of in-depth evaluation may be warranted if audit planning shows that the organization frequently misses its target costs once the product goes into production.

The primary output from the plan and define phase is the *product assurance plan.* This component, which is not directly referenced in ISO/TS 16949, has no prescribed format. The *APQP Reference Manual* says that the product assurance plan is a component of the quality plan, which is referenced in 16949. The auditor should ask, "What tools do we use to plan out and manage the project?" Verify that methods are used to define the activities, deliverables, timetables, and responsibilities associated with product and process design and development. Verify design verification planning and reporting (DVP&R) per customer requirements. If documented plans do not exist, generate an NC. Note that the auditor will want to use the part or product that is still in design and development when evaluating the product assurance plan, since there is no requirement to keep this plan as part of the PPAP package.

Once the auditor has the plan in hand, evaluate performance to the milestones reflected on the plan. The auditor should also ask, "How are we doing in meeting our milestones for this project?" Were the milestone dates met? If not, were actions taken to recover the schedule and/or capture lessons learned? Is there a pattern of not meeting launch dates? If so, and there were no steps taken to correct this systemic deficiency, issue an NC against the effectiveness of the planning process.

AUDITING THE PRODUCT DESIGN AND DEVELOPMENT PHASE

The product design and development phase takes the outputs from the plan and define phase and uses them to develop a product design and to initiate process development. It is especially important to realize that both the product and the process design and development should happen concurrently, not in series. Waiting until the product design is finalized to begin process development will limit the choices available to error-proof the process and reduce manufacturing risk.

The following components are developed or performed during this phase, shown with the key audit points that should be verified:

Component	Key Audit Points
Design failure mode and effects analysis (DFMEA)	The FMEA will be examined in more detail later in this chapter.
Design for manufacturability and assembly (DFM/DFA)	If a formal DFM/DFA process is in use (ask the lead engineer), then the auditor should ask about the process. DFM/DFA will normally be used on assemblies and subassemblies. Normally a set of guidelines or checklists will be used. Sometimes a software program will be used. Some things to look for include: • Was the number of parts minimized? • Were parts designed to be self-locating and self-aligning? • Can the part be assembled without reorientation? • Was error-proofing considered? Ask to see evidence of its application on this project. Note, if this project was only a slight modification of a previous design, then ask to see the DFM/DFA analysis of the previous project.

Continued

Component	Key Audit Points
Design verification and design reviews	Verify that the design verification activities called out in the project plan and design verification plan (DVP) were conducted by asking to see the results. Verify that actions and open issues are being followed on an open items list or equivalent. Verify that actions are being closed out. Ask to see the design review minutes or reports. Review for the following: • Was there adequate representation of the affected functions? • Did the review critically examine and challenge the design elements under review (tests, concepts, drawings, and so on)? • Were problems identified and/or actions assigned as a result of the review? Was it more than a compulsory status report?
Prototype build and prototype control plan	If the organization is involved in prototype development, ask to see the prototype control plan that was used to evaluate the prototype(s). Note that early control plans (prototype, prelaunch) usually evolve into production control plans, so there is no guarantee they will have the prototype control plan for a product that is now in production. If they do not, you may have to go outside this project and identify a project in an early stage of development to evaluate this area.
Engineering drawings, engineering specifications, material specifications, and drawing and specification changes	If your organization does not design the products it manufactures, then ask to see the customer's design drawings and note any special characteristics assigned by the customer. Jot these down on your checklist. You will want to ensure these are picked up in your process documentation and control plan later on. If you are design responsible, then check to see that your design drawings reflect any special characteristics reflected in the FMEAs and/or control plan. If you are design responsible and development of specifications was part of the project, then check to see that your specifications reflect inspection and testing requirements. Ask about the process used to control engineering changes. Is it documented? Is it followed? Pick one or more of the design drawings that have been revised (refer to the revision block or letter). Inquire about the nature of earlier changes ("What did revision B do? Revision C?") and ask for evidence of proper control of the change. Note any special testing requirements (reliability, functional, and so on) noted on the drawings or in the specifications. You will verify they were conducted and met requirements during the validation phase.
New equipment, tooling and facilities requirements, and gages/test equipment requirements	Normally, equipment and tooling identification is facilitated through the use of a checklist such as in the APQP manual. It may also be evidenced in the project planning documents or design review/status minutes. For purchased tooling and equipment, look for evidence of supplier tracking. Ask who tracks, how often, and whether equipment suppliers are members of the APQP team. Ask about lean manufacturing considerations. How are the items noted in 16949 section 6.3.1 evaluated? What methods were considered for this project?

Continued

Continued

Component	Key Audit Points
Special product and process characteristics	This item will be discussed in more detail in the section dealing with FMEA.
Team feasibility commitment and management support	Verify that a formal feasibility review and risk analysis was performed prior to accepting the manufacturing contract. A model is provided in Appendix E of the *AIAG Advanced Quality Planning and Control Plan* reference manual.

Ask the lead engineer/APQP team leader, "When is the risk assessment performed? Can I see the assessment performed on this project?"

A risk assessment is often done in conjunction with the contract review/feasibility review. The assessment points may even be incorporated into these reviews. Ask to see the evidence that the project was evaluated for:

- Program timing (Can we provide it to customer timing requirements?)

- Resources (Do we have the equipment, tooling, skills needed?)

- Development costs and investments (Can we develop the design/processes?)

- Possible failures of the organization's direct suppliers (Do we have qualified suppliers?)

Note that this evaluation may be directed at the account manager since feasibility review should be conducted as part of contract review.

For management support, ask the lead engineer/APQP team leader, "How did we keep management informed of our progress on this project?"

The standard requires that management be informed of the progress being made in design and development. They are typically informed through distribution of periodic status reports, design review summaries, and through attendance of meetings and reviews. A more difficult, but still important issue is, how did management react to slippages in schedule or problems reported in the design process? Review the reports or minutes of meetings. Is there evidence of management response when problems arise?

AUDITING THE PROCESS DESIGN AND DEVELOPMENT PHASE

The process design and development phase takes the outputs from the plan and define phase and the product design and development phases and uses them to develop the manufacturing process. The following components are developed or performed during this phase, shown with the key audit points that should be verified:

Component	Key Audit Points
Process flowchart and floor plan layout	Verify that a process flowchart has been developed. Later you will compare it to the PFMEA and the control plan. It should also be taken out on the manufacturing floor during process-based manufacturing audits to confirm its accuracy. Any discrepancies between the PFMEA and the control plan should be identified. Issue an OFI if the deficiencies are minor; issue an NC if the flowchart looks nothing like the steps reflected in the PFMEA and/or control plan. Although not specifically required by ISO/TS 16949:2002 or by the PPAP manual, most companies have floor plan layouts to aid with plant, facility, and equipment planning and documentation.
Process FMEA	The FMEA will be examined in more detail later in this chapter.
Characteristics matrix	The characteristics matrix is an optional tool and is not often subject to audit. An example is provided in the *AIAG Advanced Production Quality Planning and Control Plan* reference manual. If it is used, the auditor could verify that more significant process operations and product features are considered when assigning special characteristics and process controls.
Prelaunch control plan	Compare the verifications called out in the prelaunch control plan to the evidence of conformity contained in the PPAP package. If no evidence exists in the PPAP package to support the verifications called out in the prelaunch control plan, generate an NC. Also note that General Motors (GM) requires retention of the prelaunch control plan as part of the PPAP package.
Packaging specifications and standards	If the organization develops the packaging specifications, then ask to see the packaging standards used as a reference. If the customer provides the detailed packaging requirements, then defer evaluation of packaging compliance until the production process is audited. Note any special testing requirements involving the packaging. You will verify they were conducted during the next phase.
Process instructions	The existence of process instructions will be verified during production process audits.
Measurement systems analysis plan and preliminary process capability study plan	The MSA plan and preliminary process capability study plan, as separate documents, are optional tools and are not often subject to audit. The planning should be reflected in the other project planning documents, however, even if these tools are not used.

AUDITING THE PRODUCT AND PROCESS VALIDATION PHASE

The centerpiece of this phase is the production trial run or customer equivalent. This trial will be used to validate the process by using production equipment, materials, fixtures, measuring equipment, operators, and instructions to produce production parts. Some of these parts will then be selected for detailed dimensional and engineering testing to validate the product. The primary output of this phase should be customer approval (or provisional approval, for Toyota) for production. The following components are produced or verified during this phase, shown with the key audit points that should be verified:

Component	Key Audit Points
Production trial run	Verify that the customer-approved validation process (typically PPAP, but also subject to customer-specific supplementation like Ford's phased PPAP process) was followed. Verify that actual production equipment, tooling, facilities, materials, and operators were used during the trial. Inquire about how many parts were run. For the PPAP process, at least 300 parts, representing between one and eight hours of production, must be produced unless the customer has authorized another quantity.
	Also verify that the validation was performed to customer-specific timing requirements. These timing requirements should be shown in the initial project plan. If the validation was late, select several other recent projects to see if they were completed on time.
Measurement systems evaluation	Discussed separately later in this chapter.
Preliminary process capability study	The auditor should review the results of the process capability studies. Studies must be run on all special characteristics on the control plan that are measured using variable data. Verify that the indices were greater than 1.33 (1.67 for General Motors). Verify that at least 100 consecutive parts were used, formed into at least 20 subgroups, to perform the calculations.
Production validation testing, packaging evaluation	Inquire about any customer-specific requirements relating to validation. Have the lead engineer provide you with the requirements and show you how they were addressed during the validation. Pay particular attention to the completion of all required engineering and dimensional testing called out on the prelaunch control plan, design verification plan, and/or engineering drawings and specifications.
Production control plan	Verify that a production control plan is included in the product approval package and that it is up to date (reflects the current important process controls and revision level).

Continued

Continued

Component	Key Audit Points
Production part approval	The auditor should verify that all of the items required by PPAP are retained in the PPAP package or are available (for example, sample product and checking aids). Many of these items will have already been reviewed during the audit. A common weakness is failure to retain master parts. The checklists on the CD identify the required PPAP elements. If your customer uses a process other than PPAP, then modify the checklist to include the items required by your customer.
	The auditor may want to check several additional PPAP packages for inclusion of all of the recommended information. Focus on PPAP packages that are associated with PPAP submission levels 1, 2, or 4 (even if this means picking some projects other than the one being used as the object for this audit). Since much of the information in these packages does not have to be submitted to the customer, they are most commonly deficient.
	Pay particular attention to the completion of all required engineering and dimensional testing called out on the prelaunch control plan, design verification plan, and/or engineering drawings and specifications.
	Verify that customer approval was obtained on the warrant or customer equivalent document. If provisional approval was granted, verify that resubmission was performed prior to exceeding the quantity or date authorized.

EVALUATING DESIGN AND PROCESS FAILURE MODE AND EFFECTS ANALYSIS

The FMEA is one of the most important tools developed during the quality planning process. Some of the key audit points are provided in Figure 12.5. Each of these items will be examined in detail. Although a design FMEA is shown, the questions for a process FMEA would be similar.

• *Was a multifunction team used to develop the FMEA?* It is critical that a multi-disciplinary team be used to develop the FMEA, especially the foundation FMEA used as the baseline for other FMEAs. It is also a requirement. The auditor should, through questions, verify that the FMEA was not generated by one quality engineer sitting in an office. He or she may want to question some of the individuals identified in the core team section of the FMEA to gauge their involvement.

• *Were all realistic failure modes identified?* A key indicator that all realistic failure modes were not identified is when the FMEA only identifies one failure mode for each design function or process step. The auditor should review actual failure mode information (for example, warranty reports, product rejection reports, nonconforming product reports, and so on) prior to the audit to see what failure modes are actually occurring. These should be reflected on the FMEA. Since the FMEA is required to be

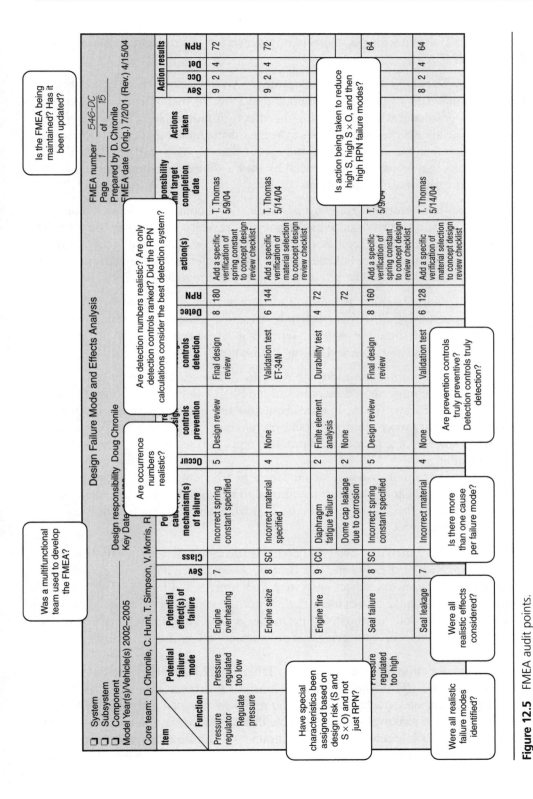

Figure 12.5 FMEA audit points.

Reprinted from the *Failure Mode and Effects Analysis (FMEA) Manual* with permission of DaimlerChrysler, Ford, and GM Supplier Quality Requirements Task Force.

maintained as a living document, there is no excuse for not reflecting actual failure modes on the FMEA.

• *Were the effects on all customers considered? Are the effects realistic?* Although the focus is usually on the end user, internal and external manufacturing customers should also be considered when identifying the effects of failure. Sometimes the effects on these other customers are more serious than the effects on the end user. Look to see if customers other than the end user were at least considered. Also verify that the effects are noted in terms that would be experienced by the customer. Also note that any given failure mode normally has multiple effects.

• *Were appropriate severity rankings assigned?* Most companies do a credible job of identifying realistic severity rankings. Ensure that severity rankings of 9 and/or 10 consider safety, health, and/or regulatory effects. Since companies can generate their own rankings, safety effects may be deleted. The FMEA reference manual cautions that severity modes 9 and 10 should be retained for safety and regulatory effects, however.

• *Was more than one cause per failure mode considered?* A dead giveaway that little effort was put into the FMEA is when only one cause is identified per failure mode. Also note that the cause should be stated in terms that can be acted on. For example, the cause *operator error* is too vague and should not be used.

• *Were realistic occurrence numbers assigned?* The assignment of occurrence rankings is one of the most abused activities in the FMEA development process. Most commonly they are artificially low. Inquire about how the rankings were determined . . . what was the basis for the assignment? Focus on rankings of 1, 2, or 3. Look over your list of defects rates, scrap, and associated problem reports to see what failure modes are actually happening.

If there is documented evidence of moderate or frequent failures in the field, in your plant, or in your customer's plant determined to be caused by manufacturing deficiencies and related to the failure mode being evaluated, and the ranking was very low (1, 2, or 3), generate an NC.

• *Were both preventive and detection controls identified? Are the preventive controls truly preventive? Were only detection controls ranked? Are the rankings realistic?* The auditor should review the detection system assignments and rankings. Are preventive controls (focused on the cause) identified? If not, are actions being taken to develop preventive controls? Focus on those failure modes with high severity and/or severity times occurrence rankings. Also, verify that only detection controls are assigned detection rankings.

Compare the detection rankings assigned to Table 4 (DFMEA) and Table 8 (PFMEA) in the *AIAG Potential Failure Mode and Effects Analysis Reference Manual*. In particular, for the PFMEA, evaluate whether the detection rankings assigned are reasonable compared to the suggested rankings in Table 8. Note that the best detection ranking that can be expected for visual inspection methods is around a 7 (for double visual inspection). It is not uncommon to find rankings of 2 or 3 assigned to visual controls. Document findings if the detection rankings appear to be significantly lower than what would be expected using the table guidance.

Also use the information gained from your review of actual occurrences escaping to the customer to determine if the detection rankings are realistic. If the data show significant amounts of bad product reaching the customer, but the detection rankings are 1, 2 or 3, then the auditor should question the detection ranking. Finally, verify that the most effective (lowest ranking) detection control was used to calculate the overall RPN.

• *Were special characteristics properly identified and assigned?* One of the primary uses of the FMEA is to identify the need for special process and verification methods. Many companies are under the mistaken impression that the assignment of special characteristics is the responsibility of the customer. While the customer does assign special characteristics, and the auditor should verify that these are reflected on the FMEA, it is the responsibility of the supplier to supplement these with its knowledge of the product (if design responsible) and the process, based on the results of the FMEA. Consideration should be given to assigning a critical characteristic to all high-severity (for example, 9 or 10) failure modes and a significant characteristic to moderate- to high-severity, moderate- to high-occurrence failure modes (severity times occurrence values greater than around 40 is a common rule.). If the auditor finds that no special characteristics have been assigned, despite the fact that there are high severity and/or high severity times occurrence failure modes, then he or she should consider generation of a finding.

• *Is action being taken, or was it taken, to address high-severity, high-severity times occurrence, and then high RPN rankings, in that order? Were new estimated rankings calculated based on the actions?* Look for actions/evaluations for all high-severity and all high-severity times occurrence (SO) rankings. Since the only way to reduce the severity rankings is a design change, it will not always be possible to take action to reduce severity. In these cases the detections systems must be improved or the production process modified to permit elimination/early detection of the cause. The RPN should be the last item considered when determining when to take action.

After actions have been assigned, look to see that new estimated rankings are assigned. Over time these estimates should be modified to reflect actual experience (that is, living document).

• *Is the FMEA being maintained as a living document?* This is one of the most important aspects of the FMEA, and one of the most often neglected. Since new FMEAs are often based on similar, current FMEAs, it is imperative that the current FMEAs be up to date, reflecting actual failure modes and realistic severity, occurrence, and detection rankings. Otherwise the new processes will be designed with the same inherent flaws of the older process. Auditors can evaluate whether the FMEA is being maintained through use of the data on actual failure modes reviewed as part of audit planning and by taking the FMEA out on the production floor and comparing the failure modes on the FMEA to the actual failure modes occurring as determined by evaluation of scrap, nonconforming product, and operator interviews.

The output of the FMEA will be used to develop the control plans. The auditor should compare the control plans to the FMEA and should ensure that all verifications/ controls associated with special characteristics have been carried over to the control plan. In addition, other routine verifications and controls may also be shown on the control plan. Note that the control plan does not have to list every control identified on the FMEA. The auditor can reference item 19 in the control plan methodology section of the *AIAG Advanced Product Quality Planning and Control Plan Reference Manual* for more guidance.

While the development of the FMEA is beyond the scope of this handbook, a thorough evaluation of the FMEA during the quality audit can identify the need to examine the methods used by the organization to generate FMEAs. The next section will examine what to look for when evaluating measurement system studies.

EVALUATING MEASUREMENT SYSTEM STUDIES

ISO/TS 16949 requires that measurement system analysis be conducted on all measurement systems shown on the control plan. The studies used to fulfill this requirement should be retained in the PPAP or customer equivalent product approval file. The following discussion relates to what the auditor should look for when evaluating gage repeatability and reproducibility (GR&R) and attribute studies. Evaluation of linearity, stability, and bias may also be examined, but are not covered in this handbook. The auditor should reference the *AIAG Measurement System Analysis Reference Manual* (MSA) for more information on these studies.

For an attribute short study, verify that:

- At least two production operators were used.

- At least 20 parts were used, with some slightly out of spec (no-go) at the high and low end (if possible).

- The actual production gages were used.

This type of study does not have a standard set of acceptance criteria. The results must be analyzed on a case-by-case basis. Use of the signal detection approach is recommended. Note that the methods recommended in the MSA reference manual now require the actual measurement of the trial parts. Also note that Ford Motor Company requires the use of 50 parts, three operators, and three trials. Refer to the Ford Motor Company customer-specific requirements.

The long attribute gage study is more complicated. It requires physical measurement of the parts (versus go/no-go determination) and requires the development of a gage performance curve by plotting on normal probability paper.

For an attribute long study, verify that:

- At least eight parts that represent the entire range of the product were used.

- The actual physical attributes of the parts are determined by layout inspection.

- Each part must be run through the attribute measurement system at least 20 times.

- The results should be plotted on normal probability paper.

This type of study does not have a standard set of acceptance criteria. The results must be analyzed on a case-by-case basis.

The variable gage short study using the range method provides a quick approximation of measurement system variability. It does not decompose the overall variability into repeatability and reproducibility. It is typically used as a quick screening mechanism and to verify that the GR&R has not changed (type II study).

The range method has the potential to detect an unacceptable measurement system 80 percent of the time with a sample size of five and 90 percent of the time with a sample size of 10.

For a range method study, verify that:

- At least two production operators were used.

- At least five parts were used.

- Each appraiser measures each part once.

The acceptance guidelines for variable studies using the methods described here are:

- Under 10 percent error—generally considered to be an acceptable measurement system.

- 10 percent to 30 percent error—may be acceptable based on the importance of the application and cost of the measurement device or repair.

- Over 30 percent error—considered to be unacceptable. Efforts should be undertaken to improve the system. Customer notification may also be required.

Variable gage study using the average and range (GR&R) method is the most common type of gage study. The average and range method will provide an estimate of both the repeatability and reproducibility. For the average and range study, verify that:

- At least two production operators were used.

- At least five parts were used (10 is more typical).

- Each appraiser measures each part at least twice.

Note that some customers (Ford and Toyota) requires three production operators, three trials, and at least 10 parts for variable gage studies.

The acceptance guidelines for variable studies using the methods described here are:

- Under 10 percent error—generally considered to be an acceptable measurement system.

- 10 percent to 30 percent error—may be acceptable based on the importance of the application and cost of the measurement device or repair.

- Over 30 percent error—considered to be unacceptable. Efforts should be undertaken to improve the system.

The auditor should verify both the methodology and the results according to these guidelines. Use of other methods or acceptance criteria requires customer approval.

EVALUATING STATISTICAL PROCESS CONTROL CHARTS

The final section in this chapter will consider the use of statistical process control. Although the principles outlined here do apply to quality planning, in the form of deciding what types of statistical methods to use and properly conducting process capability studies during the production trial run, the majority of the auditor's focus should be on the proper use of SPC on the production floor. The key audit points discussed would be evaluated during process-based production audits. They are presented here since SPC is one of the core tools.

• *Evaluation of variables data using the averages and range (X-bar and R) method.* X-bar and R charts are the most commonly used control chart. The range chart is always constructed first and tested for stability (all points on the range chart within the upper and lower control limits). This is because the calculation of the average range will be used in the formula for calculating the mean (X-bar) chart. If the range chart is out of control, then the X-bar chart is meaningless. Possible audit topics related to chart construction:

- Were at least 20 sample sets used to construct the chart?

- Was the range chart constructed first and tested for statistical control?

- Were the correct constants used for calculating control limits based on sample size?

- Was the X-bar chart in statistical control prior to fixing control limits?

• *Evaluation of variables data using the individuals and moving range (X-bar and MR) method.* There can be many instances where it is not appropriate or feasible to apply an X-bar and R or X-bar and s chart.

If it takes a long time to produce a single product, then it will take even longer to gather enough data to form a subgroup. The test to acquire the data may be destructive. Finance or accounting type data are often only generated periodically. While individuals charts may be used to monitor data obtained in these situations, there are some limitations. The most serious limitation is that the raw data itself must be normally or nearly normally distributed.

The chart is not as powerful as the *X*-bar chart is in detecting shifts in the process. If an *X*-bar and *MR* chart must be used, then be sure to check the assumption of normal data.

Possible audit topics related to chart construction:

– Was the distribution tested for normality prior to using this method?

– Were at least 50 sample sets used to construct the chart?

– If D_3 and D_4 were used to calculate control limits, were the correct constants used?

– Was the *X*-bar and *MR* chart in statistical control prior to fixing control limits?

• *Evaluation of attribute data.* When should attributes charts be used? Attribute charts should be used for count type data, such as particle counts. Use them when it is easier to classify products as nonconforming (defective) than it is to try to quantify a measurement. Also use them if it is not possible to obtain quantitative measurements (destructive testing for example).

The *p* and *np* control charts are used for nonconforming units. They are bounded charts that monitor the number of nonconforming units by inspecting a total number of units. Some definitions are needed:

– *Nonconforming unit.* A defective production unit or production batch that does not conform to its specification or performance criteria.

– *Bounded data.* The count characteristic has an upper bound on how large the value it can take, usually determined by the nature of the unit. For example, if car doors are tested in samples of 50, then there can be no more than 50 nonconforming doors.

– *Inspection total.* The total number of units tested to obtain a count of nonconforming units (either defective or not).

• Evaluation of attribute data using a *p* or *np* chart: The *p* chart is used to detect process shifts and nonrandom behavior in the proportion of nonconforming units. The *np* chart represents the actual number of nonconforming units observed in a subgroup. The only real difference between the *p* and the *np* charts is the perspective. Some users may prefer to look at proportions, where others may prefer the actual count. In either case, the configuration of the data points on the chart is the same (as long as *n* is constant) and thus, so is the interpretation.

Control charts for attributes generally require large subgroup sizes to be able to detect moderate shifts in performance. Typical subgroup size should be between 50 and 200. The formula for control limits are appropriate when the subgroup sizes are equal. Theoretically, whenever the subgroup size changes, *n* changes, and the control limits should be recalculated for each change in subgroup size. As a practical manner, the average subgroup size can be used if the variation between subgroup size is less than 25 percent.

Another key point is that data points outside the control limit should be investigated and the data points removed and control limits recalculated when establishing process capability. Once the process shows stability within the limits, the chart can be used for control. Possible audit topics related to chart construction:

– Was the subgroup size at least 50?

– Were at least 25 subgroups collected before constructing the control chart?

– Was the subgroup size constant? If not, was the variation in the samples set less than 25 percent? Where the subgroup size varies, but varies by less than 25 percent, was an average subgroup size calculated and used? As an alternative, individual control limits may be calculated for each subgroup.

– Were data points outside of the control limits removed and control limits recalculated for process capability studies?

• *Evaluation of attribute data using a* c *or* u *chart.* Control charts for nonconformities are unbounded charts that monitor the number of nonconformities observed in an inspection unit. Some definitions are in order:

– *Nonconformity.* A type of defect (scratch, dent, chip, and so on) that may result (not necessarily) in a nonconforming unit.

– *Unbounded data.* The count characteristic has no upper bound on the value it can take. For example, the number of scratches or dents on a car door has no natural upper limit.

– *Inspection unit.* The number of units tested to obtain a count of nonconformities.

The inspection unit may be a single, discrete product (such as a car windshield), a group of products (a batch of car windshields), or a portion of a product (a square foot of windshield). Like the inspection total, the inspection unit may be a constant, or it may vary. The c chart is used to detect process shifts and nonrandom behavior in the number of nonconformities in an inspection unit. The u chart represents the ratio of nonconformities per unit. As was the case with p and np charts, the only difference between the c and u charts is the perspective. The c chart monitors the actual count of defects, whereas the u chart monitors the defects per unit inspected (provided n is constant).

The c chart requires a constant sample size. It is typically applied in two situations: (1) where the nonconformities are scattered throughout a continuous flow of product (defects in wire insulation, flaws per 10 square meters) and (2) where the nonconformities from many different potential sources may be found in a single inspection unit (for example, a car).

Possible audit topics related to chart construction:

– Was the sample size constant?

– Were at least 25 subgroups collected before constructing the control chart?

   – Were data points outside of the control limits removed and control limits recalculated for process capability studies?

   • *Interpretation of control charts.* The previous section discussed control chart construction and points the auditor may confirm relating to these charts. This section considers whether personnel are reacting appropriately to what the charts are telling them. The auditor can evaluate this by reviewing the charts in use on the production floor and by asking operators involved in control chart maintenance and operation questions relating to these audit points.

   ISO/TS 16949 states that basic statistical concepts, such as variation, control (stability), process capability, and overadjustment shall be understood and utilized throughout the organization. Process operators involved in process control where SPC is used must be familiar with basic statistical concepts. The auditor must review charts in use and question operators to evaluate their knowledge of these concepts, along with their ability to recognize the indicators discussed in this section. There are two basic situations that should flag the need to take action. The first is when one or more points fall outside the control limits. See Figure 12.6.

   Statistically, about one in every 300 data points may be expected to fall outside the ±3 standard deviation control limits, if the process is in statistical control. These limits bound 99.73 percent of the expected data points for a normally distributed population.

   Since the likelihood of points falling outside the control limits is statistically low, if the process is operating under statistical control, investigation of the special causes acting on the process should be initiated for points falling outside the control limits.

   The auditor should review the control charts to identify any instances of points falling outside the control limits. If found, the auditor should determine whether the signal was recognized, recorded, and actions taken according to company policy. As a minimum, the action taken (or basis for taking no action) should be recorded.

   The second situation that should mark the need to take action is when the data show a statistically improbable run or trend. The test for points outside the control

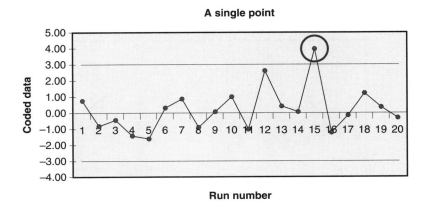

Figure 12.6 One or more points outside the control limits.

limits applies to both variables and attribute charts. The run tests apply primarily to variables data.

As in the case of points falling outside the control limits, the probability of developing certain long runs or trends is also low if the process is operating in statistical control. While there are many different rules that can be applied to help recognize such an event, organizations typically standardize on two or three. Auditors should be aware of what rules are applied in their organizations. Some of the more common rules are shown in Figure 12.7, Figure 12.8, Figure 12.9, Figure 12.10, and Figure 12.11.

The auditor should review the control charts to identify any instances of trends or runs in accordance with company policy. If found, the auditor should determine whether the signal was recognized, recorded, and actions taken according to organization procedures and reaction plans. As a minimum, the action taken (or basis for taking no action) should be recorded.

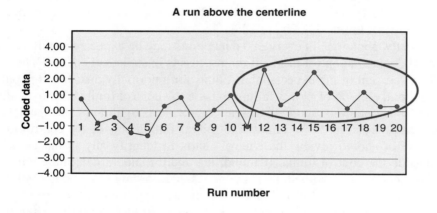

Figure 12.7 Seven or more data points above or below the centerline.

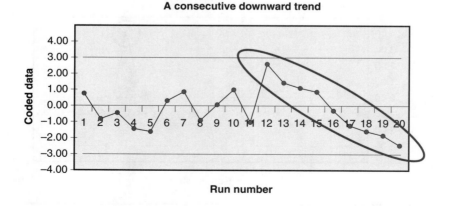

Figure 12.8 Seven consecutive points trending up or down.

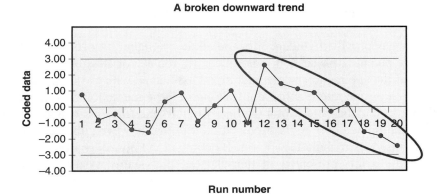

Figure 12.9 Broken run of eight of 10 points trending up or down.

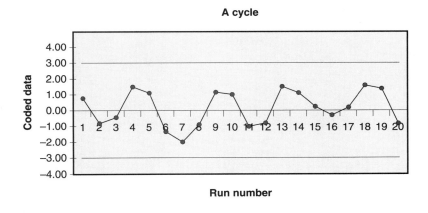

Figure 12.10 Obvious repetitive cycles.

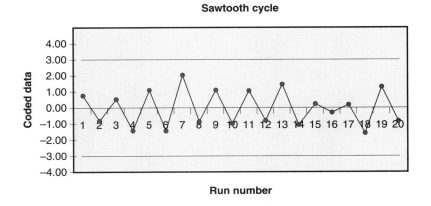

Figure 12.11 Sawtooth cycle.

SUMMARY

This chapter has provided guidance for the auditor assigned to evaluate the organization's quality planning process. It is not meant to replace or substitute for an in-depth knowledge of the application or methodologies associated with FMEAs, MSA, SPC, or the PPAP such as one might gain from training in these methodologies. Note that both General Motors and the Ford Motor Company require internal quality auditors to attend training on the related core tools. Application training, however, does not always provide insight into how to audit these tools. By combining knowledge of the methodology with the audit points presented in this chapter, the quality system auditor can be expected to find the systematic weaknesses present in the quality planning process.

13

Using Internal Audits to Identify Best Practices

T his chapter discusses another possible benefit that can be derived from the internal audit program—identifying best practices. Internal auditors are exposed to many different operations and are, therefore, in a unique position to compare processes across the organization and between different business units of the organization. With the advent of process-based auditing, auditors are also diving deeper into the activities that make up a process and can more easily identify the practices that lead to superior performance. Doing so, in a systematic fashion, can add great value to the organization.

Identifying best practices during internal audits is basically a two-step process. The first step is to identify the practices that are truly superior. The increased focus on monitoring and measuring process effectiveness in ISO 9001:2000 provides the foundation for auditors to do this. As outlined in Chapter 1, a mature organization will have in place a robust system of process metrics to indicate if its processes are achieving their intended results. Auditors can use these metrics to identify superior performance. Auditors can also use their own measures of effectiveness, as discussed in Chapter 5, to determine if the audited activity is truly excellent.

The second and more important step is to identify the drivers, or enablers, of performance. Enablers are defined as activities that lead to exceptional performance. Enablers may be in the form of:

- People (competencies, experience, or number)

- Equipment (type, age, capabilities, technology)

- Information systems (IT, databases)

- Methods (procedures, policies, workflow)

- Culture (empowerment, decision making, rewards and recognition, cooperation)

Often these enablers are the critical inputs into the process that support the transformation into outputs. As discussed throughout this book, auditors are now expected to evaluate the entire process, including the inputs, resources, controls, and the transformation of these into outputs. During their review of the critical inputs and resources into a process, auditors are now in a position to identify the critical inputs (enablers) that drive performance.

The greatest value from identifying best practices during internal audits will be to those organizations that use internal auditors to audit not only within their own business unit, but also between business units. Such a strategy allows for the exposure to similar activities in different organizational contexts and enhances the identification of best practices. It also helps if the different business units use standardized measures of performance, since this facilitates identification of best practices through the review of process performance data. Smaller, single-division companies can still identify best practices during internal audits by focusing on activities that are common across departments or teams. The gains will not be as large as those possible within a large, multidivisional corporation, however.

Besides adding direct value through the identification and communication of best practices, this internal benchmarking using the audit process can also drive a culture of learning throughout the organization. Current business dynamics demand that every organization be continuously searching for ways to improve its operations, products, and capability to satisfy customers. Business units, departments, and teams are as susceptible to the "not invented here" syndrome as are corporations. Internal benchmarking, which is in effect what we are doing through the audit program, can help to change this culture.

It must be realized that the primary goal of any internal management system audit is to find the systemic weakness in the management system. Auditors must not let the search for best practices interfere with this primary goal. By using the process and tools outlined throughout this book and in the upcoming sections, auditors should find that the extra effort required to identify and research best practices does not significantly detract from the auditor's primary mission.

THE PROCESS FOR IDENTIFYING BEST PRACTICES THROUGH THE INTERNAL AUDIT PROCESS

The process for identifying best practices using the internal audit program follows the flowchart shown in Figure 13.1 and starts with audit planning. During the planning for the audit, the auditor should review available metrics for the process(es) being evaluated. As discussed in Chapter 5, review of available metrics is important to help the auditor focus the audit on the areas of concern. The auditor can use knowledge of typical performance and performance to defined goals to identify potential best practices. The auditor might also compare the metrics to the performance measures of other, similar departments or business units, if this information is readily available (as it should be in a mature organization that has institutionalized internal benchmarking). The auditor should plan to spend an extra 10 or 15 minutes in these areas to verify the best practice and to identify the potential enablers.

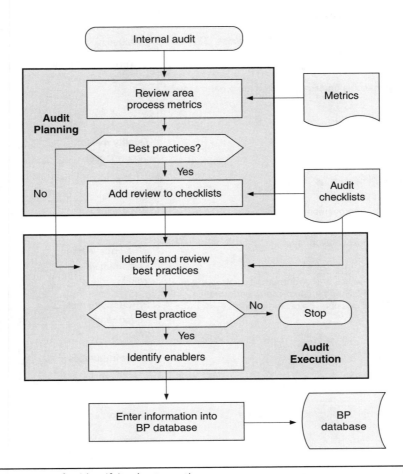

Figure 13.1 Process for identifying best practices.

During the audit, the auditor should evaluate each assigned process as described in the previous sections of this book. When the auditor comes to a process or activity that may represent a best practice, either by the metrics or by the auditor's own evaluation, then the auditor can use the best practices checklist, Figure 13.2, to quickly evaluate the process and identify the most likely enablers. Completion of this checklist should not take more than 10 or 15 minutes, maximum. Remember, the auditors are not looking for acceptable performance or even above average performance. The auditor is seeking truly superior performance or best practices.

It is also worth noting that the auditor's responsibility is to identify and communicate the best practice, not to definitively research the enablers. If another process owner determines that his or her process could benefit from the best practice, it will be up to the process owner to make contact with the owner of the best practice and to more thoroughly research its enablers and applicability to his or her process. Even so, auditors can do a credible job of identifying the most probable enablers by evaluating the

Ask the following questions once a best practice (BP) has been identified to better define the best practice and to identify the process enablers.

In what ways has this practice benefited the organization?

    Quality benefits ❑

    Cost benefits ❑

    Efficiency/time savings ❑

    Productivity improvements ❑

    Other (morale, cohesion, etc.) ❑

Summarize key metrics and performance levels in the column to the right. Summarize previous performance (before the BP), if possible, below the metric. ❑

Process: _____

Description of best practice:

Quality metric: _____
Performance: _____ Trend _____
Was:

Cost metric: _____
Performance: _____ Trend _____
Was:

Efficiency metric: _____
Performance: _____ Trend _____
Was:

Productivity metric: _____
Performance: _____ Trend _____
Was:

Other indicators:

Was/is any special training required? ❑ Yes ❑ No
If yes, describe:

How experienced or skilled are the people who perform the practice (the level of experience or skill is often one of the key enablers)?
❑ Low   ❑ Moderate   ❑ High   ❑ Very high

Is there any unique equipment, software, or information needed to perform the practice? ❑

Is there anything else that is critical to being able to perform this practice or to do it this well (research key inputs and resources)? ❑

Enablers:
1. _____
2. _____
3. _____
3. _____

Contact information:

Figure 13.2   Best practices checklist.

process as they normally would during the audit and by asking the questions on the best practices checklists.

The top section of the best practices checklist is used to gather key information for establishing a process as a best practice. It focuses on the metrics, trends, and other indicators such as awards, customer recognition, and auditee feedback that can establish the practice as truly superior. The bottom section of the checklist is used to help analyze the processes, to the extent practicable. It gathers information on the key benefits, performance measures, before and after, and potential enablers, and gathers contact information. This section can be used by potential adopters of the best practice to better evaluate whether they can adapt the best practice to their processes. By keeping the information on the checklist short and to the point, the evaluation of the best practice should not interfere with the primary goal of the audit—to identify the systemic weaknesses in the management system.

As an example of using the checklist, assume that you are evaluating a business unit's corrective action process. During the audit you review 25 corrective action requests (CARs) issued over the last nine months. This is a small number compared to other business units you have evaluated. Of course, the purpose of the corrective action process is to prevent recurrence of problems. You note that there have been no recurrences of any problem over this time frame. You also note that there were no outstanding, overdue corrective actions. You suspect that you have found a best practice and therefore ask some additional questions. You are informed that all actions are routinely completed on time, in part because of the increased awareness of the cost of the problem. The cost and other consequence of each problem is estimated and noted on the CAR. This highlights cost savings and has increased management's willingness to invest the time required to determine the real root cause. Figure 13.3 shows how this best practice might be documented using the best practices checklist.

The top section of the checklist establishes that the practice is a best practice. Potential adopters could review these performance indicators to help determine whether it is worth their time to investigate adoption of the practice in their department or business unit. The bottom section of the checklist, documenting the potential enablers, is shown in Figure 13.4.

This bottom section indicates what the owner of the practice feels is key to being able to perform the practice or to derive maximum value from its performance. It gives potential adopters some early insight into whether the practice could be adopted in their process. It also provides contact information for further investigation.

Not every best practice is quantified. The auditor can also survey process owners and operators throughout the audit by asking the questions, "What activities do you consider to be best practices?" and "Based on your experience here and at other companies, what do we do that really works well?" These questions may lead the auditor to best practices that might be overlooked, but might benefit the organization if adopted in other similar processes.

Ask the following questions once a best practice (BP) has been identified to better define the best practice and to identify the process enablers.

In what ways has this practice benefited the organization?

Quality benefits ☑ *Problem recurrence has been practically eliminated.*

Cost benefits ☑ *The elimination of recurrence has produced significant cost savings.*

Efficiency/time savings ☑ *The timeliness of corrective action is now at 100%.*

Productivity improvements ☑ *None quantified, although certainly there.*

Other (morale, cohesion, etc.) ☑ *Culturally, everyone now sensitive to cost of problems.*

Summarize key metrics and performance levels in the column to the right. Summarize previous performance (before the BP), if possible, below the metric. ☑

Process: *Corrective action process*

Description of best practice:
The estimated cost and/or other consequences of each problem is noted on the CAR form. This cost is then used to estimate dollars saved and improve awareness of the need to permanently eliminate the cause of the problem.

Quality metric: *Problem recurrence*
Performance: *0%*   Trend _____
Was: *20%*

Cost metric: *$ saved from resolution*
Performance: *$150,000* Trend *↑*
Was: *Not measured*

Efficiency metric: *% overdue*
Performance: *0%*   Trend _____
Was: *40%*

Productivity metric: *Not measured*
Performance: *Not measured* Trend _____
Was:

Other indicators: *Registrar auditors commented very favorably on this practice*

Figure 13.3   Corrective action best practice.

Was/is any special training required? ☐ Yes ☑ No
If yes, describe:

How experienced or skilled are the people who perform the practice (the level of experience or skill is often one of the key enablers)?

☐ Low   ☑ Moderate   ☐ High   ☐ Very high

Is there any unique equipment, software, or information needed to perform the practice? ☑
Standard costs for different activities associated with problem resolution had to be developed, with support from accounting.

Is there anything else that is critical to being able to perform this practice or to do it this well (research key inputs and resources)? ☑
Cost estimates must be seen as legitimate. Use accounting to help develop. Quality must support direct dollar costs.

Enablers:
1. *Standard cost categories*
2. _____
3. _____
3. _____

Contact information:
Tim Jenkins 792-985-0987
Jenkinst@wmi.com

Figure 13.4   Corrective action best practice—enablers.

COMMUNICATING BEST PRACTICES

Simply identifying and documenting best practices in an audit report is not sufficient. There must also be a systematic means of communicating best practices throughout the organization. A database must be developed to facilitate this communication. The database must allow searching by fields and keywords. As a minimum, include in the database the following information:

- Functional area or activity

- Summary description of the best practice

- Performance metrics that support best practice

- Key enablers

- Contact information

- Keywords to allow retrieval

An example of a simple Microsoft Access database that provides this information is shown in Figure 13.5. It includes this information and allows easy categorization and retrieval of the best practices. The information from the best practices checklist is used to populate the database, which can easily be entered in five minutes or less.

Large organizations that institutionalize the identification of best practices might categorize hundreds of best practices, so design for easy search and retrieval by process

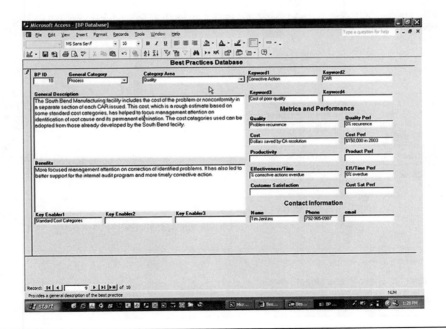

Figure 13.5 Best practices database.

owners is critical. Maintenance of the database could reside with the audit program manager, management representative, or continuous improvement coordinator. The database can also be used to generate summary reports of the best practice, an example of which is shown in Figure 13.6. If the audit program manager found that the database was not being used by process owners, then he or she could retrieve applicable best

Category Area	General Category	BP ID	Name	Phone
Engineering	Process	8	Tina Newman	734-987-9878

General Description

The Advanced Connector Team implemented a formal lessons learned design review one month after product launch. During this review, the APQP team, key suppliers, and the customer formally review what went well during the design, development, and validation phases, and what did not go well. A short, one-page summary is developed for each lesson learned and entered into the lessons learned database. The APQP process has been modified to require the APQP team to review this database during the conceptual design phase and to identify lessons learned to be incorporated into the new project. The lessons learned database has been optimized to permit easy searching and information retrieval during this early evaluation.

Benefits

The number of ECRs issued within six months after launch, normalized to 100 drawings, has been reduced from an average for 2001 of 57 to a 2003 average of 14. In addition, the percent of on-time launches (to customer agreed launch dates) has risen from 45% in 2001 to 85% in 2003 and 90% during the first six months of 2004. Cost savings have also been significant, but have not been measured.

Quality	Quality Perf	Productivity		Product Perf
# ECRs 6 mo. after launch/100 dwgs	14 ECRs/100 dwgs			
Effectiveness/Time	**Eff/Time Perf**	**Customer Satisfaction**		**Cust Sat Perf**
No. Launches on time to cust. rqmts.	90%			
Cost	**Cost Perf**	**e-mail**		
		tnewman@yazaki.com		

Key Enabler 1: Cross-functional team particip

Key Enabler 2: Lessons learned database

Key Enabler 3: Customer involvement

Figure 13.6 Best practices report.

practices by category area or keyword, print off the report, and attach it to the final audit report as an information item. The goal is to make process owners aware of methods that could make their process more effective or efficient.

Beyond documentation in audit reports and the use of a best practices database, best practices identification and adoption should be supported through newsletter articles, public presentations, bulletin boards, internal Web site communications, and ongoing staff, departmental, and work unit meetings. Remember, one of the primary goals of internal benchmarking is to foster a culture of improvement and learning throughout the organization. Best practices, when found and substantiated, should be recognized and celebrated.

LEVERAGING INTERNAL BENCHMARKING

Using the internal audit process to identify best practices also clears the way for the use of more formal methods of benchmarking. Benchmarking requires an up-front investment of time and resources. Many organizations may not want to put forth this investment without some evidence of its potential payoff. Using the internal audit process to demonstrate the value of benchmarking is a low-cost way to provide the evidence that management needs prior to committing to more aggressive forms of benchmarking.

Internal benchmarking has been shown to provide between a five percent and 10 percent improvement in performance in those activities that adopt internal best practices. External benchmarking with your key customers and suppliers (what I call value-chain benchmarking) has the potential for a 15 percent to 20 percent improvement. By far the greatest potential payoff comes from benchmarking inside and outside your industry, wherever best practices are found. This type of benchmarking can improve performance by 25 percent to 75 percent or more. Unfortunately, it also consumes significant resources to do. Using the internal audit program to prove the benefits of learning from others paves the way for an expansion of the benchmarking process. See Figure 13.7.

SUMMARY

Using the internal audit process to identify best practices brings auditing to a new level through the addition of even greater value. Organizations must provide the framework for identifying best practices by providing auditors with the tools (checklists), training, and time, and by establishing the systems needed to communicate and disseminate best practices. Best practice identification is facilitated by a robust system of process metrics and by standardization of key metrics across business units and departments. Auditors can still identify best practices, even in the absence of a robust system of metrics, by focusing on process purposes and effectiveness as shown by the corrective action example.

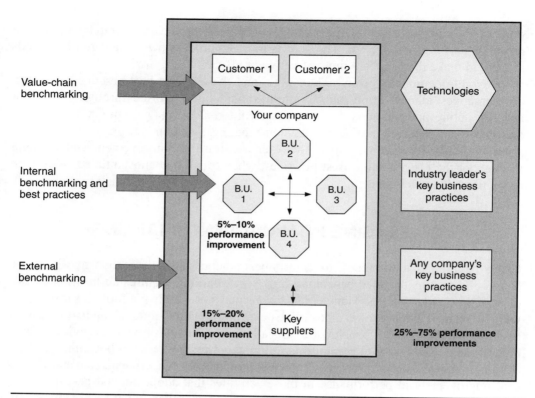

Figure 13.7 Benchmarking levels of performance.

14

Auditing for Strategic Alignment

As noted in Chapter 2, one of the potential benefits of a mature audit program is its ability to support the execution of the organization's strategy. Robert Kaplan and David Norton, in their groundbreaking book *The Balanced Scorecard,*[1] provided a model for measuring the alignment between an organization's key internal financial support and customer-oriented processes and its vision, mission, and strategy. In their follow-up book, *Strategy Maps: Converting Intangible Assets into Tangible Outcomes,*[2] they cite research that indicates between 70 percent and 90 percent of organizations fail to realize success from their strategies. In most instances this failure was not due to poor strategies, but rather from failures to properly deploy and execute their strategy. The internal audit program, coupled with a properly deployed strategic plan and a well-designed system of indicators, can help an organization execute its strategy and achieve its performance goals. In such instances, the internal audit program becomes a strategic asset and the benefit changes from potential to primary.

This topic has been saved for last simply because it is not easy to do. To be successful, the strategic elements must first be in place. These elements include a properly formulated strategic plan (based on the company's mission, vision, and values); a robust scorecard of balanced metrics that include not only financial, but also customer, process, and support system indicators; and, most importantly, strategy maps that link the strategic goals and initiatives to the internal processes that support them. In addition, the organization must have senior managers who recognize the potential of the audit program as a deployment aid and who support audits of the strategic alignment and performance of its internal processes. And finally, the organization must have experienced auditors who have the knowledge, perspective, and credibility needed to successfully evaluate and report on areas of strategic alignment (or misalignment) within the organization's systems and processes.

This chapter will review each of these components and will discuss the steps needed to transition from auditing for conformance and effectiveness to auditing for strategic alignment and performance. Making this transition should be the ultimate goal of the senior management team and the audit program manager. Both have critical roles to fill. Senior management must develop appropriate strategies, develop the strategic scorecards and strategy maps, and identify the strategic initiatives that will lead to achievement of the strategy. The audit program manager and staff must develop the strategic knowledge and perspective needed to evaluate strategy deployment and execution and must, through their other audit activities, develop the credibility with senior management needed to gain support for auditing at the strategic level. Needless to say, if the majority of the audit program's findings focus on administrative deficiencies or minor nonconformances, or if auditors lack perspective in raising issues of effectiveness, senior management will not trust the auditors to take on issues of strategic importance.

MISSION, VISION, AND STRATEGY

A strategic audit capability begins with a strategic plan. This section will present some of the basics of such a plan, how it should be linked with an organization's strategic initiatives, and how a quality management system can be used to support its deployment. Keep in mind that this is only a very basic overview of business strategy development. See the bibliography for a listing of more complete discussions on strategy development and execution.

Figure 14.1 shows the relationship between these three elements. Execution ties the three together, and as noted, is most often the weak link in achievement of the organization's vision and strategy.

The first element, the *mission*, defines why the organization exists or its basic reason for being. It is long-term in nature, providing a foundation for the organization to lock in on and to challenge its current and planned actions. It should also describe how the organization adds value in the eyes of its customers. A well-written mission statement provides guidance and inspiration. It helps motivate the organization's employees.

The second element is the organization's vision. The *vision* describes where the company wants to be in five, 10, or 20 years. It takes the mission, or core purpose, of the organization and establishes one or more long-term goals, which if achieved, will indicate success in fulfilling its mission. A well-written vision statement will be quantifiable. It will establish a target and possibly a timetable for achieving this target. It

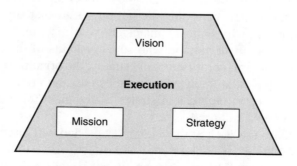

Figure 14.1 Execution, mission, vision, and strategy.

should also provide stability. With the dynamic pace of today's business environment, with initiatives and new methods (or fads, as some call them) appearing every year, the vision provides a guidepost that the company can use to challenge proposed projects by asking, "Will this help us achieve our vision? If so, how?" In doing so, it provides focus for the organization's strategic initiatives and plans.

The third element, *strategy*, is the broad formula for how the company will compete in the marketplace. A strategy will define the company's mid-range, normally one to three years, goals and objectives. It will also define the policies, tactics, and methods the company will use to achieve these goals, specific actions, and initiatives that will be undertaken, along with the overall plan to pull all these things together. In essence, the strategy lays out the path the company will follow to achieve its vision.

Although there are any number of theories on strategy that a company can adopt, most can be grouped into three generic categories as shown in Table 14.1.

The first category is *overall cost leadership,* also known as operational leadership or a defender strategy. Companies that compete with this strategy seek to be the lowest-cost provider and emphasize cost reduction and efficiency in internal operations. Quality initiatives that support this strategy include business process improvement and Six Sigma.

The next category is differentiation or *product leadership.* With this strategy the emphasis is on innovation, new product development, and product or service performance. Quality function deployment and design for Six Sigma are some initiatives that directly support this strategy.

The last category, focus or *customer intimacy,* combines elements of the other two categories, but targets a more narrow segment of the overall market and seeks to serve this segment better than anyone else. It emphasizes customer relationships and responsiveness.

Execution is the final element of our framework. Execution is the ability of an organization to implement its strategy and thereby achieve its strategic goals and objectives. Execution is based on the outcome of the strategic planning process, but is rooted in the company's people and operations. As previously noted, many organizations fail to successfully implement their strategy, primarily due to shortcomings in the competencies, assignment, or number of human resources needed to implement the strategy, or because they lack an understanding of the operational processes that must be controlled and improved in order to execute it. ISO 9001 and its many variations provide an existing framework that can be used to manage human resources and to control and monitor the processes that are critical to achieving successful implementation of the strategy.

Table 14.1 Generic strategies.[3]

Michael Porter	Treacy and Wiersema	Miles and Snow
Overall cost leadership	Operational excellence	Defender
Differentiation	Product Leadership	Prospector
Focus	Customer Intimacy	Analyzer

BALANCED SCORECARDS

Now we'll turn our attention to the balanced scorecard, and why many companies are using balanced scorecards to help achieve their strategic goals. Traditionally, strategic performance has been measured using financial indicators, such as return on investment, earnings per share, or sales growth. Such financial measures are typically results oriented, lagging, and focused on investors and shareholders. Financial measures have been and will continue to be a primary measure of how well the organization is performing.

The problem is that financial measures by themselves do not indicate what an organization needs to do in order to achieve these results or its strategic goals. Weaknesses in the use of financial measures alone to gauge corporate performance include:

- Financial measures tend to emphasize tangible assets, such as capital equipment and inventory. These measures are not reflective of many modern organizations where most of their worth is reflected in its intellectual capital. They may even value waste, such as large inventories that show up as an asset on the balance sheet.

- The most successful organizations focus on satisfying their customers, which is measured only indirectly by traditional financial measures. Problems can occur when meeting long-term customer needs conflicts with short-term shareholder expectations, as measured by the financial indicators.

- Financial measures focus on results, which while important, do not provide insight into the activities that drive these results. This is one of the greatest shortcomings of traditional financial measures, in that by failing to monitor the drivers of performance, they have limited value in predicting, and therefore influencing, future performance.

The balanced scorecard overcomes the limitations of financial metrics alone by creating a balanced set of indicators that link the desired performance results with the operational activities that drive these results. In the model given to us by Robert Kaplan and David Norton, the creators of the scorecard, an organization will use a balanced portfolio of measures categorized along four dimensions or perspectives:

- Financial (just discussed)

- Customer

- Internal business processes

- Innovation and learning (or learning and growth)

The first two perspectives are primarily results, or lagging indicators, while the last two perspectives are primarily leading indicators, or drivers. It should be noted that the ISO 9001 quality system model directly addresses key elements of each of the last three perspectives.

The *customer perspective* focuses on those indicators that measure how well we satisfy our external customers. Examples include traditional customer satisfaction indicators, along with market share, customer retention, and percent of repeat business. They are important in that improvement in these indicators should lead to improved financial results—that is, satisfied customers drive financial performance. They also provide a balance against the typically short-term interests of shareholders and investors who, while important, may not fully account for the internal investments necessary for sustained growth.

The customer perspective seeks to answer, using defined measurables, how the customer views the organization. The indicators chosen will be aligned with the strategy of the organization, including such dimensions as value (for a cost leadership position), quality and reliability (for a product leadership strategy), or responsiveness (for a focused or customer intimacy strategy). ISO 9001's primary focus is on satisfying customers; and requirements to understand customer expectations, to ensure they are met, and to measure our performance in satisfying their needs are numerous. As such, management system auditing to the ISO 9001 standard directly supports this perspective of the balanced scorecard.

The internal business process perspective measures key performance indicators associated with the activities and processes most important to the implementation of our strategy. Once an organization has identified its overall strategy and financial goals, and what it must do from a customer perspective to be able to achieve these goals, it must identify those processes at which it must excel. These processes must then be properly resourced, tightly controlled, and carefully monitored to ensure superior performance. Examples may include:

- The product development cycle, for a company using a product leadership strategy

- Manufacturing productivity and business process improvement, for a company using a low-cost provider strategy

- Sales, marketing, engineering, and customer service, for an organization using a customer intimacy strategy.

Essentially this perspective seeks to address the question of what the company must excel at in order to satisfy its customer, which, in turn, leads to financial success. Since the premise behind the ISO 9001 model is understanding, controlling, monitoring, and, where needed, improving your processes, there is a natural alignment between ISO 9001 and this perspective. The organization must go beyond the minimum requirements of ISO 9001, however, in these important processes if it is to be successful.

The innovation and learning perspective focuses on internal capabilities, in the form of infrastructure and intangible assets, needed to excel in those activities and processes essential to the company's attainment of its strategic goals and vision, and to sustain superior performance for the long-term. Examples of innovation and learning indicators may include:

- The number of new products launched or percent of sales from new products for a company committed to a product leadership position.

- The number of, or money saved from, business process improvement initiatives such as Six Sigma for a cost leadership strategy.

- Employee motivation and attitudes, which can be especially important for a company pursing a customer intimacy strategy.

This perspective seeks to answer the question, "What capabilities and resources do we need to be able to perform at a high level and to sustain this performance over the long haul?" ISO 9001 naturally aligns with this perspective through its focus on process inputs and resources, infrastructure, continual improvement, and the identification and achievement of employee competency. Success in this perspective drives excellence in internal business processes, which, in turn, leads to satisfied customers, which, in turn, leads to financial performance. Together, the scorecard's portfolio of financial, internal business process, learning and growth, and customer metrics combine to provide a balanced system of indicators, both leading and lagging, which, if properly developed and deployed, will help the organization accomplish its mission and achieve its vision through the successful implementation of its strategy.

The organization's ISO 9001 quality management system can significantly assist in the deployment and monitoring of the balanced scorecard, *if* it is properly aligned with the company's scorecard and strategy. The key to successful implementation lies with the deployment of the top-level metrics down to the operational level. This requires the development of process-specific metrics that align with and support the top-level scorecard metrics. This is one area where ISO 9001, and its requirements to monitor process performance, can greatly assist in the execution of the scorecard.

It has been noted that when balanced scorecards have failed, it is primarily due to a failure to fully establish the cause-and-effect relationships between the indicators and goals, and the activities or processes necessary to achieve the goals. This is often termed *strategy mapping*. Coming up with metrics for each perspective is not sufficient . . . the company must fully map the drivers of performance to the desired outcomes. It must then link these drivers to specific organizational processes and establish criteria for process performance that support the strategic goals.

As an example of a strategy map, assume a company establishes financial goals to improve its return on equity, revenue growth, and profit per employee by maintaining its cost leadership position and improving its market share in the automotive market. To do this the company sees a need to increase the loyalty of its existing customers based on value, while becoming the supplier of choice in its industry among automotive customers, which it knows will require a reputation for world-class quality, responsiveness, and efficiency. In essence, the company will attempt to establish a customer intimacy strategy within the automotive sector, while maintaining a cost leadership strategy within its industry as a whole.

To do this, it has determined that it must improve its understanding of its automotive customers (sales, marketing, and organizational learning processes), it must improve its time to market for new automotive products (product development processes, innovation processes), and it must improve its customer relationship and technical support capabilities, especially within the automotive group, all while lowering its production and inventory costs. Organizational capabilities and initiatives that will support this are a robust business process improvement (BPI) capability, including Six Sigma, improved competencies in some critical areas, and a system that supports the collection, categorization, and dissemination of organizational learning. See Figure 14.2.

Now let's look at an example of how a scorecard may be developed. Our example company's balanced scorecard may appear as shown in Figure 14.3.

The company would first develop strategic objectives in each of the scorecard perspectives that will support the chosen strategy. Note that these objectives are quantified, where practical. The organization then develops the scorecard indicators that will be

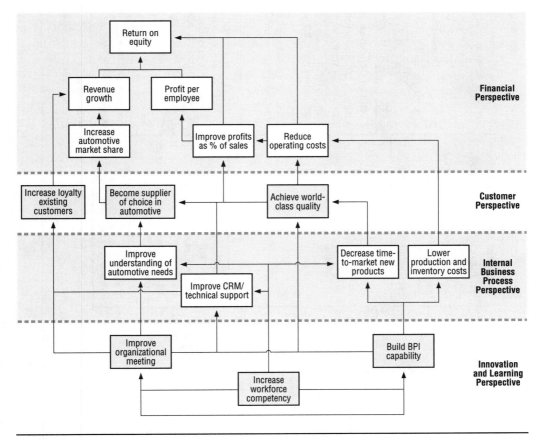

Figure 14.2   Strategy map.

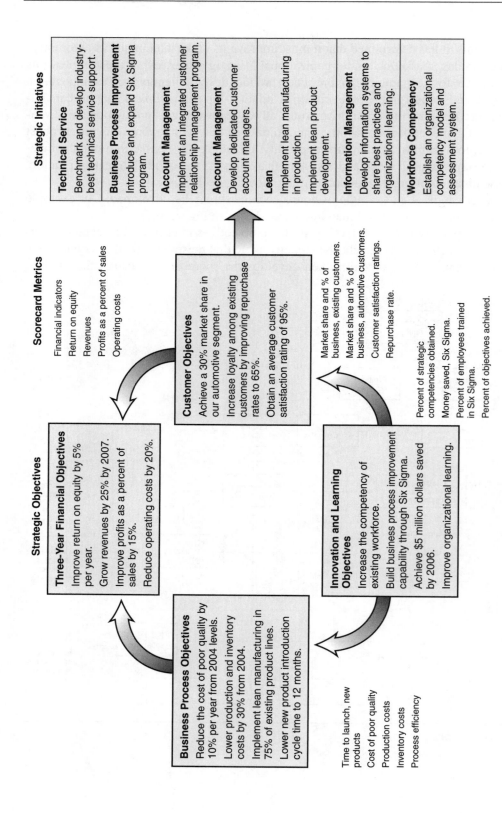

Figure 14.3 Developing a balanced scorecard.

used to monitor achievement of the objectives. The financial and customer indicators are primarily lagging, or results based, while the business process and innovation and learning indicators are primarily leading, or drivers of performance. Although not shown at this level, deployment of the indicators would continue down to the process level of activities seen as critical to execution of the strategy.

Next the organization would identify the specific initiatives, or actions, that will be used to drive improvement and performance in selected areas. These initiatives are each evaluated for their alignment with, and ability to support, execution of the organization's strategy. Note that ISO 9001:2000 requires an organization to set and deploy objectives throughout each relevant level and function of the organization. Audit program managers can and should consider the scheduling of evaluations of major initiatives such as Six Sigma, lean manufacturing, and 5S. These initiatives are processes in themselves and need to be properly resourced, controlled, and monitored if they are to deliver on their expected promises. Lean manufacturing and 5S could be evaluated during process-based audits of the production process, and Six Sigma would fit nicely within a process-based audit of the improvement process.

While the ISO management system standards require control of each of the organization's important processes, those that are considered drivers of the organization's strategy, as evidenced by their linkage to the balanced scorecard, must receive increased attention in the form of inputs, resources, controls, and monitoring. In particular, this may mean assigning additional quality or service criteria and performing additional monitoring to ensure they are performed at a very high level. It also means that auditors engaged in evaluating one of these strategic processes must understand and verify the linkages to the strategic goals of the organization.

As already mentioned, success in implementing the balanced scorecard depends on identifying the activities and processes that drive performance in areas critical to the strategy and then linking these with the scorecard objectives in a cause-and-effect relationship. Setting up an ISO 9001 quality management system involves identifying those processes that need to be included in the system and showing their interrelationships. This same concept can be used to link the critical internal business processes from the scorecard to the inputs, resources, and other processes needed to ensure their satisfactory performance.

As previously noted, both the balanced scorecard and ISO 9001 require the monitoring of process performance. Alignment of these metrics provides important benefits to both. From a balanced scorecard perspective, measuring the performance of strategically important processes on a daily, weekly, and/or monthly basis provides early and continuous feedback and allows for early intervention if performance is not satisfactory. From a quality management system standpoint, linking process metrics to strategic needs provides increased focus and interest on the part of senior management. Resources to correct poor performance or to improve existing performance are much more likely to be supplied when the executive team understands the linkage between process performance and achievement of the strategic objectives.

A properly implemented quality system based on ISO 9001:2000 makes process improvement the norm, rather than the exception. Whether it is corrective action or continual improvement, action to achieve planned results should become a way of life. This cycle can be interrupted, however, when management fails to see the significance of process improvement and settles for current performance as good enough. When management understands the linkage between process performance and strategy execution, and has access to detailed data that shows performance, resources for improvement are made available. Improvement initiatives undertaken to support the execution of the strategy can be used to satisfy ISO 9001 quality system requirements and receive better management support than do those that are not aligned with the scorecard objectives.

To align an existing quality management system to a balanced scorecard, first link the strategic objectives to the key processes by developing a strategy map. Codify the relationship by including it in the purpose and scope statement of the process procedure, if there is one. Next deploy the scorecard indicators down to the process level by establishing or expanding process metrics where appropriate. Then link strategic targets to key processes by establishing the appropriate service standards and process objectives needed to achieve strategic targets and objectives. This is shown in Figure 14.4.

Figure 14.5 provides an example of a typical process procedure for an ISO 9001 company. The procedure has the normal purpose and responsibility sections, and the company has included process inputs, outputs, and metrics to support the process approach of ISO 9001:2000. The focus of the procedure is on the typical manufacturing outputs of quality and delivery performance.

Assume this company has adopted a low-cost provider strategy and has identified manufacturing as an internal business process that is a key driver of performance on its scorecard. Also assume that it has established strategic objectives to lower its manufacturing costs and improve production efficiencies through cycle time reduction.

What might its procedure look like after alignment with its balanced scorecard? See Figure 14.6.

Note that the focus on manufacturing costs has been added to the purpose statement to reinforce this strategic objective. Also note that both cycle time and production costs have been recognized as key process outputs. Since these outputs are key drivers of strategic performance, the organization has expanded its monitoring of the production process to include them. In addition, criteria have been established to help drive process improvement. Finally, ongoing criteria for performance have been added to reinforce ongoing performance to the strategic objectives. Obviously this organization has gone beyond the minimum required to meet the ISO 9001 requirements for process performance monitoring. This is appropriate for this process, since it has been identified as key driver of strategic results.

BUILDING AUDITOR KNOWLEDGE AND COMPETENCY

Auditing for strategic alignment and execution requires that the auditor understand the organization's desired strategy and how each organizational process fits into this strategy. It is fair to say that not all processes are created equal, especially when considering

Objective	Measurement	Target	Initiatives/Programs	Processes
Increase automotive market share	Market share, automotive	25% of total sales	Account management, automotive customers	Business development process, CRM process
Improve profits	Profitability as % of sales	5% improvement	BPI initiative, Lean initiative	All targeted processes
Reduce operating costs	Operating		BPI initiative	All targeted processes
Increase existing customer loyalty	Percent o...		...itiative	CRM process, Technical support process
Become supplier of choice in automotive	Percent o... automot...			Business development process, Order fulfillment process, Technical support process
	Customer satisfaction	ratings		
Achieve world-class quality	Customer satisfaction, Quality yield, ppm	98% rating, < 50 ppb	BPI initiative	Order fulfillment process, Product development process
Improve understanding of automotive needs	No. of contacts, No. of CSRs trained	150 contac..., 100% CSF...		CRM process, Training process
Decrease time-to-market of new products	Time-to-launch, Percent projects using rapid prototyping			CRM process (VOC), Product development process
Improve CRM and technical support	No. of CSRs trained	100% CSF	BPI initiative	CRM process, Technical support process
Lower production and inventory costs	Production cost/unit, Total inventory costs, No. lean initiates launched	30% reduction in cost/unit and total inventory costs	BPI initiative, Lean initiative	Order fulfillment process, Warehouse/distribution process, Purchasing process
Ir...		75% critical competencies achieved	Workforce competency initiative	Training process
B...		TBD individually, 50% of employees trained	BPI initiative, MIS initiative	Training process, Continual improvement process, IT support process
Ir... learning	achieved	75% of strategic objectives and programs achieved	BPI initiative, MIS initiative	IT support processes, Communication process

Overlay callout boxes:

- Link strategic objectives to key processes through purpose and scope where appropriate.
- Link balanced scorecard measurements to key processes through process metrics where appropriate.
- Link strategic targets to key processes through process criteria, service standards, and objectives.

Figure 14.4 Mapping strategic objectives, targets, and initiatives to internal processes.

Purpose	This procedure describes the process used to plan, schedule, and control production operations.
Responsibility	The ACA manufacturing and maintenance managers are assigned ownership for this process. Other functions within ACA will support these responsbilities to the extent noted.
Inputs Resources	Customer production and quality requirements.
	Process control plans, inspection and monitoring plans, and other production-related documents and outputs from the quality planning and process design process.
	Production plans.
	Purchase orders from ACA sales affiliates and electronic orders from customers.
	Customer-owned tooling and/or equipment.
	Supplier materials and/or component parts.
Outputs	Products that meet customer quality and delivery requirements.
	Processes that meet ongoing process capability requirements.
Metrics	Final product quality, as measured by PRRs, QPRs, and/or other customer feedback.
	On-time delivery to customer delivery requirements.
	Ongoing process capability, measured against customer requirements.

Figure 14.5   Typical production control procedure.

Purpose	This procedure describes the process used to ensure the effective planning, scheduling, and control of production operations *and associated costs.*
Inputs Resources	Customer production and quality requirements.
	Process control plans, inspection and monitoring plans, and other production-related documents and outputs from the quality planning and process design process.
	Production plans.
	Purchase orders from ACA sales affiliates and electronic orders from customers.
	Customer-owned tooling and/or equipment.
	Supplier materials and/or component parts.
	Estimated costs.
Outputs	Products that meet customer quality and delivery requirements.
	Processes that meet ongoing process capability and cycle time requirements.
	Products that meet targeted costs/unit.
Metrics	Final product quality, as measured by outgoing quality and/or customer feedback.
	• *Quality objective < 50 ppm.*
	On-time delivery to customer delivery requirements.
	Ongoing process capability, measured against customer requirements.
	• *Minimum Cpk objective 2.0 production cycle time efficiency.*
	• *Minimum cycle time efficiency of 25% total cost per completed unit.*
	• *Total cost/unit < targeted cost per unit.*

Figure 14.6   Production control procedure with emphasis on strategic objectives.

their contribution to the success or failure of the strategic plan. Auditors must be shown or be able to develop the connections between the strategy and the processes being evaluated. The auditor will then be in a position, using the techniques and methods already described in this handbook, to determine the degree of alignment between the strategy and the processes' inputs, resources, and metrics and performance in support of the strategic goals.

To accomplish this, auditors should be provided additional training on how the organization develops and deploys its strategy as follows:

- The organization's vision, mission, and values

- The organization's strategy

- The balanced scorecard or other dashboard of strategic indicators used by the organization to measure strategic performance, and how these support the chosen strategy

- The strategic plan and initiatives needed to execute the chosen strategy

- The organization's strategy maps, or linkages to the specific processes and activities that support the strategy

- Key process metrics that were derived to deploy the strategy to these processes

These topics help provide the business perspective that the auditors will need when evaluating what is most important and where they should allocate their time during the evaluation.

In addition, auditors will need training and experience in tracing these linkages and in reporting the results. This training and experience can be provided locally. Another option is to use auditors with previous experience as examiners for any of the state or national quality awards patterned after the Malcolm Baldrige National Quality Award (MBNQA). The Baldrige model focuses on the development and deployment of a strategy based on the organization's vision, mission, and values and the expectations of its customers and stakeholders. It also focuses on the alignment of the organization's internal processes to the strategy and on the achievement of business results. During a MBNQA examination, the examiners evaluate the extent to which the organization has successfully deployed this model by reviewing the strategy, the alignment of internal business processes to the strategy, and its success in producing business results. The seven major areas of focus for the Baldrige model are:

- Leadership

- Strategic planning

- Customer and market focus

- Measurement, analysis, and knowledge management

- Human resource focus

- Process management

- Business results

The rating system used during a Baldrige examination is quite different from that used during an internal management system audit. The examiner's ability to recognize and evaluate the alignments between an organization's strategy and its internal processes, resources, and controls is, however, applicable to any management system audit. The knowledge and experience gained from serving as an examiner for one of the award programs based on the Baldrige model broadens the perspective of the internal auditor and gives him or her the capability to evaluate strategic alignment and performance during management system audits.

As a minimum, all auditors should receive the training on the organization's strategy and strategy deployment previously mentioned. In addition, it would be desirable to have a limited number of auditors with enhanced skills. Audit program managers have options in developing this enhanced capability. They can allow auditors to serve as examiners on one of the state award programs. Recognize that this does require a significant commitment of time, however, probably between 10 to 15 days. Second, they can download the Baldrige training materials from the National Institute of Standards and Technology Web site and use the case studies and other materials to train the auditors internally.[4] The audit program manager could tailor this material and the training toward a management system audit. This training, together with the training mentioned earlier on the organization's strategy, could be accomplished in a three-day session. As a goal, it would be recommended that all full-time auditors receive enhanced training.

AUDITING FOR STRATEGIC ALIGNMENT AND PERFORMANCE

Auditing for strategic alignment means evaluating the processes the auditor has been assigned to examine with the perspective of how this process supports the attainment of the organization's strategic goals. For example, assume that the company is committed to a low-cost provider strategy, and the auditor has been assigned to an audit of the production process. The auditor should put additional emphasis on locating waste or unnecessary costs in the manufacturing process. He or she should look beyond the normal audit areas of scrap and rework and should also look for excessive inventories, material obsolescence, and successive layers of overinspection. Weaknesses in these areas, if found, represent *strategic* opportunities for improvement. Likewise, the auditor may find that the process metrics being used do not really take into account the strategic priority of the process, similar to the example provided in Figure 14.5. The auditor may then decide to issue an opportunity for improvement to consider adding the metrics shown in Figure 14.6.

The auditor may also find weaknesses during the evaluation of individual inputs, resources, and controls. Assume the auditor knows that one of the strategic initiatives deployed to help the organization reduce its costs is the rollout of lean manufacturing in two key areas. The auditor notes that there has been little activity in these areas despite the launch of this program several months ago. During review of production worker's competencies, the auditor notes that the organization has fallen far behind in providing the training on lean principles needed to support the rollout. If there was a detailed plan for the rollout and it clearly indicates that the training is significantly behind schedule with no actions to recover, the auditor should cite an NC. Even if there is no plan, the auditor should consider citation of an opportunity for improvement given the strategic importance of the program. The executive team needs to be made aware that actions needed to support its strategy are not on track. Hopefully, this awareness will be made early enough to allow recovery.

Beyond simple notification, the auditor is also in a position to find out why certain problems exist. The auditor may learn that the training has not been initiated because of inadequate funding or because of a high level of turnover in the two areas. This information gives management the opportunity to reevaluate the importance of the initiative to the achievement of the strategy and to take the necessary actions to increase the funding or to stabilize the workforce, should the initiative still be considered to be important. The auditor is now reinforcing the linkages between the strategy, the process (manufacturing), the strategic initiative (lean manufacturing), and the finance or human resources functions. Any misalignment between these processes and objectives will cause the strategy to fail.

To provide another example, assume that the company is committed to a customer intimacy strategy with a particular focus on its growing automotive customer base. To support this it has restructured its technical service center to provide a central point of contact to its major automotive customers. During the evaluation, the auditor notes that despite the reorganization, customer satisfaction ratings have not increased and customer complaints have even started to rise. Because of the strategic nature of this weakness, the auditor should probe deeper into this area. It may be that the major source of complaints is the increased time that it takes to provide an answer to a customer's technical questions. In the old system all calls were answered as they came in, but were immediately routed by a service representative with expertise in the problem area. While this caused some delay, it was less than the new system wherein all calls, in or out, go through the central point of contact, who in most cases is not an expert in the problem. Because this contact must first discuss the problem with the subject matter expert, almost all problem calls now require a callback versus being answered on the first call, greatly extending the time needed to get an answer back to the customer. Senior management needs to be made aware of this problem and the insights gained by the auditor. Although the supervisor or first-line manager may already be aware of the issue, he or she may be reluctant to raise it because of the effort that was expended to restructure the service center.

To summarize, the auditor can audit for strategic impact by using the methods and techniques provided elsewhere in this handbook and by asking the following questions for each area evaluated:

- Is this process important to the organization's ability to achieve its strategic goals? If so, how does it contribute?

- Do the process owners recognize the strategic importance of this activity, and have they aligned the process with the strategic goals?

- Is this strategic process provided with the resources and inputs it needs to be able to support accomplishment of the strategy? If not, are actions being taken to acquire the needed resources?

- Are the process metrics aligned with the strategic goals in a meaningful way?

- Is there evidence that the process is contributing to achievement of the strategic goals?

REPORTING STRATEGIC WEAKNESSES AND OPPORTUNITIES FOR IMPROVEMENT

Probably the most difficult, and possibly the most important step in strategic auditing, is documenting the weaknesses. Rather than just reporting nonconformances to requirements, plans, and miscellaneous opportunities for improvement, the auditor must capture the strategic nature of the finding in the write-up. This requires good perspective and that the auditor put himself or herself in the shoes of the executive team.

Perspective is vitally important. Not every weakness impacts on the organization's ability to achieve its strategic goals, although almost any weakness could be indirectly tied to the same. For instance, assume the auditor finds that the area supervisor did not approve the 5S area plan as required. The auditor could cite:

> The 5S plan for the injection molding area was not approved by the area supervisor. The 5S plan is an important component of the 5S Program, which is part of the lean manufacturing initiative. Failure of the 5S Program could jeopardize the accomplishment of lean manufacturing and in so doing, impact on the organization's ability to achieve the cost reductions targeted in the strategic plan.

Trying to tie this minor administrative nonconformance to the success or failure of the organization's strategic initiatives demonstrates a lack of perspective and would possibly do irreparable damage to the audit program. Meaningful audit findings having strategic impact need to be cited as such, but there must be direct line-of-sight connection to the organization's strategy. As an example:

> Training in lean manufacturing methods is seriously behind schedule. Only three of nine training events scheduled to date have been accomplished. This has impacted the rollout of lean, with both pilot areas more than three months behind schedule. It is noted that the implementation of lean manufacturing in these areas is a strategic initiative deployed to support the organization's cost

reduction goals. No actions are currently in place to recover the training schedule. It was reported that high employee turnover in the two pilot areas is a major reason for the failure to accomplish required training.

As another example:

Customer complaints in the service center have increased 25 percent over the last four months. Seventy-five percent of the increase has been from automotive customers. It is further noted that no improvement in automotive customer satisfaction ratings has been made over the past 12 months, despite reorganization of the service center as part of a strategic realignment in support of the organization's strategic goals to increase the market share of automotive customers to 25 percent by the end of calendar year 2005. It was reported that the service center restructuring may in part be a reason for the increase in customer complaints. No further actions have been identified to address the current trends in customer satisfaction or complaints.

A final example:

The organization has established a strategic goal to reduce manufacturing costs by 25 percent from 2004 levels by the end of calendar year 2005. It was noted that there are currently few routinely monitored metrics in place to measure manufacturing process costs or efficiency. The only metrics available are outgoing quality (PPM), direct labor costs, overhead, and total inventory costs. Consideration should be given to establishing more operational metrics that focus on cost and/or production efficiency.

The linkage to the organization's strategy in each of the last three examples is clear and line-of-sight. While senior managers may choose not to act on some, they at least have the awareness of the issue and the opportunity to reevaluate the importance of their strategic goals and/or initiatives relative to the auditor's findings. Because of the importance of clearly communicating the strategic impact of these types of findings, it may be appropriate for the audit program manager to review such findings prior to presentation to the auditee, at least until experience shows that the organization's auditors have the experience and perspective needed to properly identify the strategic linkages.

SUMMARY

To summarize this chapter, the increased scope of the ISO management system's coverage and the focus on process-based auditing has given the management system audit function new opportunities to transition from a process conformance to a strategic performance role. To successfully make this transition requires cooperation between the organization's senior management team and its internal auditors. Senior management must develop the strategy, the strategic objectives and plans, and a scoreboard, and must map the strategy to the internal processes that support the objectives. Internal auditors must become knowledgeable of the strategic plan and its linkages to the organization's processes, and must develop the perspective and capability to be able to identify the line-of-sight linkages and to report weaknesses and opportunities for improvement in terms that are meaningful to management. Filling this role will provide significant additional value to the organization.

Notes

Chapter 1

1. ANSI/ISO/ASQ ISO 9001:2000, *Quality management systems—Requirements* (Milwaukee: American Society for Quality, 2000).

2. ISO/TS 16949:2002, *Quality management systems—Particular requirements for the application of ISO 9001:2000 for automotive production and relevant service parts organizations* (International Automotive Task Force, 2002).

3. ANSI/ISOASQ E14001–2004, *Environmental management systems— Requirements with guidance for use* (Milwaukee: American Society for Quality, 2004).

4. OHSAS 18001:1999, *Occupational health and safety management systems— Specification.* (British Standards Institute, 2002).

5. AS9100, *Quality management systems—Aerospace—Requirements* (Society of Automotive Engineers, 2004).

6. ISO 13485:2003, *Medical devices—Quality management systems— Requirements for regulatory purposes* (Geneva, Switzerland: International Organization for Standardization, 2003).

7. The QuEST Forum, *TL 9000 Quality System Requirements,* Book One, Release 3.0 (Milwaukee, ASQ Quality Press, 2001).

8. AIAG, *Advanced Product Quality Planning and Control Plan Reference Manual* (Southfield, MI: Automotive Industry Action Group, 1994).

9. AIAG, *Production Part Approval Process* (Southfield, MI: Automotive Industry Action Group, 1999).

10. AIAG, *Measurement Systems Analysis Reference Manual* (Southfield, MI: Automotive Industry Action Group, 2002).

11. AIAG, *Potential Failure Mode and Effects Analysis Reference Manual* (Southfield, MI: Automotive Industry Action Group, 2001).

12. AIAG, *Statistical Process Control Reference Manual* (Southfield, MI: Automotive Industry Action Group, 1995).

Chapter 2

1. Robert Kaplan and David Norton, *The Balanced Scorecard* (Boston: Harvard Business School Press, 1996).

Chapter 3

1. United States Food and Drug Administration, *Guide to Inspections of Quality Systems* (Washington, D.C.: United States Food and Drug Administration, 1999).

Chapter 4

1. ANSI/ISO/ASQ QE19011S-2004, *Guidelines for quality and/or environmental management systems auditing—U.S. version with supplemental guidance added* (Milwaukee: American Society for Quality, 2004).

Chapter 6

1. Stephen Covey, *The 7 Habits of Highly Effective People* (New York: Simon & Schuster, 1989).

Chapter 8

1. ANSI/ISO/ASQ ISO 9001:2000, *Quality management systems—Requirements* (Milwaukee: American Society for Quality, 2000).

2. ISO/TS 16949:2002, *Quality management systems—Particular requirements for the application of ISO 9001:2000 for automotive production and relevant service parts organizations* (International Automotive Task Force, 2002).

Chapter 9

1. ANSI/ISO/ASQ E14001–2004, *Environmental management systems— Requirements with guidance for use* (Milwaukee: American Society for Quality, 2004).

Chapter 10

1. OHSAS 18001:1999, *Occupational Health and Safety Management Systems—Specification* (British Standards Institute, 2002).

Chapter 11

1. ANSI/ISO/ASQ ISO 9001:2000, *Quality management systems—Requirements* (Milwaukee: American Society for Quality, 2000).

2. ANSI/ISO/ASQ E14001–2004, *Environmental management systems—Requirements with guidance for use* (Milwaukee: American Society for Quality, 2004).

3. OHSAS 18001:1999, *Occupational Health and Safety Management Systems—Specification* (British Standards Institute, 2002).

Chapter 12

1. AIAG, *Advanced Product Quality Planning and Control Plan Reference Manual* (Southfield, MI: Automotive Industry Action Group, 1994): 5.

2. AIAG, *Potential Failure Mode and Effects Analysis Reference Manual* (Southfield, MI: Automotive Industry Action Group, 2001): 36.

3. AIAG, *Measurement Systems Analysis Reference Manual* (Southfield, MI: Automotive Industry Action Group, 2002).

4. AIAG, *Production Part Approval Process* (Southfield, MI: Automotive Industry Action Group, 1999).

5. AIAG, *Statistical Process Control Reference Manual* (Southfield, MI: Automotive Industry Action Group, 1995).

6. ISO/TS 16949:2002, *Quality management systems—Particular requirements for the application of ISO 9001:2000 for automotive production and relevant service parts organizations* (International Automotive Task Force, 2002).

Chapter 14

1. Robert Kaplan and David Norton, *The Balanced Scorecard* (Boston: Harvard Business School Press, 1996).

2. Robert Kaplan and David Norton, *Strategy Maps: Converting Intangible Assets into Tangible Outcomes* (Boston: Harvard Business School Press, 2004).

3. Naceur Jabnoun, Azaddin Khalifah, and Attahir Yusuf, "Environmental Uncertainty, Strategic Orientation, and Quality Management: A Contingency Model," *Quality Management Journal* 10, no. 4 (2003).

4. Readers can download copies of the Malcolm Baldrige criteria and case studies at the NIST Web site http://baldrige.nist.gov.

Glossary

active listening—The act of focusing all of an auditor's attention on the communication from the auditee. Includes observation of the words being used; the tone, pitch, and inflection of the words; and the nonverbal communications being expressed.

advanced product quality planning (APQP)—Common guidelines for a structured approach for defining and establishing the steps needed to ensure a quality product and robust production processes within the automotive industry.

AS9100—The version of ISO 9001 modified to suit the aerospace industry.

audit nit—An audit finding that while valid, has no consequence and provides no value if corrected.

audit plan—A document that details the major processes or areas to be reviewed, the auditor for each process, and the dates and/or time frames for each evaluation. Audit plans often also identify the individual to be interviewed, when appropriate.

balanced scorecard—A balanced set of indicators that link the desired performance results with the operational activities that drive these results. Often categorized along four dimensions or perspectives of financial, customer, internal business processes, and innovation and learning indicators.

balanced scorecard perspective—An area of focus for the balanced scorecard such as financial, internal business process, or customer.

benchmarking—The systematic identification of superior practices through comparison to benchmarks and indicators of performance, and the discovery of the enablers or drivers of the superior performance.

best practice—An activity or process that represents superior performance.

beyond compliance—Environmental principle that emphasizes performance over that required by environmental regulations and laws. Also emphasizes source reduction over pollution control.

centralized support processes—Support processes, or parts thereof, that are not normally evaluated during other process-based audits.

characteristics matrix—A tool that shows the relationship between product design features and the manufacturing operations that generate those features.

client—The person who commissions or sponsors the audit. Normally the audit program manager.

conformance verification—That portion of the audit that focuses on verifying compliance to requirements (for example, customer requirements, organizational requirements, government legislation, and the management system standard).

control plan—A summary document of the important controls used to ensure the quality product and/or stability of a manufacturing process. Primarily used in the automotive industry.

core process—Processes that support the primary purpose of the business. Examples would include production and launch planning for a manufacturing organization, patient assessment and primary care for a health care organization, and market analysis, sales, and customer support for a consumer services company.

criteria—Current standards or levels of performance to be achieved. Can also be defined as requirements to be met.

customer-oriented processes—Processes that directly provide value to an organization's customers.

design for manufacturability and assembly (DFM/DFA)—A structured method for analyzing a product concept in order to optimize its manufacturability, assembly, quality, and cost.

echoing—A short repeat, in the form of a question, of a topic the auditor wants an auditee to expand on.

effectiveness confirmation—That portion of the audit that evaluates the level of performance of the process against planned results.

environmental aspect—An element of an organization's activities, products, or services that can interact with the environment.

environmental impact—The actual effect that an environmental aspect has on the environment.

failure mode and effects analysis (FMEA)—A systematic and disciplined approach for anticipating failure modes associated with a product or process, determining their likelihood of occurrence, their causes, and countermeasures to prevent their occurrence or to detect them prior to delivery to the customer.

first-party audit—An audit by an organization of its own operations.

funnel approach—A strategy for asking questions that begins with a broad, open-ended question relating to the area to be evaluated followed by clarifying questions that focus on the missing information or points of interest.

guide—An individual representing the audited organization who provides liaison and confirmation for the auditor.

inspection escapes—A term that describes defects that passed through the organization's detection systems to the customer.

ISO 13485—The version of ISO 9001 for the medical device industry.

ISO 19011—The international standard published by the International Organization for Standardization that provides general guidelines and principles for setting up, conducting, and controlling an audit or audit program.

ISO/TS 16949—The version of ISO 9001 for the automotive industry.

job hazard analysis (JHA)—Systematic analysis of the hazards associated with tasks and the risk that these hazards present to human operators and equipment.

key support process—Processes that provide significant support for the organization's core processes.

layered audits—A series of focused process audits by team leaders, managers, and top management.

Malcolm Baldrige National Quality Award—National award given to organizations demonstrating the highest level of performance according to the award's business excellence model.

measurements—Specific measurements made to evaluate product, process, or system performance, normally implemented after ongoing monitoring indicates problems or concerns.

measurement systems analysis (MSA)—Statistical analysis of the sources of variation within a measurement system and comparison of this variation to either the process variation or the product tolerance for the purpose of determining measurement system acceptability.

monitoring—High-level scanning of a product, process, or system for the purpose of tracking performance.

muda—Waste, or any activity that does not add value.

nonconformance—An audit finding that represents a violation of a requirement.

minor nonconformance—A nonconformance that does not represent a total failure of the system to address a customer or standard requirement and will not likely lead to release of defective product to the customer.

major nonconformance—A nonconformance that represents a total failure of the system to address a customer or standard requirement, which has a high probability of allowing defective product to reach the customer.

objective evidence—Evidence, typically in the form of records, direct observations, or documentation, of the conformance or nonconformance of a process or activity to a requirement or planned results.

one-liner form—An optional audit tool that helps organize numerous audit findings.

opportunities for improvement—An audit finding that represents, in the judgment of the auditor, an opportunity to improve. Note that an opportunity for improvement does not represent a violation of a requirement.

plan–do–check–act (PDCA)—Systematic and ongoing process of planning, implementation, measurement of the results, and action to further improve the process. Also referred to as the Deming cycle.

process approach—A management approach that seeks to optimize results by controlling all aspects of the process—inputs, resources, controls, the transformation itself, outputs, and the interrelationships with other interdependent processes. Also an audit approach that considers the entire process and not just compliance to the steps of the procedure.

process capability study—A statistical study used to compare the amount of inherent process variation to product tolerances for the purpose of determining process acceptability and anticipated performance.

production part approval process (PPAP)—Automotive methodology used to determine if all customer engineering design record and specification requirements are properly understood and that the process has the potential to produce product consistently meeting these requirements during an actual production run at the quoted production rate.

registrar—An organization that contracts to perform independent assessments for the purposes of certification of the management system.

second-party audit—An audit of a supplier or potential supplier organization.

silo approach—Situation where individual departments within an organization seek to maximize their performance against department objectives to the detriment of the organization as a whole.

special characteristic—An assignment made to product features or manufacturing operations to identify the need for special process controls to minimize variation that could significantly affect item fit, form, function, durability, maintainability, or safety, health, or regulatory conformity.

statistical process control (SPC)—The application of statistical techniques to monitor, analyze, and improve processes.

strategy map—The mapping of the strategic objectives, indicators, and goals of the organization to the specific business processes that most contribute to their attainment.

sustainable development—Economic development that meets the needs of today without compromising the ability of future generations to meet their own needs.

technical expert—A resource to the audit team who brings unique and specific knowledge about an audited process or activity.

third-party audit—An audit performed by an organization independent of the audited organization.

TL 9000—The version of ISO 9001 for the telecommunications industry.

trace back—An audit strategy that starts at the end of a process and traces backward through the process to the beginning.

trace forward—An audit strategy that starts at the beginning of a process and proceeds through each activity to the end of the process.

value stream—A system of interrelated processes that together focus on providing value (typically goods and services) to an organization's customers.

verbal door opener—A short, nonintrusive comment used to encourage an auditee to continue to communicate.

Further Reading

BOOKS AND ARTICLES

Bogan, Christopher, and Michael English. *Benchmarking for Best Practices.* New York: McGraw-Hill, 1994.

Bossidy, Larry, and Ram Charan. *Execution—The Discipline of Getting Things Done.* New York: Crown Business, 2002.

Cascio, Joseph. *The ISO 14000 Handbook.* Milwaukee: ASQ Quality Press, 1996.

Cianfrani, Charles, Joseph Tsiakals, and John E. (Jack) West. *The ASQ ISO 9001:2000 Handbook.* Milwaukee: ASQ Quality Press, 2002.

Kaplan, Robert, and David Norton. *The Balanced Scorecard.* Boston: Harvard Business School Press, 1996.

———. *Strategy Maps.* Boston: Harvard Business School Press, 2004.

Liebesman, Sandford, Alka Jarvis, and Ashok Dandekar. *TL 9000 Release 3.0—A Guide to Measuring Excellence in Telecommunications.* Milwaukee: ASQ Quality Press, 2002.

Niven, Paul. *Balanced Scorecard Step-by-Step.* New York: John Wiley and Sons, 2002.

Swartz, George. *Job Hazard Analysis—A Guide to Identifying Risks in the Workplace.* Rockville, MD: Government Institutes, 2001.

REFERENCE MANUALS

Automotive Industry Action Group. *Advanced Product Quality Planning and Control Plan Reference Manual.* Southfield, MI: Automotive Industry Action Group, 1994.

———. *Measurement Systems Analysis Reference Manual,* 3rd ed. Southfield, MI: Automotive Industry Action Group, 2002.

———. *Potential Failure Mode and Effects Analysis Reference Manual,* 3rd ed. Southfield, MI: Automotive Industry Action Group, 2001.

———. *Statistical Process Control Reference Manual,* 2nd ed. Southfield, MI: Automotive Industry Action Group, 1995.

STANDARDS AND SPECIFICATIONS

ANSI/ISO/ASQ E14001–2004. *Environmental management systems—Requirements with guidance for use.* Milwaukee: American Society for Quality, 2004.

ANSI/ISO/ASQ ISO 9001:2000. *Quality management systems—Requirements.* Milwaukee: American Society for Quality, 2000.

AS9100. *Quality Management Systems—Aerospace—Requirements.* Society of Automotive Engineers, 2004.

ISO 13485:2003. *Medical devices—Quality management systems—Requirements for regulatory purposes.* Geneva, Switzerland: International Organization for Standardization, 2003.

ISO/TS 16949:2002. *Quality management systems—Particular requirements for the application of ISO 9001:2000 for automotive production and relevant service parts organizations.* Geneva, Switzerland: International Automotive Task Force, 2002.

OHSAS 18001:1999. *Occupational Health and Safety Management Systems—Specification.* British Standards Institute, 2002.

The QuEST Forum. *TL 9000 Quality System Requirements, Book One, Release 3.0.* Milwaukee: ASQ Quality Press, 2001.

WEB SITES

The Environmental Protection Agency Web site provides many valuable environmental resources and training guides that can be downloaded for free. Visit it at http://www.epa.gov.

The OSHA Web site, maintained by the U.S. Department of Labor, provides useful safety and health tools and training materials for a variety of industries. Visit this site at http://www.osha.gov.

The National Institute of Standards and Technology maintains a site dedicated to the Malcolm Baldrige National Quality Award. Award criteria, scoring guidelines, and training materials can be downloaded from this site for free. Visit it at http://baldrige.nist.gov.

Index